STATISTICAL DECISION THEORY
IN ADAPTIVE CONTROL SYSTEMS

MATHEMATICS
IN SCIENCE
AND ENGINEERING

A SERIES OF MONOGRAPHS AND TEXTBOOKS

Edited by Richard Bellman
University of Southern California

MATHEMATICS IN SCIENCE AND ENGINEERING

In preparation

STATISTICAL DECISION THEORY
IN ADAPTIVE CONTROL SYSTEMS

Yoshikazu Sawaragi and Yoshifumi Sunahara

Department of Applied Mathematics and Physics
Kyoto University, Kyoto, Japan

and

Takayoshi Nakamizo

Department of Mechanical Engineering
Defense Academy of Japan
Yokusuka, Japan

ACADEMIC PRESS　　New York　·　London　　1967

ACADEMIC PRESS INC.
111 Fifth Avenue, New York, New York 10003

United Kingdom Edition published by
ACADEMIC PRESS INC. (LONDON) LTD.
Berkeley Square House, London W.1

LIBRARY OF CONGRESS CATALOG CARD NUMBER: 66-30099

PRINTED IN THE UNITED STATES OF AMERICA

PREFACE

The history of automatic control can, in large measure, be traced to the end of the 18th century and the work of James Watt on the speed regulation of steam engines. From this point to the beginning of the 1940's, one finds practically no development of comprehensive techniques, as we know them today, for the analysis and synthesis of automatic control. Since the end of World War II, however, aided by the development of electronics, spectacular advances have been made in both the variety and number of automatic control systems. During the 1950's the basic concept of automatic control was firmly established, embodied in a simple feedback diagram. These years saw also the development of the frequency response concept of linear feedback control systems for the analysis of the system, stability theory, and feedback system design by simple lead and/or lag compensation techniques. In more recent years, interest has grown in the effect on the performance of control systems of nonlinearities which appear in practice. Both the describing function technique and the phase plane method proved to be very useful in the design and analysis of various nonlinear control systems.

One of the most fruitful harvests of the development of control theory was the discovery of the dependence on system inputs of the dynamic behavior of nonlinear control systems. It became of considerable importance to consider the behavior of control systems on the basis of stochastic theory for randomly varying signals which, in practice, characterize the input. Although hundreds of papers have been written to explain the mysteries of systems response to random inputs, these were always based on the simple feedback control concept.

As the uses of automatic control have increased, much attention has been directed to the control of large scale industrial plants with complex facilities. Simultaneously, the demands placed on the control systems have severely taxed the designers to analyze the dynamic behavior of existing systems more precisely and to improve the control performance.

As a result, the control concept can no longer be represented by a simple feedback loop. With the help of high speed digital computers, one strives to establish the "best" possible strategy to reach a desired goal or "optimum." This trend in automatic control is due to a remarkable growth of interest in problems of systems optimization and of optimal control, which have seen active development only within the past seven or eight years. Examples are R. Bellman's dynamic programming and the application of L. S. Pontryagin's maximum principle to control systems theory.

However, we cannot overlook the vital lack of modern control theory in practical applications. In fact, the dynamical characteristics of a dynamical system cannot be duplicated by a mathematical model but undergo drastic changes with time and environment. To counteract unduly large changes in a dynamical system which is to be controlled, it becomes necessary to vary characteristics of the controller while it is in operation. Thus one becomes concerned with the concept of adaptive control, and this may be approximately realized by measurement and computation using a form of logic programming. The words "approximately realized" are very significant here. The mathematical modeling itself cannot be realized in an absolutely accurate fashion for randomly varying characteristics but can only be performed in an approximate fashion in the stochastic sense. Thus one strives for a best approximation, recognizing the uncertainty of phenomena. This art of approximation in automatic control can be created by invoking the principles of statistical decision theory. If these principles are properly introduced and applied, the possibility of realizing a situation in which the ultimate optimization is performed on the basis of sequences of decisions identifying the characteristics of the controlled system will not be only an ideal for the remote future.

With the above viewpoint in mind, the authors have devoted the present volume to the combination of control theory with statistical decision theory. Chapter 1 serves as a brief review of the history of control theory and emphasizes the need for the introduction of statistical decision theory. Chapter 2 reviews the mathematical background that plays so important a role in the present studies. Chapter 3 presents the basic concept of statistical decision theory, and Chapter 4 describes the method of solving statistical decision problems. The application of statistical decision concepts to control problems is explained in Chapter 5, including simple numerical examples. Chapter 6 describes a method of designing an adaptive control system from the nonsequential point of view. An application of the sequential decision procedure to the design of decision adaptive control systems is illustrated in Chapter 7. Comparison of the sequential decision procedure with the nonsequential one is also discussed in some detail. Chapter 8 is devoted to the description of a method of the adaptive adjustment of parameters contained in nonlinear control systems. In this chapter, a new idea for constructing the decision adaptive logic programming is presented.

It is the authors pleasure to acknowledge the encouragement of Professor Richard Bellman and to thank him for taking this volume into his authoritative series for Academic Press. The authors wish specifically to thank Professor Walter M. Wonham of the Division of Applied Mathematics, Brown University for his valuable suggestions. The encouragement extended by Professor Hiroshi Nishihara of the Department of Nuclear Engineering of Kyoto University is gratefully recorded. Finally, the authors would like to express their thanks to Miss Hideko Iwamoto, who typed the final manuscript and helped in various ways.

Kyoto   Yoshikazu Sawaragi
Kyoto   Yoshifumi Sunaharu*
Yokosuka   Takayoshi Nakamizo

March 1967

* Present address: Center for Dynamical Systems, Division of Applied Mathematics, Brown University, Providence, Rhode Island.

CONTENTS

Chapter 4. Evaluation Functions and Solutions in Statistical Decision Theory

Chapter 5. Statistical Decision Concept in Control Processes

Chapter 6. Nonsequential Decision Approaches in Adaptive Control Systems

Chapter 7. Sequential Decision Approaches in Adaptive Control Systems

Chapter 8. **Adaptive Adjustment of Parameters of Nonlinear Control Systems**

Chapter 9. **Some Future Problems in Applications of Statistical Decision Theory to Control Processes**

CHAPTER 1

Introduction

1.1 Historical Development of Automatic Control

Automatic control may be defined as follows: automatic control is the means of automatically keeping a physical variable as faithfully as possible to a desired state by cancelling the disturbance of environments. A control system consists of a controlled system or a process which is to be controlled, a device for measuring the instantaneous value of the

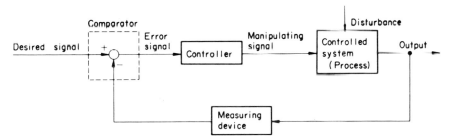

FIG. 1.1. Basic concept of automatic control: a simple feedback loop.

system output, a comparator for generating an error signal measuring the deviation of the output signal from the desired value, and a controller which modifies the error signal and generates a manipulating signal for correcting the state of the controlled system in such a way as to reduce the error toward zero. The basic concept may thus be embodied in a simple feedback loop, as shown in Fig. 1.1. In its primitive stage this loop was responsible for the widespread use of the practical technique of automatic control. It is well known that the basic principle of feedback control shown in the figure has already been utilized in electronic communications engineering. The modern intense interest in automatic

1

control has evolved from the work on electronic feedback amplifiers of Nyquist[1] and others at Bell Telephone Laboratories in 1932. Early in the development of control theory attention in electronic communications engineering was shifted directly from electronic feedback amplifiers to feedback control circuits. For example, if we consider a transfer element whose stationary magnitude of output is linearly related to the small magnitude of input around the balancing point, the relation between the

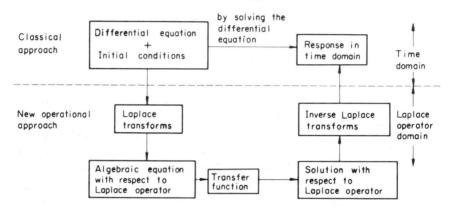

FIG. 1.2. Approach for linear automatic control systems.

output $x(t)$ and the input $y(t)$ is expressed by a linear differential equation with constant coefficients. This means that the transfer characteristic of the element can be considered approximately linear in the small range of magnitude of the input signal.

Such an idealized situation provides the possibility of introducing the linear integral transformation, which is the well-known Laplace transformation. The Laplace transformation is a very useful tool for analyzing system performance. It is the transfer function $G_0(s)$, defined by $G_0(s) = L[x(t)]/L[y(t)]$, where $x(t)$ and $y(t)$ are the output and input signals, respectively. The method of Laplace transformation was a kind of operational calculus in the first stages of control theory, and it was very much more useful than the method of solving the differential equation, even though it seems to be a bypass (see Fig. 1.2), because the frequency transfer function was introduced by letting $s = j\omega$, where $\omega = 2\pi f$, and it provided much useful information touching on system performance in the frequency domain. The 1950's saw the development

[1] H. Nyquist, Regeneration theory. *Bell System Tech. J.* **11**, 126 (1932).

of the frequency response concept of linear feedback control systems for evaluating system performance, stability, and feedback system design. Although this was the birth of linear feedback control theory and was built up around the Laplace transformation, the problems encountered with it were concerned only with properties that can be associated with the configuration of the system—first by virtue of the configuration alone and then by virtue of specific transfer functions within that configuration. For example, a fundamental problem in feedback theory is the determination of the extent to which a given parameter can change without causing instability of the system. Once this analytical problem is solved, the same technique by which it was solved can be utilized to design a system in which the sensitivity to a particular parameter is controlled both by the choice of an appropriate configuration and by the selection of suitable transfer functions.

In spite of the systematic establishment of linear control theory and the numerous contributions made to it by many scientists the phenomena of actual control systems have yielded a wide variety of mathematical problems which the theory cannot solve. It is quite certain that many control engineers were mystified by the fact that an automatic control system, well designed by linear control theory, fluctuates with constant amplitude and frequency around its balancing level. This phenomenon, which cannot be solved by linear control theory, has been called the limit cycle, and it is due to nonlinear transfer characteristics existing within the feedback control circuit. Consequently, we are forced to take into account an extended region of the input magnitude. Our analytical field of vision must be extended to various kinds of nonlinear characteristics which are always present in control systems, whether intentionally placed there or not. Much attention has, therefore, been directed to the existence of nonlinear characteristics. The most important contribution in this area was the development of the describing function technique for quasilinearization, proposed by Kochenburger,[2] in which a nonlinear element with a single input and the corresponding output is approximately represented by an equivalent transfer function, dependent upon the amplitude of the sinusoidal input signal which is applied to the nonlinear element. Although the describing function method is particularly useful for determining the steady-state response and the existence of limit cycles, it cannot provide information concerning the transient state of

[2] R. J. Kochenburger, *Trans. AIEE* **69,** Pt. I (1950).

system responses. The phase plane technique[3,4] is particularly useful for exploring precisely the nature of the transient behavior of nonlinear control systems with various classes of deterministic input signals. The so-called bang-bang control systems are particularly important. The fact that, when a bang-bang control system is disturbed from its zero-error position, it comes back to that position with maximal power is itself more satisfactory, from the point of view of rapid response for the correction, than the behavior of a conventional linear servo system. However, a disadvantage of an on-off servo system is that there is risk of overshooting the newly desired level and producing steady-state oscillations. This disadvantage may be avoided if changes in the transient state are systematically forecast in such a way that there is no overshooting. With respect to its special performance the on-off system is superior to any linear servo system that is limited to the same maximal torque. The theoretical aspect of the synthetical technique mentioned above relates to the optimization of bang-bang servo systems. It cannot be overlooked in this period that as small-size high-speed digital computing equipment has become more practical, more and more control systems for industrial applications incorporate a digital computer as one of its elements. The widespread use of practical electronic computers—first the analog type, about 1957, and later the digital type, about 1959—has greatly extended the ability of control engineers to analyze and design control systems.

Gradually, as the uses of automatic control have multiplied in process industries, in manufacturing, in the steering and operation of modern weapons, and in setting the attitude for flight of artificial satellites, the demands placed on control systems have also severely taxed the designers and forced them to analyze the dynamic behavior of existing systems more precisely to improve control performance. By inserting a digital computer the control designer achieves the possibility of much greater flexibility in the transfer characteristics of the controller, so that it is better able to take automatically into account changes in the environment and in the nature of the signals. Both such types of change (or, more broadly, changes in Nature) are random, because random noise may be generated within the system or the input signal contaminated

[3] I. Flügge-Lotz, "Discontinuous Automatic Control." Princeton Univ. Press, Princeton, New Jersey, 1953.

[4] Ya. Z. Typkin, "The Theory of Relay Systems of Automatic Control." Gostekhizat, Moscow, 1955.

with random noise. Since random changes are an inevitable feature of any physical system, they must be considered in any proper control system design. Random noise may be defined as any random time function whose magnitude at any given moment cannot be predicted with certainty from either experience or studies of preceding values. It is, therefore, quite apparent that the conventional continuous time functions used for describing sinusoidal waves or waves involving harmonics cannot be used for describing random signals, and it is natural that a statistical technique must be applied to control theory.

In the analysis and synthesis of linear control systems the principle of superposition allows the performance specification of a linear control system subjected to an arbitrary input to be evaluated, if the behavior for a unit impulse signal is known. So far, step responses and sinusoidal response measurements have, therefore, been an accepted method of describing control performance and of synthesizing control systems. Perhaps the most significant work in control theory to evolve from research during World War II was the basic study of the design of optimal linear filters for the processing of random signals. Wiener[5] had developed analytical methods of finding the optimal linear predictor, or filter. The earliest statistical approach to control engineering was made by James et al.[6] Excellent introductions to the subject are given by Truxal,[7] Solodovnikov,[8] and Gibson,[9] and many recent textbooks on control theory make mention of it. Unquestionably, the prime results of these studies were the entirely novel viewpoint introduced into control system design and the recognition of problems associated with the mathematical characterization of actual signals.

The gradual acceptance of the importance of nonlinear characteristics shifted attention to the nature of input signals and to changing modes of control action in adaptive, self-optimizing, and computer control systems, which affected system performance in a manner which could not be easily predicted. Control theory and its practice were placed in a new

[5] N. Wiener, "Extrapolation, Interpolation and Smoothing of Stationary Time Series with Engineering Applications." Wiley, New York, 1948.

[6] H. M. James, N. B. Nichols, and R. S. Phillips, "Theory of Servomechanisms," MIT Radiation Lab. Series, Vol. 25. McGraw-Hill, New York, 1947.

[7] J. G. Truxal, "Automatic Feedback Control System Synthesis." McGraw-Hill, New York, 1955.

[8] V. V. Solodovnikov, "Introduction to the Statistical Dynamics of Automatic Control." Dover, New York, 1960.

[9] J. E. Gibson, "Non-Linear Automatic Control." McGraw-Hill, New York, 1963.

situation, in which the characteristics of the control elements were non-linear; these undergo drastic changes in the stochastic sense, according to time and environment. It was the birth of theoretical studies of adaptive control concepts.

As supporting background for our development of the analytic aspect, the next section is a brief introduction to stochastic methods. No attempt is made to give a comprehensive treatment, for which the reader is referred to the literature.[10–15]

1.2 Control Systems and Stochastics

Randomness or unpredictability can enter a control system in the following ways: the information signal generated by the source may not be completely predictable, the control system may be randomly disturbed, and parameters of the control system may randomly change with time. Thus, the output of control systems becomes a random time function.

It is quite apparent that the conventional continuous functions used for describing a sine wave [Fig. 1.3(top)] or waves with harmonics cannot be used for expressing a random process actually observed [Fig. 1.3 (bottom)]. Naturally, it is impossible to predict the exact value of a random time function at any given instant of time, as can be done with conventional functions. We must, therefore, relax our demands concerning the description of the random signal shown in Fig. 1.3 (bottom). Concerning the mathematical description of random time functions, it is, at best, possible only to say that the function will probably be within certain limits with respect to the statistical mean. Thus, it is clear that the mathematics pertinent to a study of random signals

[10] J. S. Bendat, "Principles and Applications of Random Noise Theory." Wiley, New York, 1959.

[11] H. L. Newton, L. A. Gould, and J. F. Kaiser, "Analytic Design of Linear Feedback Controls." Wiley, New York, 1957.

[12] D. Middleton, "An Introduction to Statistical Communication Theory." McGraw-Hill, New York, 1961.

[13] G. J. Thaler and M. P. Pastel, "Analysis and Design of Non-Linear Feedback Control Systems." McGraw-Hill, New York, 1962.

[14] See Ref. 6.

[15] See Ref. 7.

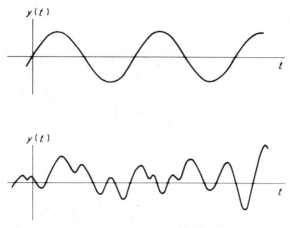

$y(t)$

t

$y(t)$

t

FIG. 1.3. A sine wave and a random process: (top) a sine wave $y(t) = A_y \sin \omega_0 t$; (bottom) a random process $y(t)$.

and noise in control systems is modern stochastic theory. Relevant portions of modern stochastics in the field of control theory will be introduced in sufficient detail, so that readers previously unfamiliar with the subject may become acquainted with the tools they need for the main part of this book.

1.3   Adaptive Control and Decision Theory

As we have already pointed out, the birth of the concept of adaptive control took place during the second half of the 1950's, and the control engineer turned gradually to the new computer tool. Up to the present time much attention has been directed to the design of adaptive or self-optimizing control systems, which automatically measure and compensate for parameter variations in some part of the system, bringing the control performance within a prescribed tolerance.

In the early years of the development of adaptive control we could have said that its basic concept was realized by two different modes. The first was originated by Draper and Li[16]; in this mode attention is

[16] Y. T. Li, The philosophy of adaptive control; automatic and remote control. *Proc. First IFAC Congress, Moscow, USSR, June, 1960.* Butterworths, London and Washington, D.C., 1960.

focused on the realization of an optimal static condition of the control
operation for the process. The second involves adaptivity in the sense
that variations in process dynamics are automatically corrected for.
This is the type of control system usually termed the adaptive control
system. It is characterized by a group of components for the automatic
measurement of process dynamics and another group for the automatic
adjustment of controller parameters.[17] The concept of adaptive control
has thus been loosely defined as one involving automatic measurement

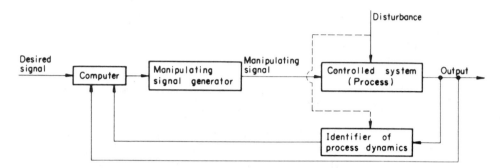

FIG. 1.4. Typical configuration of an adaptive control.

of a desired signal in the presence of random noise, process dynamics,
and subsequent self-adjustment of control parameters so as to maintain
satisfactory dynamic control. This definition reveals that the systems are
often specific types of computer control systems, because they involve a
measurement of process dynamics in some form, and that two connected
elements, identification and optimization, always appear in some form.
Identification signifies the measurement of the system dynamics to be
controlled, and optimization signifies the generation of an appropriate
actuating signal. Figure 1.4 shows a typical configuration of an adaptive
control system.

The first essential in an approach to control system design in an
adaptive sense is, therefore, the establishment of identification methods,
because the adaptivity depends upon an exact and rapid solution of the
identification. A typical adaptive control system contains a process
identifier constructed according to a mathematical model of the process.

[17] J. A. Aseltine, A. R. Mancini, and C. W. Sartue, A survey of adaptive control
systems. *IRE Trans. Automatic Control* **6**, 102 (1958).

The second essential is the optimization. Once the identification problem is solved, then the result is used to produce the manipulating signal, which drives the process and maintains optimal control by a specific performance criterion. Generally, the procedure of optimization takes the form of parameter adjustment of the controller. However, very often it is unnecessarily restricted in flexibility. Recent configurations of adaptive control systems circumvent this restriction by a method in which the manipulating signal is directly generated by a computer in accordance with observations of the system input, the system response, and the identified process dynamics.

Nevertheless, in practice there exist many fundamental difficulties in solving the identification problem, such as limits on the measuring equipment and constraints on the time permitted for the measurement. In other words, various identification schemes proposed up to the present can only be approximately accurate, and process parameters can be measured only by the manner in which their variations are reflected in the difference between the output of the true system and the mathematical model. An error-free identification is almost impossible to establish because of the following inevitable factors:

1. It is impossible to make the measuring time short without deteriorating its accuracy, therefore, the time must be fairly long. However, a long time is not favorable. Hence we must look for a compromise between the measuring time interval and the accuracy.

2. The measuring results are generally obscured by the existence of random noise or disturbance in the input and output of the system, and the incoming signal to the measuring device is probably contaminated with random noise. Both internal and external noises contribute to the ambiguity of the information to be identified.

3. Other factors are incompleteness of equipment and error induced in the signal conversion.

Thus, the central problem of identification in adaptive control systems is to determine the true value of a parameter from incomplete information. The principal line of attack is to apply statistical decision theory which, in fact, provides a very general optimal synthesis method for statistical inference and, hence, for the design of the adaptive loop. Figure 1.5 is a possible configuration of an adaptive control system, taking the desired generality mentioned above into account. The adaptive loop of this system consists of a process identifier, a signal identifier, and a decision computer. The identification problem is solved by the process identifier. The signal identifier extracts the properties of the input signals in the presence of random noise as a basis for the selection of control performance or optimization criteria. Utilizing the results of both process and the signal identifiers, the decision computer determines the optimal control strategy. The controller shown in Fig. 1.5 may be a time-variant gain or time-variant transfer characteristic or, alternatively,

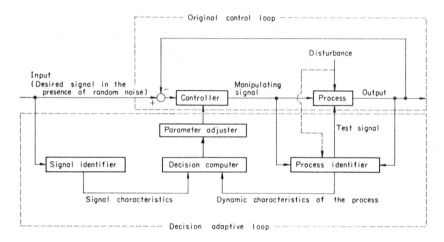

FIG. 1.5. Typical configuration of an adaptive control system containing a decision computer.

a function generator, the output of which is the manipulating signal selected by the decision computer.

Decision adaptive control not only is the most practical type of automatic control we have at present, but also indicates a high degree of performance in future control. In spite of its importance, however, major efforts have been directed only to developing the process identifier. Even with the concentrated work on identification technique there still exist a great many unsolved problems of fundamental significance. For example: in the presence of random noise in measurements what time interval is required for determining the process dynamics to a specified accuracy?

A powerful approach to such a difficult problem unquestionably is statistical decision theory. Up to the present, the chief applications of this theory have been in the field of communications theory, particularly to radar detection problems. Broadly speaking, since decision theory is concerned with making an optimal decision in the face of several choices we must find the corresponding optimal control strategy in accordance with changes of a process dynamics or system input by sequences of decisions. Thus, decision theory is both a basis of signal identification and a guide to the design of adaptive control systems.

CHAPTER 2

Mathematical Description of Random Processes

2.1 Introductory Remarks

The reason for the randomness we observe in a physical phenomenon may be that we did not know, and so could not adjust, all the initial states and causal forces, or the relation between the causal forces and their combined effects is inherently indeterminable, or we do not have enough data on the factors in our problem. If all the conditions were perfectly known, then the situation would become deterministic; however, such a situation is an entirely ideal one in the field of system science.

One means of mathematically describing a random phenomenon is the probability concept, which is established by the statistical regularity of random phenomena. Thus, the classical theory of probability and statistics is basic to the notion of random processes; it will be explained in the following sections. The purpose of this chapter is to show the development of the modern stochastic theory of random processes. However, since this will be done without any pretense at mathematical rigor, the authors should like to recommend the reading of several excellent books[1-6] to anyone wishing to study the mathematical theory of random processes.

[1] J. L. Doob, "Stochastic Processes." Wiley, New York, 1953.
[2] H. Cramer, "Mathematical Methods of Statistics." Princeton Univ. Press, Princeton, New Jersey, 1946.
[3] M. Loève, "Probability Theory." Van Nostrand, Princeton, New Jersey, 1955.
[4] M. S. Bartlett, "An Introduction to Stochastic Processes." Cambridge Univ. Press, London and New York, 1955.
[5] A. M. Yaglom, "An Introduction to the Theory of Stationary Random Functions." Prentice-Hall, Englewood Cliffs, New Jersey, 1962.
[6] W. Feller, "Probability Theory and its Applications—I." Wiley, New York, 1950.

2.2 Probability

Let us toss a uniform and symmetric die. As the result of our throw one of six faces, having from 1 dot to 6 dots, appears. Table 2.1 shows the results of ten trials, in which the symbol x_i $(i = 1, 2, \ldots, 10)$ expresses the result of the ith trial. Since we cannot predict the result because of such indeterminable factors as the initial state of the die in our palm, the initial angle of throw, the initial velocity of the die, and the smoothness of the table on which the die falls, the appearance of any

TABLE 2.1

Numerical Results of Ten Trials of Tossing a Die

	Trial No., N									
	I	II	III	IV	V	VI	VII	VIII	IX	X
Trials x_i	x_1	x_2	x_3	x_4	x_5	x_6	x_7	x_8	x_9	x_{10}
Result, M	1	4	5	3	1	2	6	4	2	5

particular face is a random event. This means that the value of x_i cannot be uniquely determined. In fact, it might seem that there is no regularity in this event. However, if the number of trials is sufficiently large, some regularity appears. For example, suppose that we observe M particular events, say "even face," in N trials of tossing a die; then the fraction M/N is called the frequency of appearance of the particular result "even face." If N is sufficiently large, the frequency leads us to the concept of probability. However, since it is impossible to define directly the probability by the limiting form $\lim_{N \to \infty} (M/N)$, we introduce the concept of sets and define the probability.

The primitive notion of the theory of probability is that of a set of elementary events. Naturally, it is possible to record the results of a long series of trials, such as that mentioned above, in the form of Table 2.1. The result x_i $(i = 1, 2, \ldots, 10, \ldots, N)$ is, of course, the appearance n of any particular die face, where $n = 1, 2, 3, 4, 5, 6$. It is often convenient to consider an experiment and its possible outcomes as defining, respectively, a Euclidean space and points in it. We may consider a point called the sample point, or elementary event. The appearance of any particular face is an elementary event, which is expressed by e_n. We thus can construct a set, the points x_i corresponding to the appearance n of the face when the number of trials, N, is sufficiently large, and this set is expressed by the symbol $\mathscr{E}$. Since the set $\mathscr{E}$ may be considered the totality of sample points corresponding to the aggregate of all possible outcomes of the experiments, it is often called the sample space. As stated above, the whole set $\mathscr{E}$ of elementary events contains the six elements e_1, e_2, e_3, e_4, e_5, e_6. It is obvious that as a result of a throw we shall certainly obtain one of the faces having 1 to 6 dots. We are, therefore, sure that one of the elementary events e_i of the set $\mathscr{E}$ will appear.

For example, the symbol x_i in Table 2.1 expresses the value of the realization of an elementary event e_i. We recall our problem. We are investigating the random event A that an even face appears. If we express the event A, consisting of the elementary events face 2, face 4, and face 6, by the symbol (e_2, e_4, e_6), then this event appears when the result of a throw is the face 2, 4, or 6. In other words, the event consisting of the elementary events limited to the faces 2, 4, and 6 is examined.

Another example follows. We investigate the appearance of an arbitrary face that is not 6. The random event A in this case consists of five elements, $(e_1, e_2, e_3, e_4, e_5)$. Since there exist many possible investigations of random events, we can form a set $\mathscr{F}$ of random events, which is a set of all subsets of the set $\mathscr{E}$.

Moreover, we shall consider the event in which a face with a number higher than 6 appears. Such an event is, of course, impossible to realize, and usually is not considered a random event; however, we shall consider it an elementary event of the set $\mathscr{E}$ and express it as an "empty" set by using the symbol zero, 0. Since we shall be obliged to perform such mathematical computations under the operation of complementation, finite union and finite intersection in working with the sets theory, the properties of sets in which the probability is defined must be characterized. We define the property of the set $\mathscr{F}$ described above:

1. The set $\mathscr{E}$ is contained in the set $\mathscr{F}$.
2. If the random event A is contained in the set $\mathscr{F}$, the complement A^C of the random event A is also contained in the set $\mathscr{F}$.
3. If the random event A_j ($j = 1, 2, \ldots, n$) is contained in the set $\mathscr{F}$, then the event appearing if and only if the event A_j has occurred is also contained in the set $\mathscr{F}$.

Here $\mathscr{F}$ is the so-called Borel field of sets,[7] and every element of the Borel field $\mathscr{F}$ of subsets of the set $\mathscr{E}$ of elementary events is called a random event. By considering the Borel field of the set the probability is defined as follows:

DEFINITION. A nonnegative real number $\Pr(A)$ is assigned to each set $\mathscr{A}$ in the set $\mathscr{F}$. This number $\Pr(A)$ is called the probability of the random event A.

Naturally, the set $\mathscr{A}$ is a subset of the set $\mathscr{E}$; this notion is illustrated in Fig. 2.1, where the area E represents the set of elementary events $\mathscr{E}$

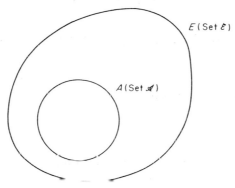

FIG. 2.1. The sets $\mathscr{E}$ and $\mathscr{A}$ associated with the definition of probability.

and the circle A represents the subset $\mathscr{A}$ of the set $\mathscr{E}$. The probability can now be understood as the ratio of the area A to the area E. It is also, thus, a measure given by the ratio of the subset $\mathscr{A}$ to the set $\mathscr{E}$. The space in which the probability is defined as a measure is called the probability space.

Although the probability has now been defined, the mathematical aspect of probability is not yet made precise. If the mathematical properties are to be made precise, a system of axioms formalizing them must be constructed. Although many studies have been devoted to the axiomatization of the theory of probability, the system of axioms described briefly in this section was constructed by Kolmogorov.[8]

[7] R. von Mises, "Mathematical Theory of Probability and Statistics." Academic Press, New York, 1964.

[8] A. N. Kolmogorov, "Foundations of the Theory of Probability." Chelsea, New York, 1956.

As we have said, the notion of probability means the statistical regularity of random events. It has, then, been observed that the frequency of occurrence of a random event will oscillate about some fixed number when the number of trials is sufficiently large. This regularity and the fact that the frequency is a nonnegative fraction which is less than or equal to 1 lead us to accept the following axioms of Kolmogorov[8]:

AXIOM 1.   There is a certain number $\Pr(A)$, called the probability of every random event A. This number $\Pr(A)$ satisfies the inequality

$$0 \leq \Pr(A) \leq 1 \tag{2.1}$$

The second axiom is easily accepted by taking the property of the sure event into account.

AXIOM 2.   The probability of the sure event is

$$\Pr(E) = 1 \tag{2.2}$$

We know that the frequency of appearance of the particular face 1 when a die is tossed oscillates about the number $1/6$. The same may be said of frequency of appearance of the particular face 2. These two events are exclusive. The frequency of occurrence of *either* face 1 or face 2 oscillates about the number $1/3$, which equals the sum of their frequencies. By taking this property of the frequency of alternative of events into account we find the third axiom:

AXIOM 3.   If there is a finite or countable sequence of exclusive events A_k $(k = 1, 2, \ldots)$, then the probability of the alternative of exclusive events equals the sum of the probabilities of these events; that is,

$$\Pr(A_1 \cup A_2 \cup \cdots \cup A_n \cup \cdots) = \sum_{k=1}^{\infty} \Pr(A_k) \tag{2.3}$$

The property expressed by Axiom 3 is called the countable additivity of probability.

2.3 Joint Probability

In the preceding section we have been primarily concerned with the results of a single experiment. In practice, however, we consider the results of several different experiments: for instance, the outcome of throwing a pair of dice or the magnitude of a randomly time-varying signal at several different instants of time. Suppose we wish to know the probability that one die will show the face with three dots and the other the face with six dots. The probability relating to such combined experiments is called the joint probability. The joint probability has the same basic properties as those described in the preceding section. If the probability that both the mth result of experiment A and the nth result of the experiment B occur is expressed by $\Pr(A_m, B_n)$, then it follows from Eq. (2.1) that

$$0 \leq \Pr(A_m, B_n) \leq 1 \tag{2.4}$$

If there exist M possible outcomes $\{A_m\}$ and N possible outcomes $\{B_n\}$ and, moreover, all the trials are mutually exclusive, it further follows that

$$\sum_{m-1}^{M} \sum_{n-1}^{N} \Pr(A_m, B_n) = 1 \tag{2.5}$$

2.4 Conditional Probability

Here is a problem: What is the probability of an event A when another event B has already occurred? We do not focus our attention on the joint probability of the combined results with respect to the events A and B, but on the conditional probability corresponding to the conditional frequency of the event A, provided that the event B has already occurred. See Fig. 2.2. Let B be an event in the set $\mathscr{E}$ of elementary events. The set $\mathscr{B}$ is, therefore, an element of the Borel field $\mathscr{F}$ of subsets of the set $\mathscr{E}$ of all elementary events. The probability of the event B is expressed by $\Pr(B)$ and $\Pr(B) \geq 0$.

We shall consider another arbitrary event A. In Fig. 2.2 the event expressed by the symbol AB contains all the results, i.e., sample points, which are common to A and B. Of course, if the events A and B exclude each other, then there are no points common to A and B, and the event included in the area AB cannot occur. The hatched area in the figure represents the random event B. The crosshatched area represents the random event A, which occurs provided that B has occurred. The latter clause is written $A \mid B$. The probability of the event $A \mid B$ is $\Pr(A \mid B)$; since this may be defined by a concept similar to that outlined in the

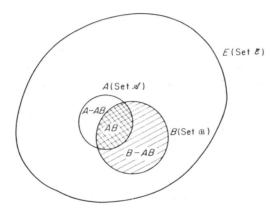

FIG. 2.2. The conditional probability.

previous section, there is no need to postulate the existence of probability $\Pr(A \mid B)$ and its properties.

To show an important equality we shall consider a simple experiment. Suppose that we have performed N random experiments and observed that the event B occurred M times. Moreover, we observed the event A to occur K times, where $K \leq M$ in these experiments. The frequency of event B is M/N, and the frequency of AB, the event in which both A and B occur, is K/N. The frequency of A when B has already occurred is K/M. Therefore, we have

$$\frac{K}{M} = \frac{K/N}{M/N} \qquad (2.6)$$

By observing this formula we can accept the following equality.

Let the probability of the event B be $\Pr(B)$ and let $\Pr(B)$ be greater than 0. The conditional probability of the event A when event B has occurred is given by

$$Pr(A \mid B) = \frac{Pr(A, B)}{Pr(B)} \tag{2.7a}$$

Similarly,

$$Pr(B \mid A) = \frac{Pr(A, B)}{Pr(A)} \tag{2.7b}$$

where $Pr(A) > 0$. From Eqs. (2.7) it follows that

$$Pr(A, B) = Pr(B) \, Pr(A \mid B) = Pr(A) \, Pr(B \mid A) \tag{2.8}$$

Now let $A_1, A_2, \ldots, A_{n-1}, A_n$ be n random events. An extension of the relation given by Eq. (2.8) to the n-dimensional case is the following relation, which is easily obtained:

$$Pr(A_1, A_2, \ldots, A_n) = Pr(A_1) \, Pr(A_2 \mid A_1) \, Pr(A_3 \mid A_1, A_2)$$

$$\cdots Pr(A_n \mid A_1, A_2, \ldots, A_{n-1}) \tag{2.9}$$

If the occurrence of event B does not influence the occurrence of the event A, we may say that the occurrence of A is independent of the occurrence of B. Therefore, since

$$Pr(A, B) = Pr(A) \, Pr(B) \tag{2.10}$$

then formulas (2.7a) and (2.7b) may be expressed, respectively, as

$$Pr(A \mid B) = Pr(A) \tag{2.11a}$$

and

$$Pr(B \mid A) = Pr(B) \tag{2.11b}$$

2.5 Bayes' Theorem

The most typical problem that will lead us to an understanding of Bayes' theorem is the problem of picking up a particular ball stored in many urns. We consider two urns. There are three white and four black balls in the first urn and two white and four black balls in the second. From an urn selected at random we pick one ball up at random. What is the probability of picking up a white ball if the probability of selecting each of the urns is given? We express the events of selecting the first urn and of selecting the second urn by A_1 and A_2, respectively. The event of selecting a white ball is denoted by B. Since event B may occur together with either event A_1 or event A_2, and since the events A_1B and A_2B are mutually exclusive, we have

$$Pr(B) = Pr(A_1, B) + Pr(A_2, B) \qquad (2.12)$$

By applying Eq. (2.7b) to Eq. (2.12), we obtain

$$Pr(B) = Pr(A_1)\,Pr(B\,|\,A_1) + Pr(A_2)\,Pr(B\,|\,A_2) \qquad (2.13)$$

When the probability of selecting each of the urns equals 1/2, we have $Pr(A_1) = Pr(A_2) = 1/2$, $Pr(B\,|\,A_1) = 3/7$, and $Pr(B\,|\,A_2) = 1/3$. Therefore, with these values Eq. (2.13) becomes

$$Pr(B) = (\tfrac{1}{2}\cdot\tfrac{3}{7}) + (\tfrac{1}{2}\cdot\tfrac{1}{3}) = 0.38 \qquad (2.14)$$

From the example given above we can obtain the following theorem:

THEOREM. If the random events $A_1, A_2, \ldots$ are exclusive, then for any random event B we have

$$Pr(B) = Pr(A_1)\,Pr(B\,|\,A_1) + Pr(A_2)\,Pr(B\,|\,A_2) + \cdots \qquad (2.15)$$

Now we consider the inverse situation. Suppose that the event B has occurred. What is the probability of the events A_i, where in this example i is equal to 1 or 2? By substituting A_i for A in Eq. (2.8) we obtain

$$Pr(A_i\,|\,B) = \frac{Pr(A_i)\,Pr(B\,|\,A_i)}{Pr(B)} \qquad (2.16)$$

Since $\Pr(B)$ is given by Eq. (2.15), Eq. (2.16) becomes

$$\Pr(A_i \mid B) = \frac{\Pr(A_i)\,\Pr(B \mid A_i)}{\Pr(A_1)\,\Pr(B \mid A_1) + \Pr(A_2)\,\Pr(B \mid A_2)} \qquad (2.17)$$

This formula is called Bayes' formula and is the probability of the event A_i after the event B has occurred; therefore it is also called the formula for a posteriori probability. The probabilities $\Pr(A_i)$ are called the a priori probabilities. In the example given in this section the formula gives us the answer to the question, "What is the probability that a white ball will be obtained from the first urn?"

2.6 Probability Distribution and Probability Density Function

As we have seen, we can assign a number to every elementary event in the set $\mathscr{E}$. We can assign to every result of a die throw one of the numbers n ($n = 1, 2, \ldots, 6$) corresponding to the number of dots appearing on the face. If now we identify the point k with the event that k dots appear when we throw the die, then the function $x(k) = k$ is considered a variable, such that $x(k)$ equals the number of dots. Functions such as $g(k) = k^2$ and $g'(k) = \exp(k^2)$ may also be considered. All these functions are called random variables.* A single-valued real function whose probability is defined on the set $\mathscr{E}$ is called a random variable.[9] Therefore, a random variable is a function defined on the result of a random event. Conversely, every numerically valued random event may be interpreted as the value of a random variable X, namely, the random variable X defined on the real line for every real number x by $X(x) = x$. Roughly speaking, a quantity X is said to be a random variable, or an observed value of a numerically valued random event, if for every real number x there exists a probability $\Pr(X \leq x)$ that X is less than or equal to x.

Once again we shall consider the example of tossing a die. It is easily observed that the random variable may take six values $x_n = n$ ($n = 1,$ 2, 3, 4, 5, 6) with the same probabilities. Therefore, the following ranks

---

* The term "random variable" is somewhat confusing. Although the "random function" would be more appropriate, the term used here is due to tradition.

[9] E. Parzen, "Modern Probability Theory and Its Applications." Wiley, New York, 1960.

of probability may be given:

$$\Pr(X < x) = 0 \qquad\qquad\qquad\qquad \text{for} \quad x < 1$$
$$\Pr(X < x) = \tfrac{1}{6} \qquad\qquad\qquad\qquad \text{for} \quad x < 2$$
$$\Pr(X < x) = \Pr(X = 1) + \Pr(X = 2) = \tfrac{1}{3} \qquad \text{for} \quad x < 3$$
$$\Pr(X < x) = \Pr(X \le 6) = \sum_{n=1}^{6} \Pr(X = n) = 1 \qquad \text{for} \quad x \le 6$$

In general, we may define a mathematical function as

$$\Pr(-\infty < X \le x) = P(x) \tag{2.18}$$

and this function is called the probability distribution of the random variable X. From the axioms of Kolmogorov the properties of the probability distribution are easily stated:

1. For $-\infty < x < \infty$, $P(x) \ge 0$. $\qquad\qquad\qquad$ (2.19a)

2. $0 \le P(x) \le 1$ $\qquad\qquad\qquad\qquad\qquad\qquad\qquad$ (2.19b)

    $\lim\limits_{x \to \infty} P(x) = 1$ $\qquad\qquad\qquad\qquad\qquad\qquad\qquad$ (2.19c)

    $\lim\limits_{x \to -\infty} P(x) = 0$ $\qquad\qquad\qquad\qquad\qquad\qquad$ (2.19d)

3. $P(x)$ is a monotone increasing function with respect to the condition $x \to \infty$.

It further follows that the probability that the random variable x will fall within the interval $[a, b]$ is simply the difference between the values of the probability distribution determined at both endpoints of the interval; that is,

$$\Pr(a < x \le b) = P(b) - P(a) \tag{2.20}$$

There are three types of random variables: the continuous type, the discrete type, and the mixed type.

An example of the first type is the random variable thermal noise, which is measured at a specified instant of time and may take arbitrary values between plus and minus infinity. A random variable for which the probability distribution is everywhere continuous is called a continuous random variable. In such case we may define the probability density function $p(x)$ as the derivative of the probability distribution.

By letting $b = x + \epsilon$ and $a = x - \epsilon$ in Eq. (2.20) we find that the probability density function $p(x)$ may be defined as

$$p(x) = \lim_{\epsilon \to 0} \frac{P(x + \epsilon) - P(x - \epsilon)}{2\epsilon} = \frac{d}{dx} P(x) \qquad (2.21)$$

Since this equation also may be expressed as

$$P(x) = \int_{-\infty}^{x} p(x)\, dx \qquad (2.22)$$

we may state that a random variable X is said to be of the continuous type if there exists a nonnegative function, which is called the probability density function $p(x)$, given by Eq. (2.22), where $P(x)$ is the probability distribution. The properties of the probability density function may be summarized as follows:

1. Since the probability distribution is a nondecreasing function, the probability density function $p(x)$ is always $p(x) \geq 0$ with respect to all values of x between minus and plus infinity.

2. From Eqs. (2.19c) and (2.22) it follows that

$$\int_{-\infty}^{\infty} p(x)\, dx = 1 \qquad (2.23)$$

3. The relation between the probability density function and the probability distribution is given by Eq. (2.22).

An example of the probability distribution and the corresponding probability density function for a continuous random variable is shown in Fig. 2.3.

The second type of random variable, the discrete type, is as follows. If X can take only a finite number of values in an arbitrary finite interval, then we call the random variable x a discrete random variable. The complete set of probabilities $\Pr(X = x_k)$ with respect to the possible values x_k of x is determined as

$$\Pr(-\infty < X \leq x) = \sum_{x_k \leq x} P_k \qquad (2.24)$$

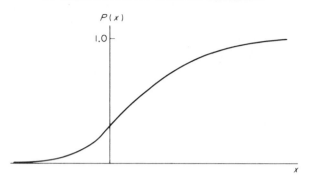

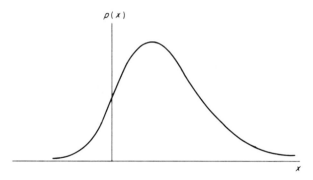

FIG. 2.3. Example of the probability distribution and probability density function of a continuous random variable: (top) probability distribution in the continuous case; (bottom) probability density function in the continuous case.

where

$$\Pr(X = x_1) = P_1$$
$$\Pr(X = x_2) = P_2$$
$$\cdot$$
$$\cdot \qquad\qquad (2.25a)$$
$$\cdot$$
$$\Pr(X = x_k) = P_k$$

$$\sum_{k=1}^{n} P_k = 1 \qquad\qquad (2.25b)$$

We apply the limiting expression for the probability density function to a random variable of the discrete type. Then the probability density function must be defined as

$$p(x) = \sum_{k=1}^{n} P_k \, \delta(x - x_k) \tag{2.26}$$

where $\delta(\xi)$ is Dirac's delta function. In fact, if the definition of the probability density function for a random variable of the discrete type is given by this formula, then Eq. (2.23) holds; that is,

$$\int_{-\infty}^{\infty} p(x) \, dx = \sum_{k=1}^{n} P_k \int_{-\infty}^{\infty} \delta(x - x_k) \, dx = 1 \tag{2.27}$$

It can also be observed that

$$P(x) = \int_{-\infty}^{x} p(x) \, dx = \sum_{k=1}^{n} P_k \int_{-\infty}^{x} \delta(x - x_k) \, dx = \sum_{x_k \leq x} P_k$$

The probability distribution and the associated probability density function for a particular random variable of the discrete type are shown in Fig. 2.4.

Finally, we have the random variable of mixed type, whose probability distribution may be decomposed into two parts: a staircase function having jump discontinuities at those points for which $P(X = x) > 0$ (that is, a discrete probability distribution, such as shown by the first curve of Fig. 2.4) and a part which is everywhere continuous. We may generally be safe in an ignorance of the detailed aspects of this type of random variable, because both its probability distribution and its probability density function are easily discussed by reference to random variables of the discrete and continuous types.

2.7   Joint Probability Distribution and Joint Probability Density Function

In the preceding section the probability density function for a single random variable was defined as the derivative of the probability distribution. Similarly, if X and Y are two random variables and x and y are

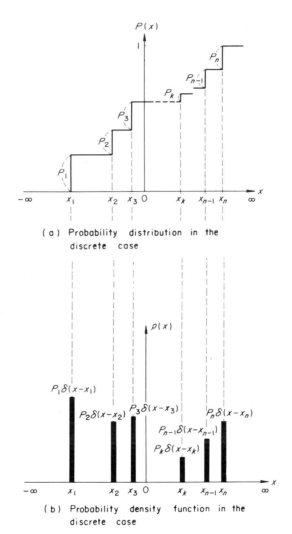

(a) Probability distribution in the discrete case

(b) Probability density function in the discrete case

FIG. 2.4. Example of the probability distribution and probability density function of a discrete random variable.

the respective values that can be assumed on any one trial, then we may define the joint probability distribution as

$$\Pr(-\infty < X \le x, -\infty < Y \le y) = P(x, y) \qquad (2.28)$$

and the associated joint probability density function as

$$p(x, y) = \lim_{\substack{\Delta x \to 0 \\ \Delta y \to 0}} \frac{\Pr(x - \Delta x < X \le x, y - \Delta y < Y \le y)}{\Delta x\, \Delta y} = \frac{d^2 P(x, y)}{dx\, dy}$$

$$(2.29)$$

From Eq. (2.22), we have

$$P(x, y) = \int_{-\infty}^{x} \int_{-\infty}^{y} p(x, y)\, dx\, dy \qquad (2.30)$$

Since the joint probability distribution is a nondecreasing function of its arguments, the probability density function is always nonnegative:

$$p(x, y) \ge 0 \qquad (2.31)$$

From the definition given by Eq. (2.22), it follows that the probability that a random variable s falls in a region R of the probability space, $\Pr(s \in R)$, is given by the integral of the joint probability density function over that region:

$$P(s \in R) = \int\int_{R} p(x, y)\, dx\, dy \qquad (2.32)$$

Consequently, the region of interest is the entire x-y plane. Then this equation becomes

$$\int_{-\infty}^{\infty} \int_{-\infty}^{\infty} p(x, y)\, dx\, dy = 1 \qquad (2.33)$$

In particular, if we allow only one of the upper limits to recede to infinity, then from Eq. (2.32) we obtain

$$\int_{-\infty}^{\infty} \int_{-\infty}^{x} p(x, y)\, dx\, dy = \int_{-\infty}^{x} p(x)\, dx = P(x) \qquad (2.34)$$

2.8   Conditional Probability Distribution and Conditional Probability Density Function

We consider the probability that the random variable Y is less than or equal to a particular value y, subject to the hypothesis that another random variable X falls within the interval $[x, x + \epsilon]$. From the definition of conditional probability, Eq. (2.7a), it follows that

$$\Pr(-\infty < Y \le y \mid x < X \le x + \epsilon)$$
$$= \frac{\Pr(-\infty < Y \le y, x < X \le x + \epsilon)}{\Pr(x < X \le x + \epsilon)} \quad (2.35)$$

By using Eq. (2.34) in this formula we have

$$\Pr(x < X \le x + \epsilon) = \int_{x}^{x+\epsilon} dx \int_{-\infty}^{\infty} p(x, y)\, dy \quad (2.36a)$$

$$\Pr(x < X \le x + \epsilon, -\infty < Y \le y) = \int_{x}^{x+\epsilon} dx \int_{-\infty}^{y} p(x, y)\, dy \quad (2.36b)$$

and so Eq. (2.35) yields

$$\Pr(-\infty < Y \le y \mid x < X \le x + \epsilon) = \frac{\int_{x}^{x+\epsilon} dx \int_{-\infty}^{y} p(x, y)\, dy}{\int_{x}^{x+\epsilon} dx \int_{-\infty}^{\infty} p(x, y)\, dy} \equiv P(y \mid x)$$
$$(2.37)$$

The function $P(y \mid x)$ is called a conditional probability distribution; it is the probability distribution of the random variable Y given the hypothesis $X = x$.

We shall now define the conditional probability density function. First, we consider the integral

$$\int_{x}^{x+\epsilon} dx \int_{y_a}^{y} p(x, y)\, dy \quad (2.38)$$

The value of this integral is equal to the volume of the body ABCDEFGH shown in Fig. 2.5. We consider the shaded area PQRS, which is the section of the body ABCDEFGH constructed by the plane $x = x_0$. Since this area is calculated by the integral

$$\int_{y_a}^{y} p(x_0, y)\, dy \qquad (2.39)$$

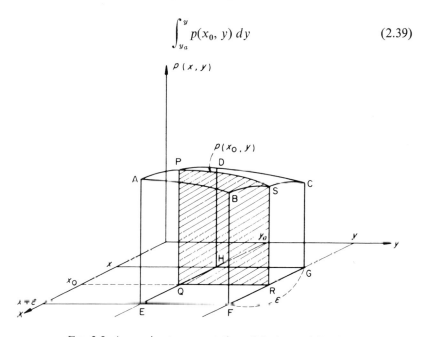

FIG. 2.5. Approximate computation of the integral (2.38).

then the volume ABCDEFGH can be approximated as

$$\epsilon \int_{y_a}^{y} p(x_0, y)\, dy \qquad (2.40)$$

where the value of ϵ is, of course, very small. Therefore the value of the integral equal to this volume (2.38) above can be approximately obtained as

$$\int_{x}^{x+\epsilon} dx \int_{y_a}^{y} p(x, y)\, dy \cong \epsilon \int_{y_a}^{y} p(x_0, y)\, dy \qquad (2.41)$$

This holds for arbitrary values of y_a and y. In particular, we can let

$y_a = -\infty$. Thus Eq. (2.41) becomes

$$\int_x^{x+\epsilon} dx \int_{-\infty}^y p(x, y) \, dy \cong \epsilon \int_{-\infty}^y p(x_0, y) \, dy \qquad (2.42a)$$

In a similar manner it can easily be shown that

$$\int_x^{x+\epsilon} dx \int_{-\infty}^\infty p(x, y) \, dy \cong \epsilon \int_{-\infty}^\infty p(x_0, y) \, dy = \epsilon p(x_0) \qquad (2.42b)$$

If the usual continuity requirements for the joint probability density function are now satisfied, we may define the conditional probability density function $p(y \mid x)$ as the derivative of the conditional probability distribution; that is,

$$p(y \mid x) = \frac{d}{dy} [\lim_{\epsilon \to 0} \Pr(-\infty < Y \leq y + \epsilon \mid x < X \leq x + \epsilon)]$$

$$= \frac{d}{dy} \left(\lim_{\epsilon \to 0} \frac{\displaystyle\int_x^{x+\epsilon} dx \int_{-\infty}^{y+\epsilon} p(x, y) \, dy}{\displaystyle\int_x^{x+\epsilon} dx \int_{-\infty}^\infty p(x, y) \, dy} \right) \qquad (2.43)$$

If Eqs. (2.42) are applied to Eq. (2.43), the conditional probability density function may be expressed as

$$p(y \mid x) = \frac{d}{dy} \left(\frac{\displaystyle\int_{-\infty}^y p(x, y) \, dy}{p(x)} \right) = \frac{p(x, y)}{p(x)} \qquad (2.44)$$

where, because the value of ϵ tends to zero, the value of x_0 approaches the value of x; thus we may use x instead of x_0 in the calculation of this equation. The following relation is used:

$$\frac{d}{dx} \left[\int_a^x f(u) \, du \right] = f(x)$$

The conditional probability density function is, of course, nonnegative:

$$p(y \mid x) \geq 0 \qquad (2.45)$$

Let us consider Eq. (2.43), since

$$p(y \mid x) = \frac{d}{dy} P(y \mid x) \qquad (2.46a)$$

that is,

$$\Pr(-\infty < Y \le y \mid X = x) = \int_{-\infty}^{y} p(y \mid x)\, dy \qquad (2.46b)$$

then it follows that the probability that the values of Y will fall within the interval $[a < Y \le b]$, under the hypothesis that $X = x$ is given by the integral of the conditional probability density function over that interval, is

$$\Pr(a < Y \le b \mid X = x) = \int_{a}^{b} p(y \mid x)\, dy \qquad (2.47)$$

If, now, the integral limits in this equation recede to infinity, we obtain

$$\int_{-\infty}^{\infty} p(y \mid x)\, dy = 1 \qquad (2.48)$$

If the random variables X and Y are mutually independent, then

$$p(x, y) = p(x)\, p(y) \qquad (2.49)$$

In this case the conditional probability density function defined by Eq. (2.44) becomes

$$p(y \mid x) = p(y) \qquad (2.50)$$

2.9 Statistical Parameters of Random Variables

We have already pointed out that the probability distribution or the probability density function describes the long-run behavior of random variables. It will be seen that such averages of random variables as the mean, the mean square, the variance, etc., can be determined through the use of the probability density function. In this section we develop the averaging aspect of probability theory, although only the process of statistical averaging is given, and we study several pertinent averages.

2.9-1   Statistical average or expectation.   We shall first consider $y = f(x)$, where x is a discrete random variable taking on any one of M possible values x_m, and $f(x)$ is a single-valued real function of x. We determine here the average of $f(x)$. We repeat N times an experiment which defines the random variable x. Suppose that the event corresponding to x_m occurs $n(x_m)$ times in the N repetitions. The arithmetic average of $f(x)$, $f(x)\big|_{\text{a.av.}}$, becomes

$$f(x)\big|_{\text{a.av.}} = \sum_{m=1}^{M} f(x_m) \frac{n(x_m)}{N} \qquad (2.51)$$

As described in Sect. 2.2, the probability $P(x_m)$ represents the limit of the frequency $n(x_m)/N$ as $N \to \infty$. The expectation of the discrete random variable $f(x)$ is therefore defined by

$$E[f(x)] = \sum_{m=1}^{M} f(x_m)\, P(x_m) \qquad (2.52)$$

Given that x is a continuous random variable with the probability density function $p(x)$ and $f(x)$ is a single-valued function of x, suppose that x can be approximated by a discrete random variable x', which takes on the values x'_m with probability $p(x'_m)\, \Delta x'_m$, where we partition the sample space of x into M intervals $\Delta x'_m$. Then, from Eq. (2.52) we have

$$E[f(x')] = \sum_{m=1}^{M} f(x'_m)\, p(x'_m)\, \Delta x'_m \qquad (2.53)$$

If we let all the $\Delta x'_m \to 0$ (that is, $M \to \infty$), the limiting value of the sum given by this equation becomes

$$E[f(x)] = \int_{-\infty}^{\infty} f(x)\, p(x)\, dx \qquad (2.54)$$

This is the definition of the expectation of the continuous random variable $f(x)$. Inversely, by applying the definition given by Eq. (2.26) to Eq. (2.54) the expectation of the discrete random variable $f(x)$ given by Eq. (2.52) is also obtained:

$$E[f(x)] = \int_{-\infty}^{\infty} f(x) \sum_{m=1}^{M} P(x_m)\, \delta(x - x_m)\, dx$$

$$= \sum_{m=1}^{M} f(x_m)\, P(x_m) \tag{2.55}$$

2.9-2   Statistical moments.   One set of averages of the functions of a random variable x that is of particular interest is the νth moment of the probability density function of the random variable x. This moment is defined as the statistical average of the νth power of x:

$$\mu'_\nu \equiv E[x^\nu] = \int_{-\infty}^{\infty} x^\nu\, p(x)\, dx \tag{2.56}$$

When $\nu = 1$ in Eq. (2.56), we have the definition of the mean value of the random variable x as the first moment:

$$m_x = E[x] = \int_{-\infty}^{\infty} x\, p(x)\, dx \tag{2.57}$$

The νth central moment μ_ν of the probability density function of the random variable x is defined as

$$\mu_\nu \equiv E[(x - m_x)^\nu] = \int_{-\infty}^{\infty} (x - m_x)^\nu\, p(x)\, dx \tag{2.58}$$

The second central moment μ_2, which is often of particular interest, is commonly expressed by the symbol ψ_x or σ_x^2:

$$\psi_x = \sigma_x^2 = \mu_2 = E[(x - m_x)^2] = \int_{-\infty}^{\infty} (x - m_x)^2\, p(x)\, dx$$

$$= E[x^2] - (E[x])^2 \tag{2.59}$$

The second central moment ψ_x of a random variable x defined by Eq. (2.59) has the special name variance or dispersion. The positive square root σ_x of the variance ψ_x is known as the standard deviation of the random variable x.

2.9-3   Characteristic functions.   Another statistical average of considerable importance in our work is the characteristic function $\varphi(w)$ of
the probability density function of a real random variable x; it is defined
as the statistical average of $\exp(jwx) = f(x)$ in Eq. (2.54);

$$\varphi(w) = E[\exp(jwx)] = \int_{-\infty}^{\infty} \exp(jwx)\, p(x)\, dx \qquad (2.60)$$

where w is real and $j^2 = -1$.   Since the probability density function is
nonnegative, we have

$$|\varphi(w)| = \left| \int_{-\infty}^{\infty} p(x) \exp(jwx)\, dx \right|$$

$$\leq \int_{-\infty}^{\infty} |p(x) \exp(jwx)|\, dx$$

$$= \int_{-\infty}^{\infty} p(x)\, dx$$

$$= 1 \qquad (2.61)$$

Hence, the characteristic function always exists, and the following
relation may be observed:

$$|\varphi(w)| \leq \varphi(0) = 1 \qquad (2.62)$$

The conjugate property of the characteristic function $\varphi(w)$ is easily shown
to be

$$\varphi(-w) = \int_{-\infty}^{\infty} p(x) \exp(-jwx)\, dx = \varphi^*(w) \qquad (2.63)$$

Multiplying both sides of Eq. (2.60) by

$$\frac{1}{2\pi} \exp(-jwx)$$

and integrating over the region $(-\infty, \infty)$ gives

$$\frac{1}{2\pi} \int_{-\infty}^{\infty} \varphi(w) \exp(-jwx)\, dw = \frac{1}{2\pi} \int_{-\infty}^{\infty} \int_{-\infty}^{\infty} p(x') \exp\{jw(x' - x)\}\, dx'\, dw$$

$$(2.64)$$

When the definition of Dirac's delta function[10] is introduced,

$$\int_{-\infty}^{\infty} \exp(jwx)\, dw = 2\pi\delta(x) \tag{2.65}$$

then Eq. (2.64) becomes

$$\frac{1}{2\pi}\int_{-\infty}^{\infty}\int_{-\infty}^{\infty} p(x')\exp\{jw(x'-x)\}\, dx'\, dw = \int_{-\infty}^{\infty} p(x')\,\delta(x'-x)\, dx'$$

$$= p(x) \tag{2.66a}$$

That is, when Eq. (2.66a) is combined with Eq. (2.64), then

$$p(x) = \frac{1}{2\pi}\int_{-\infty}^{\infty} \varphi(w)\exp(-jwx)\, dw \tag{2.66b}$$

From this result it is easily seen that the characteristic function and the probability density function of a random variable x are connected by a pair of Fourier transforms.

2.9-4 Cumulants, or Thiele's semi-invariants. We take the derivative of the characteristic function with respect to w. Since the relation

$$\left| \frac{d^{\nu}}{dw^{\nu}} [\exp(jwx)] \right| = |x|^{\nu} \tag{2.67}$$

holds, then by taking the νth derivative of the characteristic function with respect to w we obtain

$$\varphi^{(\nu)}(w) = \frac{d^{\nu}}{dw^{\nu}} [\varphi(w)] = j^{\nu}\int_{-\infty}^{\infty} x^{\nu}\, p(x)\exp(jwx)\, dx \tag{2.68}$$

Evaluating at $w = 0$, we find that the integral given by this equation

---

[10] D. Middleton, "An Introduction to Statistical Communication Theory." McGraw-Hill, New York, 1961.

becomes the νth moment of the random variable x. Therefore,

$$\varphi^{(\nu)}(0) = j^\nu \int_{-\infty}^{\infty} x^\nu \, p(x) \, dx = j^\nu \mu_\nu' \tag{2.69}$$

On the other hand, suppose that the characteristic function has a Maclaurin series expansion:

$$\varphi(w) = \varphi(0) + \sum_{k=1}^{n} \frac{1}{k!} w^k \varphi^{(k)}(0) + O(w^{n+1}) \tag{2.70a}$$

By using Eqs. (2.62) and (2.69) we may express Eq. (2.70a) as

$$\varphi(w) = 1 + \sum_{k=1}^{n} \frac{\mu_k'}{k!} (jw)^k + O(w^{n+1}) \tag{2.70b}$$

Suppose, further, that the logarithmic form of the characteristic function has a Maclaurin series expansion:

$$\log \varphi(w) = \sum_{k=1}^{n} \frac{K_k}{k!} (jw)^k + O(w^{n+1}) \tag{2.71}$$

where K_k are the coefficients of the Maclaurin series expansion of the logarithmic form of the characteristic function. We shall consider the expression of the coefficients K_k with respect to the νth moment μ_ν' of the random variable x.

By neglecting the terms of higher order than $n + 1$ in the respective expansion given by Eqs. (2.70b) and (2.71), we obtain

$$\log \varphi(w) = \log\left(1 + \sum_{k=1}^{\infty} \frac{\mu_k'}{k!} (jw)^k\right) \tag{2.72a}$$

$$= \sum_{k=1}^{\infty} \frac{K_k}{k!} (jw)^k \tag{2.72b}$$

Since from Eqs. (2.72) with the use of the expansion of the logarithmic function we have

$$\sum_{k=1}^{\infty} \frac{K_k}{k!} (jw)^k = \sum_{k=1}^{\infty} \frac{\mu_k'}{k!} (jw)^k - \frac{1}{2}\left(\sum_{k=1}^{\infty} \frac{\mu_k'}{k!} (jw)^k\right)^2 + \frac{1}{3}\left(\sum_{k=1}^{\infty} \frac{\mu_k'}{k!} (jw)^k\right)^3 + \cdots \tag{2.73}$$

then, by comparing the same powers of $(jw)^k$ on the both sides of Eq. (2.73) we find that

$$K_1 = \mu_1' = m_x$$
$$K_2 = \mu_2' - \mu_1'^2 \qquad (2.74)$$
$$K_3 = \mu_3' - 3\mu_1'\mu_2' + 2\mu_1'^3$$

If we use the central moment μ_v defined by Eq. (2.59), instead of the μ_v' in these equations, we have

$$K_1 = m_x$$
$$K_2 = \mu_2$$
$$K_3 = \mu_3 \qquad (2.75)$$
$$K_4 = \mu_4 - 3\mu_2^2$$

The coefficients K_k of the expansion in Eq. (2.71) can, then, be expressed only by the statistical moment μ_v; these coefficients are called the cumulants, or Thiele's semi-invariants.

2.9 5   Cross moments of multiple random variables.   The concept of statistical moments of the probability density function may, of course, be extended to those of joint probability density function. In general, for example, an $(n + k)$th-order moment of the joint probability density function of the two random variables x and y is defined by

$$E[x^n y^k] = \int_{-\infty}^{\infty} \int_{-\infty}^{\infty} x^n y^k \, p(x, y) \, dx \, dy = \mu_{nk}' \qquad (2.76)$$

The cross central moment μ_{nk} is given by

$$\mu_{nk} = E[(x - m_x)^n (y - m_y)^k] \qquad (2.77)$$

where m_x and m_y are the mean values of the random variables x and y, respectively. In the case in which $n = k = 1$ the cross moment given by Eq. (2.77) becomes

$$\mu_{11} = E[(x - m_x)(y - m_y)] \qquad (2.78)$$

and this is called the covariance of the random variables x and y.

2.9-6 Joint characteristic functions. The statistical average of $\exp(jw_1x + jw_2y)$,

$$\varphi(w_1, w_2) = E[\exp(jw_1x + jw_2y)]$$

$$= \int_{-\infty}^{\infty} \int_{-\infty}^{\infty} \exp(jw_1x + jw_2y)\, p(x, y)\, dx\, dy \qquad (2.79)$$

is called the joint characteristic function of the joint probability distribution of the two random variables x and y. It can, therefore, be understood that the joint characteristic function is the 2-dimensional Fourier transform of the joint probability density function with respect to the random variables x and y. Then the joint probability density function can also be derived by using the inverse Fourier transformation, as

$$p(x, y) = \frac{1}{4\pi^2} \int_{-\infty}^{\infty} \int_{-\infty}^{\infty} \varphi(w_1, w_2)\exp[-(jw_1x + jw_2y)]\, dw_1\, dw_2 \qquad (2.80)$$

From Eq. (2.79), some properties of the joint characteristic function may be derived. First we find that

$$\varphi(0, 0) = 1 \qquad (2.81)$$

As in Eq. (2.62) it further follows from Eq. (2.79) that

$$|\varphi(w_1, w_2)| \leq \varphi(0, 0) = 1 \qquad (2.82)$$

Next, suppose that we take the lth partial derivative of the joint characteristic function with respect to w_1 and the mth partial derivative with respect to w_2. The result is

$$\frac{\partial^{l+m}\varphi(w_1, w_2)}{\partial w_1^l\, \partial w_2^m} = j^{l+m}\int_{-\infty}^{\infty} \int_{-\infty}^{\infty} x^l y^m \exp(jw_1x + jw_2y)\, p(x, y)\, dx\, dy$$

$$(2.83)$$

Setting both w_1 and w_2 equal to zero, we easily obtain the expression of the cross moments:

$$E[x^l y^m] = (-j)^{l+m} \frac{\partial^{l+m}\varphi(w_1, w_2)}{\partial w_1^l\, \partial w_2^m}\bigg|_{\text{at } w_1=w_2=0} \qquad (2.84)$$

This equation shows that various orders of cross moments of the random variables x and y may be calculated by their joint characteristic function through successive differentiations.

2.10 Stochastic Processes

So far we have treated only of random events, without considering the time dependence of phenomena. For example, although in trials of tossing a die time entered the scope of our discussion implicitly, our attention was directed only to the random event itself; the time instant and the time interval between the nth and $(n + 1)$th trials were omitted in our treatment, because they had no particular bearing on the problem at hand. However, since all random phenomena naturally may be observed as random time functions, time-dependent statistical behavior of random phenomena must be taken into account. These situations reveal that both the time instant of the occurrence of a random phenomenon and the mutual correlations of random phenomena observed at different time instants are of considerable importance in the study of random signals actually encountered in control systems as, for example, in problems involving random signal and noise.

It is well known that the output of a device when no signal is present is not always zero, but fluctuates more or less irregularly around some average value. On an oscilloscope, for instance, the fluctuations produce the typical noise that often prevents weak signals from being detected. This noise has several sources such as thermal and diode circuit noises. Our problem is, therefore, how to describe quantitatively the random signal. We attempt to show how the previous notions of probability and random variables may be extended to cover this situation.

To establish the basic idea of the variation of random phenomena with time, we recall a sequence of N throws of a die such as described in Sect. 2.2 and shown in Table 2.1. First, suppose that the particular face with $k(n)$ dots appears on the nth throw where $k(n)$ is any integer between 1 and 6 and corresponds to x_i ($i = 1, 2, \ldots, 6$). As already stated in Sect. 2.1, we can discuss the statistical regularity of this experiment by means of the concept of probability, by considering an appropriate sample space for the nth throw consisting of six elements from 1 to 6. The probability that the particular face with $k(3) = 5$ dots, as shown in Table 2.1, will appear on the third throw can be estimated from the results of simultaneously throwing a large number of dice. Similarly, by repeating the experiments we can estimate the probability that the particular face with $k(n)$ dots will appear on the nth throw and also the joint probability that the face with $k(3) = 5$ dots will appear on the third throw and the face with $k(5) = 1$ dot will appear on the fifth throw. The specification of such a set of experiments with probability distributions defines a stochastic process. For a more rigorous definition of the stochastic process we consider next a particular sequence of die throws. The real numbers $k(n)$, which are obtained in this sequence of throws,

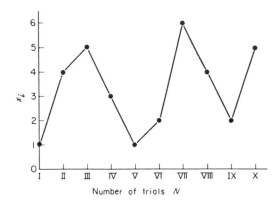

FIG. 2.6. A sample function.

are called sample values. When we express the result of the sequence of throws, shown in Fig. 2.6, a function of the index n is obtained, and this is called a sample function. We may also consider a set of all possible such sample functions by again performing the experiment of simultaneously throwing a large number of dice.

Although the example given here is concerned with a discrete case, the consideration is easily extended to a continuous one.

For example, consider the thermal-agitation noise voltage $y(t)$ generated in a resistor in an environment of a given temperature.

In particular, we consider the measured voltage $y(t_1)$ at an instant of time t_1. Since the measured voltage can take any value between plus and minus infinity, the sample space in this case is the real line $(-\infty < x < \infty)$, and the random variable is the measured voltage $y(t_1) = y_1$. If we have available a large number of macroscopically identical resistors, called an ensemble of resistors, we can simultaneously measure a number of values of voltages, $\{y(t_1)\}$; see Fig. 2.7. At a definite instant of time t_1 we can observe the fraction of the total number

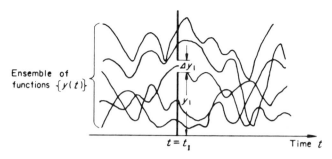

FIG. 2.7. The probability density function $p_1(y_1, t_1)$.

n_1 of cases in which $y(t_1)$ occurs in a given interval y_1 and $y_1 + \Delta y_1$ among the total number N of the measured voltages. This fraction is the frequency of occurrence of events of the type

$$\Pr(y_1 < y \le y_1 + \Delta y_1, t_1) = n_1/N \qquad (2.85)$$

and this provides the measure of the probability; that is, by considering that Δy_1 is very small and that $N \to \infty$ we have

$$\lim_{\substack{N \to \infty \\ \Delta y_1 \to dy_1}} \Pr(y_1 < y \le y_1 + \Delta y_1, t_1) = p_1(y_1, t_1)\, dy_1 \qquad (2.86)$$

Hence it is apparent that the probability density function depending on an instant of time t_1 can be defined. The probability density function defined here is written $p_1(y_1, t_1)$.*

Next we consider all the pairs of values of y occurring at two given arbitrary time instants t_1 and t_2. As shown in Fig. 2.8, from the fraction

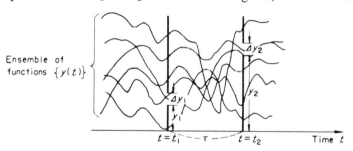

FIG. 2.8. The joint probability density function $p_2(y_1, t_1; y_2, t_2)$.

* Henceforth, to describe the n-dimensional joint probability density function, we shall use the symbol $p_n(y_1, t_1; y_2, t_2; \ldots; y_n, t_n)$.

of the total number of pairs in which y occurs in the range $(y_1, y_1 + \Delta y_1)$ at t_1 and in the range $(y_2, y_2 + \Delta y_2)$ at t_2 we can obtain the joint frequency and, hence, the joint probability density function $p_2(y_1, t_1; y_2, t_2)$:

$$\lim_{\substack{N \to \infty \\ \Delta y_1 \to dy_1 \\ \Delta y_2 \to dy_2}} \Pr(y_1 < y \leq y_1 + \Delta y_1, t_1; y_2 < y \leq y_2 + \Delta y_2, t_2)$$

$$= p_2(y_1, t_1; y_2, t_2)\, dy_1\, dy_2 \quad (2.87)$$

Similarly, we can make measurements at n instants of time, such as t_1 through t_n, as shown in Fig. 2.9, and obtain a measure of the n-dimensional

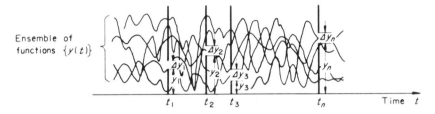

FIG. 2.9. The n-dimensional probability density function $p_n(y_1, t_1; y_2, t_2; \ldots; y_n, t_n)$.

joint probability density function $p_n(y_1, t_1; y_2, t_2; \ldots; y_n, t_n)$:

$$\lim_{\substack{N \to \infty \\ \Delta y_1 \to dy_1 \\ \Delta y_2 \to dy_2 \\ \cdots \\ \Delta y_n \to dy_n}} \Pr(y_1 < y \leq y_1 + \Delta y_1, t_1; y_2 < y \leq y_2 + \Delta y_2, t_2; \ldots; \\ y_n < y \leq y_n + \Delta y_n, t_n)$$

$$= p_n(y_1, t_1; y_2, t_2; \ldots; y_n, t_n)\, dy_1 \cdots dy_n \quad (2.88)$$

Thus we may say that a random phenomenon $y(t)$ varying with time is said to be a stochastic process if $y(t)$ may be considered a member function of the ensemble of functions, $\{y(t)\}$, and if the corresponding probability distribution may be defined.

2.11   Stationary Random Processes

As stated in the preceding section, we can estimate the probability density function $p(y_1)$ from the data $y(t_1) = y_{t_1}$ observed at the time

instant t_1, and we can estimate the probability density function at a
different time instant $t_1 + t$. We can also estimate the joint probability
density function $p_n(y_{t_1+t}, \ldots, y_{t_n+t})$ from the data $y(t_1 + t) = y_{t_1+t}, \ldots,$
$y(t_n + t) = y_{t_n+t}$ obtained at the n instants of time $t_1 + t$ through $t_n + t$.
An important question arises: whether the two sets of probability
density functions are identical or not. To answer this we must distinguish
between stationary and nonstationary random processes. A stationary
random process is defined as one in which the statistical properties do
not change with time or, more precisely, one in which all the probability
density functions and the joint probability density functions that define
a random process are invariant under a shift of the time origin. Often
processes may be so described in this strict sense of the term. Naturally,
there are others said to be nonstationary. The definition of a stationary
random process in the wide sense of the term will be given at the end of
this section.

   For an example of a stationary random process we may consider the
thermal-agitation noise generated at temperature T in a registor with
resistance R, which is connected in parallel with a condenser with
capacitance C. Even if only one value of R, C, and T varies with time,
the process is nonstationary.

   According to the hypothesis described above, since the probability
density function does not depend on the time, it may be expressed as
$p_1(y_1)$ instead of $p_1(y_1, t)$. The joint probability density function, for example $p_2(y_1, t_1 ; y_2, t_2)$, depends upon only the time interval $t_2 - t_1 = \tau$.
Consequently, we may use the symbol $p_2(y_1, y_2 ; \tau)$ instead of $p_2(y_1, t_1 ;$
$y_1, t_2)$. The following parameters are thus determined (where the subscript
sav means "statistical average").*

Mean value (angular braces, $\langle\ \rangle$):

$$m_y = \langle y(t)\rangle_{\text{sav}} = \int_{-\infty}^{\infty} y\, p_1(y)\, dy \qquad (2.89a)$$

Mean square value:

$$\langle\{y(t)\}^2\rangle_{\text{sav}} = \int_{-\infty}^{\infty} y^2\, p_1(y)\, dy \qquad (2.89b)$$

* In this book the symbol $\langle y(t)\rangle_{\text{sav}}$ represents the ensemble average of the random
process $y(t)$; on the other hand, the symbol $\langle y(t)\rangle_{\text{av}}$ expresses the time average of the
random process $y(t)$.

Variance:

$$\psi_y = \langle\{y(t) - m_y\}^2\rangle_{\text{sav}} = \int_{-\infty}^{\infty} \{y(t) - m_y\}^2 \, p_1(y) \, dy \qquad (2.89c)$$

Characteristic function:

$$\varphi(w) = \langle\exp(jwy)\rangle_{\text{sav}} = \int_{-\infty}^{\infty} p_1(y) \exp(jwy) \, dy \qquad (2.89d)$$

Covariance:

$$\psi_y(\tau) = \langle\{y(t) - m_y\}\{y(t + \tau) - m_y\}\rangle_{\text{sav}}$$

$$= \int_{-\infty}^{\infty} \int_{-\infty}^{\infty} (y_1 - m_y)(y_2 - m_y) \, p_2(y_1, y_2; \tau) \, dy_1 \, dy_2 \qquad (2.90)$$

In Eq. (2.90), $y_1 = y(t)$ and $y_2 = y(t + \tau)$. A random process whose first- and second-order statistical moments, such as the mean value and the variance, are invariant under a shift of time origin is called a stationary random process in the wide sense of the term.

2.12 Ergodic Hypothesis and Time Averages

In the preceding section we defined the statistical average of a random process with sample functions $\{y(t)\}$ as a function of time, $\langle y(t)\rangle_{\text{sav}}$. This is an average of a random process at a particular instant of time t, let us say $t = t_1$. Therefore, the ensemble average shows a procedure of "across the process" at $t = t_1$. On the other hand, it is natural to consider also averages that show a procedure of "along the process." This means time averages of individual sample functions. Although it is almost impossible actually to acquire the data of a random process as a sample function extending in time to infinity, we define the time average as

$$\langle y(t)\rangle_{\text{av}} = \lim_{T \to \infty} \frac{1}{2T} \int_{-T}^{T} y(t) \, dt \qquad (2.91)$$

if this limit exists. The present problem is to inquire what relation exists between the ensemble average and the time average. The answer to this question is the ergodic hypothesis, which states that the ensemble average $\langle y(t)\rangle_{sav}$ of a random process $y(t)$ equals its time average $\langle y(t)\rangle_{av}$ with probability 1, if $y(t)$ is a stationary random process. The precise description of the ergodic hypothesis is beyond the scope of this book; however, we may state that we can expect the ensemble of functions $\{y(t)\}$ to exhibit statistical behavior if we observe the sample function $y(t)$ for a sufficiently long time. By invoking the ergodic hypothesis we may express the parameters given by Eqs. (2.89) and (2.90) as time averages in the following forms.

Mean value:

$$m_y = \langle y(t)\rangle_{av} = \lim_{T\to\infty} \frac{1}{2T}\int_{-T}^{T} y(t)\,dt = \int_{-\infty}^{\infty} y\,p_1(y)\,dy \quad (2.92a)$$

Mean square value:

$$\langle\{y(t)\}^2\rangle_{av} = \lim_{T\to\infty} \frac{1}{2T}\int_{-T}^{T} y^2(t)\,dt = \int_{-\infty}^{\infty} y^2\,p_1(y)\,dy \quad (2.92b)$$

Variance:

$$\psi_y = \langle\{y(t) - m_y\}^2\rangle_{av} = \lim_{T\to\infty} \frac{1}{2T}\int_{-T}^{T}\{y(t) - m_y\}^2\,dy$$

$$= \int_{-\infty}^{\infty}\{y(t) - m_y\}^2 p_1(y)\,dy \quad (2.92c)$$

Characteristic function:

$$\varphi(w) = \langle\exp\{jwy(t)\}\rangle_{av} = \lim_{T\to\infty} \frac{1}{2T}\int_{-T}^{T}\exp\{jwy(t)\}\,dt$$

$$= \int_{-\infty}^{\infty}\exp(jwy)\,p_1(y)\,dy \quad (2.92d)$$

Covariance, or autocorrelation function:

$$\psi_y(\tau) = \langle\{y(t) - m_y\}\{y(t + \tau) - m_y\}\rangle_{av}$$

$$= \lim_{T\to\infty} \frac{1}{2T}\int_{-T}^{T}\{y(t) - m_y\}\{y(t + \tau) - m_y\}\,dt$$

$$= \int_{-\infty}^{\infty}\int_{-\infty}^{\infty}(y_1 - m_y)(y_2 - m_y)\,p_2(y_1, y_2 ; \tau)\,dy_1\,dy_2 \quad (2.93)$$

2.13   Stationary Gaussian Random Processes

Although we shall not present here any practical examples of random processes whose probability distribution becomes gaussian, and we shall also omit any description of the need for them, the gaussian random process is of special importance in studying stochastic aspects of control systems.[11] We shall briefly investigate some of its properties in this section.

2.13-1   Gaussian random variables.   A random variable y having the probability density function

$$p_1(y) = \frac{1}{(2\pi\psi_y)^{1/2}} \exp\left\{-\frac{(y-m_y)^2}{2\psi_y}\right\}$$ (2.94)

shown in Fig. 2.10 is a gaussian random variable with mean value m_y

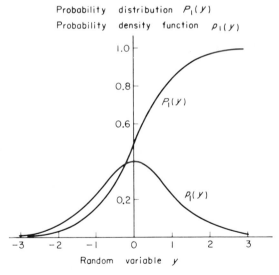

FIG. 2.10. Examples of gaussian probability distribution and gaussian probability density function.

[11] Y. Sawaragi and Y. Sunahara, "Introduction to Stochastic Theory of Control Systems" (in Japanese). Ohm, Tokyo, 1966.

and variance ψ_y. The corresponding probability distribution is obtained from Eq. (2.94) as

$$P_1(y) = \Pr(-\infty < Y \le y)$$

$$= \frac{1}{(2\pi\psi_y)^{\frac{1}{2}}} \int_{-\infty}^{y} \exp\left\{-\frac{(y-m_y)^2}{2\psi_y}\right\} dy \qquad (2.95)$$

By letting $(y - m_y)/(2\psi_y)^{\frac{1}{2}} = \lambda$ we may write this equation as

$$P_1(y) = \frac{1}{\pi^{\frac{1}{2}}} \int_{-\infty}^{(y-m_y)/(2\psi_y)^{\frac{1}{2}}} \exp(-\lambda^2)\, d\lambda$$

$$= \frac{1}{\pi^{\frac{1}{2}}} \int_{-\infty}^{0} \exp(-\lambda^2)\, d\lambda + \frac{1}{\pi^{\frac{1}{2}}} \int_{0}^{(y-m_y)/(2\psi_y)^{\frac{1}{2}}} \exp(-\lambda^2)\, d\lambda \quad (2.96)$$

If we introduce the error function,

$$\mathrm{erf}(z) = \frac{2}{\pi^{\frac{1}{2}}} \int_{0}^{z} \exp(-\lambda^2)\, d\lambda \qquad (2.97)$$

then Eq. (2.96) yields

$$P_1(y) = \frac{1}{2}\left[1 + \mathrm{erf}\left(\frac{y-m_y}{(2\psi_y)^{\frac{1}{2}}}\right)\right] \qquad (2.98)$$

The probability distribution given by Eq. (2.98) is also shown in Fig. 2.10.

2.13-2   Statistical moments of a gaussian random variable.   In this section first- and second-order statistical moments of a gaussian random variable are calculated with the aid of Eq. (2.94).   First, the statistical moment of the first order is given by

$$\mu_1' = \int_{-\infty}^{\infty} y\, p_1(y)\, dy = \frac{1}{(2\pi\psi_y)^{\frac{1}{2}}} \int_{-\infty}^{\infty} y \exp\left\{-\frac{(y-m_y)^2}{2\psi_y}\right\} dy \quad (2.99)$$

Much as in the calculation of Eq. (2.96) this equation becomes

$$\mu_1' = \left(\frac{2\psi_y}{\pi}\right)^{\frac{1}{2}} \int_{-\infty}^{\infty} \lambda \exp(-\lambda^2)\, d\lambda + \frac{m_y}{\pi^{\frac{1}{2}}} \int_{-\infty}^{\infty} \exp(-\lambda^2)\, d\lambda$$

$$= m_y \qquad (2.100a)$$

Second, the second-order moment μ_2' can be calculated as

$$\mu_2' = \int_{-\infty}^{\infty} y^2 p_1(y)\, dy = \int_{-\infty}^{\infty} (y - m_y)^2 p_1(y)\, dy + m_y^2$$

$$= \frac{1}{(2\pi\psi_y)^{1/2}} \int_{-\infty}^{\infty} (y - m_y)^2 \exp\left\{-\frac{(y - m_y)^2}{2\psi_y}\right\} dy + m_y^2$$

$$= \psi_y + m_y^2 \tag{2.100b}$$

By a similar method we can successively calculate the third order, the fourth order, etc. The results are summarized as

$$\mu_1' = m_y$$
$$\mu_2' = \psi_y + m_y^2$$
$$\mu_3' = 2m_y^3 - 3m_y\mu_2'$$
$$\mu_4' = 3\psi_y^2 + 4\mu_1'\mu_3' - 6\mu_1'^2\mu_2' + 3\mu_1'^4 \tag{2.101}$$
$$\cdot$$
$$\cdot$$
$$\cdot$$

If a random variable has zero mean, then the statistical moments shown in Eq. (2.101) become

$$\mu_1 = 0$$
$$\mu_2 = \psi_y$$
$$\mu_3 = 0$$
$$\mu_4 = 3\psi_y^2 \tag{2.102}$$
$$\cdot$$
$$\cdot$$

2.13-3 Bivariate and multivariate gaussian random variables. The foregoing remarks may be extended to the more general situation involving a pair of random variables y_1 and y_2. We suppose that the random variables y_1 and y_2 are obtained by the observation of a random process at the two instants of time t and $t + \tau$, respectively. These random variables are called gaussian random variables if they have a bivariate probability density function of the form

$$p_2(Y_1, Y_2) = (2\pi)^{-1}[\psi_y^2(0)(1 - \rho^2)]^{-\frac{1}{2}} \exp\left[-\frac{Y_1^2 - 2\rho Y_1 Y_2 + Y_2^2}{2\psi_y(0)(1 - \rho)^2}\right]$$

$$(2.103)$$

where

$$Y_1 = y(t) - m_y$$
$$Y_2 = y(t + \tau) - m_y$$

$$(2.104a)$$

and

$$\rho = \psi_y(\tau)/\psi_y(0) \qquad (2.104b)$$

We further suppose that the random variables $y_1, y_2, \ldots, y_{n-1}, y_n$ are obtained by observing a random process at n instants of time, $t_1, t_2, \ldots, t_{n-1}, t_n$.

The multivariate joint probability density function of n random variables is defined as follows. The n random variables $y_1, y_2, \ldots, y_{n-1}, y_n$ are said to be gaussian random variables if they have the multivariate probability density function of the form

$$p(y_1, y_2, \ldots, y_n) = \frac{1}{(2\pi)^{n/2}(|M|)^{\frac{1}{2}}} \exp\left(-\tfrac{1}{2}R'M^{-1}R\right) \quad (2.105)$$

Here M is a covariant matrix $\|\langle(y_i - m_{y_i})(y_j - m_{y_j})\rangle_{\text{sav}}\|$, where $(i, j = 1, 2, \ldots, n)$, which possesses an inverse M^{-1} and determinant $|M|$. The symbol R is the column vector with $y_1 - m_{y_1}, y_2 - m_{y_2}, \ldots, y_n - m_{y_n}$ as its elements and R' is the transposed vector of the column vector R. A random process is said to be a gaussian random process, if for every finite set of time instants t_n the random variables $y_n = y(t_n)$ possess a joint probability density function of the gaussian type given by Eq. (2.105). If the mean value and the covariance of the given gaussian random process are invariant under a shift of time origin, then the random process is called a stationary gaussian random process.

CHAPTER 3

Basic Concept of Statistical Decision Theory

3.1 Introductory Remarks

Most of the classical theory of communications and control engineering is based on the evaluation of spectral densities, correlation functions, and signal-to-noise ratios associated with system dynamics. However, as we know, account must be taken of the fact that only a finite time interval is available for data observation and processing. Under this restriction on practical operations, the following are the basic needs of communications and control engineering:

1. Methods of evaluating a message signal contaminated by random noise.
2. Methods of determining the structure of the optimal system for the problem at hand.
3. Methods of evaluating the performance of the optimal system.

Modern communications and control engineering, then, require the establishment of a general and powerful approach, in which all available information is utilized. The basic purpose underlying the many studies being made is that of obtaining the best estimate of the nature of a signal in the presence of random noise. This concept is embodied in statistical decision theory, which concerns making the optimal decision in the face of several possibilities.

The primary emphasis of decision theory may be found in the theory of testing hypotheses, originated by Neyman and Pearson.[1] The extension of their principle to all statistical problems was proposed by Wald[2] in

[1] J. Neyman and E. S. Pearson, The testing of statistical hypothesis in relation to probability a priori. *Proc. Cambridge Phil. Soc.* **29**, 492 (1933).
[2] A. Wald, "Statistical Decision Functions." J. Wiley, New York, 1950.

1939. The importance of his approach has been widely recognized, and decision theory has been adopted in many recent studies of statistics. As has been stated a number of times, the use of statistical concepts is inevitable, because we are not always concerned with the transfer and reception of only one particular signal corresponding to a message but, rather, with an ensemble of all possible messages in the presence of random noise. Hence, it is quite natural that decision concepts were adopted in communications theory. Since the early 1950's many investigations into reception problems have been made, including those concerned with solving problems of optimal detection and extraction of message signals in the presence of random noise. Among these are a number of remarkable contributions, developed by Middleton,[3] that have played an important role in unifying the structure of statistical decision theory and in establishing ways of designing reception and extraction systems. In this chapter the general scope of decision theory is briefly reviewed. Some terminologies are introduced, taken partly from the field of pure statistics and partly from the field of applied communications engineering.

3.2 General Description of the Decision Situation

We are always confronted with problems of measuring or receiving message signals in the presence of random noise. Such problems arise when it is necessary to make a specified type of judgement based on observations during a finite time interval. The judgement in reception problems concerns the presence or absence of message signals. It is called detection. On the other hand, a judgement may sometimes be an estimate of such features of a signal as the amplitude, frequency, and waveform. This is called extraction. A system designed in accordance with the concept of extraction provides an actual estimate of descriptive parameters of the signal as output. In either case the goal is to design a receiving system that will best produce an output quantity corresponding to the required judgement by processing the data with the help of already available, a priori, information. Therefore, there is an essential difference between systems designed by the concept of decision

[3] D. Middleton, "An Introduction to Statistical Communication Theory." McGraw-Hill, New York, 1961.

theory and those designed in the classical manner. Systems in which the decision concept has not been introduced are not designed to yield the information that would be required for a judgement, but only to produce outputs containing a posteriori information that the observer himself must use for making a decision. With this introduction, let us formulate the problems of decision processes.

To explain the general scope of decision theory we first attempt to formulate rather simply the decision situation and then to describe the major types of decision and the way in which a decision procedure is established.

Let θ^* be the true value which is to be divined. This may be a message signal in the presence or absence of random noise, for example, a target signal to radar servosystems or a waveform in a communications channel. We may assume here that there are n possible states represented by $\theta_1^*, \theta_2^*, \ldots, \theta_n^*$ and that each of them may occur with the a priori probability distributions $P(\theta_i^*)$. These a priori probability distributions play an important role in the first step of the decision situation.

Let θ be an observation. The message signal contaminated by random noise is part of this observation. We assume that there are m possible values of the observation, represented by $\theta_1, \theta_2, \ldots, \theta_m$. For a particular value θ_i^* of the message signal θ^* there exists the conditional probability distribution $P_{ij} = P(\theta_j \mid \theta_i^*)$, representing the probability that the result of the observation will be θ_j if the message signal has taken the value θ_i^*. We can construct the following matrix with elements P_{ij}:

$$
\begin{array}{cc}
\begin{array}{c} \text{message} \\ \text{signals} \end{array} &
\begin{array}{cccc} \multicolumn{4}{c}{\text{observations}} \\ \theta_1 & \theta_2 & \cdots & \theta_m \end{array}
\end{array}
$$

$$
\begin{array}{c}
\theta_1^* \\
\theta_2^* \\
\cdot \\
\cdot \\
\cdot \\
\theta_n^*
\end{array}
\begin{bmatrix}
P_{11} & P_{12} & \cdots & P_{1m} \\
P_{21} & P_{22} & \cdots & P_{2m} \\
\cdot & \cdot & & \cdot \\
\cdot & \cdot & & \cdot \\
\cdot & \cdot & & \cdot \\
P_{n1} & P_{n2} & \cdots & P_{nm}
\end{bmatrix}
\tag{3.1}
$$

Constructing this matrix with the data is the second step of the decision situation.

Let δ_k be the decision that θ_k^* is the true value of the message signal. We can now construct a matrix describing the relative cost associated with every possible mistake we could make in making a decision. Let L_{ik} be a number expressing the relative cost of making the decision that θ_k^* is the true value of the message signal when in fact it is θ_i^*. This may be represented in the form of a cost matrix, as follows:

$$
\begin{array}{cc}
\begin{array}{c} \text{message} \\ \text{signals} \end{array} & \begin{array}{cccc} & \text{decisions} & & \\ \delta_1 & \delta_2 & \cdots & \delta_n \end{array} \\
\begin{array}{c} \theta_1^* \\ \theta_2^* \\ \cdot \\ \cdot \\ \cdot \\ \theta_n^* \end{array} &
\begin{bmatrix}
L_{11} & L_{12} & \cdots & L_{1n} \\
L_{21} & L_{22} & \cdots & L_{2n} \\
\cdot & \cdot & \cdots & \cdot \\
\cdot & \cdot & \cdots & \cdot \\
\cdot & \cdot & \cdots & \cdot \\
L_{n1} & L_{n2} & \cdots & L_{nn}
\end{bmatrix}
\end{array}
\tag{3.2}
$$

Here the rows correspond to the different message signals and the columns to the different decisions. For example, the element L_{21} is the loss or cost associated with decision δ_1 when the actual signal is θ_2^*.

The construction of a cost matrix is the final step. The three steps make up a complete description of the decision situation. However, we have now heard a few unfamiliar terms, such as "loss," "cost," and "cost matrix." To learn the characters and behaviors of these quantities we shall consider a simple example.

We consider a transfer channel of information with a binary pulse code ONE and ZERO, in which only two forms, [1, 1] and [0, 0], are the message words. The probabilities that a ZERO is received as a ZERO and a ONE as a ONE are assumed to be, respectively, P_1 and P_2. We further assume that the probability that a ZERO is received as a ONE is Q_1 and the probability that a ONE is received as a ZERO is Q_2. Then P_1^2 and P_2^2 express the corresponding probabilities that the message words [1, 1] and [0, 0] will be correctly received. However, in practice we must consider the possibility of observing all the words: [1, 1], [1, 0], [0, 1], and [0, 0]. Therefore the observation matrix in this case becomes:

$$
\begin{array}{cc}
\begin{array}{c} \text{message} \\ \text{signals} \end{array} &
\begin{array}{cccc} & \text{observations} & & \\ [1, 1] & [1, 0] & [0, 1] & [0, 0] \end{array} \\
\begin{array}{c} \theta_1^* = [1, 1] \\ \theta_2^* = [0, 0] \end{array} &
\begin{bmatrix}
P_2^2 & P_2 Q_2 & Q_2 P_2 & Q_2^2 \\
Q_1^2 & Q_1 P_1 & P_1 Q_1 & P_1^2
\end{bmatrix}
\end{array}
\tag{3.3}
$$

In this example we consider the two possible decisions δ_1 and δ_2; decision δ_1 means that the observation of the message word [1, 1] is a true one, and δ_2 means that the observation of the message word [0, 0] is a true one. These correct decisions imply that there is no loss and no error cost. Hence, when we consider the following loss matrix corresponding to formula (3.2),

$$
\begin{array}{cc}
\begin{array}{c} \text{message} \\ \text{signals} \end{array} & \begin{array}{cc} \text{decisions} \\ \delta_1 \quad \delta_2 \end{array}
\end{array}
$$

$$
\begin{array}{c}
\theta_2^* = [1, 1] \\
\theta_1^* = [0, 0]
\end{array}
\begin{bmatrix}
L_{11} & L_{12} \\
L_{21} & L_{22}
\end{bmatrix}
\tag{3.4}
$$

the elements L_{ii} ($i = 1, 2$) of the main diagonal of the loss matrix should be zero. The variation of the off-diagonal elements, indicating relative costs of different kinds of errors, depends upon the error criterion adopted for the optimization. Therefore, generally we may write the loss matrix in this example as follows:

$$
\begin{array}{cc}
\begin{array}{c} \text{message} \\ \text{signals} \end{array} & \begin{array}{cc} \text{decisions} \\ \delta_1 \quad \delta_2 \end{array}
\end{array}
$$

$$
\begin{array}{c}
\theta_1^* = [1, 1] \\
\theta_2^* = [0, 0]
\end{array}
\begin{bmatrix}
0 & L_{12} \\
L_{21} & 0
\end{bmatrix}
\tag{3.5}
$$

When we let $L_{12} = L_{21} = 1$, the two errors of mistaking [1, 1] for [0, 0] and of mistaking [0, 0] for [1, 1] are equally important. Furthermore, if we let $L_{12} = 2$ and $L_{21} = 1$, then the first of the two errors carries twice the penalty that the second carries.

Let us summarize the situation so far. Three steps may be described as follows.

1. Description of the a priori probabilities: by this we may estimate, for instance, the relative frequencies of some input signals.

2. The observation matrix: since this describes the statistical characteristics of the random noise, its elements can often be evaluated from them.

3. The loss matrix: the determination of the elements of the loss matrix reflects the purposes of the designer.

When the description of the decision situation is given, the decision problem is to find the rule by which decision δ_k is to be made, so that the error cost or the loss becomes minimal. Of course, the situation mentioned above is rather general. We shall next briefly introduce some special situations concerning the n possible values mentioned above.

3.3   Signal Detection

The decision situation in which the number of possible values n is just equal to 2 is called the problem of testing hypothesis. The purpose (in our examples) is to test the hypothesis that the message signal alone is present and the hypothesis that it is not, on the basis of some observed data and with the least average loss. When we consider the example given in the preceding section, we see that the two possible values are, respectively, "signal present," [1, 1], and "no signal present," [0, 0]. In communications engineering the problem of testing hypotheses is frequently called the problem of signal detection.

Signal detection has four chief elements: (1) the number of message signals to be classified, (2) the class of the hypotheses, (3) the stochastic nature of the observed data and their processing, and (4) the joint statistics between message signal and noise.

3.3-1   Number of signals to be classified.   In the example given in the preceding section we saw two decisions corresponding to two hypotheses. Such a problem is, therefore, called a problem of binary detection. Naturally, the problem of multiple alternative detection involves more than two decisions. The number of message signals to be classified, including the null state (that is, no message signal), is equal to the number of hypotheses.

3.3-2   Type of the hypothesis.   A hypothesis which asserts the presence of a nonrandom message signal in the input is called a simple hypothesis, and a hypothesis which asserts the presence of noise alone is called the null hypothesis. Further details concerning types of hypothesis are omitted, because they are of no importance to us here.

3.3-3 Observations and data processing. Our observations, made on a mixture of message signals and random noise during an observation period, may consist of a continuum of values throughout the interval (continuous or analog sampling) or a discrete set of values (discrete or digital sampling). The observation interval is a time interval during which a decision system can store the data for making its decision. There are two kinds of decision making, depending on whether the observation interval is fixed or variable. The former is called nonsequential detection and the decision making for the detection is made on the data observed during the preassigned interval. The latter case is called sequential detection and this proceeds in steps, including at each stage the decision whether to terminate the test or postpone the decision and repeat the test with the introduction of additional data.

3.3-4 Joint statistics for observed data. Joint statistics between message signals and noise are of considerable importance in problems of signal detection. In general, because an individual sample value, as an observed datum, cannot be considered statistically independent, correlations between individual sample values over an observation period, fixed or variable, are an essential aspect of decision problems. Obviously, joint statistics of high order often will be required.

3.4 Signal Extraction

When we must estimate a message signal itself or one or more of its descriptive parameters, the decision processes are related to the extraction of message signals. Problems of signal extraction have recently received considerable attention under the name of parameter estimation. As in problems of signal detection, there exists a wide variety of possible situations corresponding to the type of the estimate, the data acquisition and their processing, and joint statistics of message signal and noise.

In the case where the message signal itself or one or more of its parameters has a definite value, which is constant over the observation interval, the extraction is called a point estimate. For example, when we estimate the amplitude of a message signal, such as a sinusoidal wave contaminated with random noise, we make a point estimate. On the other hand, when the values have certain probabilities, we make what is called an interval estimate. An estimate of the signal itself over the observation interval is an example of an interval estimate.

Of course, there is a wide variety of extraction problems, considered from the viewpoint of the stochastic nature of the observed data and the joint statistics of the message signal and noise. Since they concern mainly the theoretical aspects of communications engineering, a detailed description of them will not be given here.

CHAPTER 4

Evaluation Functions and Solutions in Statistical Decision Theory

4.1 Introductory Remarks

The basic concept and the general scope of decision situations were outlined in Chapter 3. The three steps in a decision situation were also pointed out, and a simple but practical example was given. In this chapter we give the general formulation and the mathematical aspect of a solution of decision problems. Our first task is to establish basic assumptions as analytical expressions of the three steps described in Chapter 3.

4.2 Basic Assumptions

In our present formulation of decision problems some assumptions are necessary for mathematical expressions concerning the statistics of message signals, noise, and observed data.

We assume here that the data are acquired in a discrete form, within a finite time T, during which n samples of the observed data are acquired, and that the sampling interval is equally fixed. We furthermore assume that the statistics of both message signals and noise are known a priori and that the combination of message signals and noise may be considered additive, as shown in Fig. 4.1.*

---

* Of course, the additive situation of the combination of message signals and noise is not common; there are more cases in which the combination is multiplicative. However, in many practical instances the sources of message signals and noise are mutually independent. There is, therefore, no need to take into account the cross-correlation between the message signal and noise components. This fact establishes the additive combination of message signals and noise.

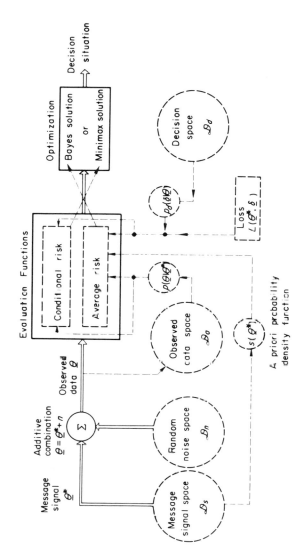

FIG. 4.1. The mathematical notion of decision-making.

According to the first assumption, the acquired data are represented as a vector with n components,

$$\boldsymbol{\theta} = (\theta_1, \theta_2, \ldots, \theta_n) \qquad (4.1)$$

where $\theta_1 = \theta(t_1)$, $\theta_2 = \theta(t_2)$, $\ldots$, $\theta_{n-1} = \theta(t_{n-1})$, $\theta_n = \theta(t_n)$. Although the true value of a message signal cannot be observed because of its being contaminated additively by random noise, we may express this, too, as a vector process,

$$\boldsymbol{\theta}^* = (\theta_1^*, \theta_2^*, \ldots, \theta_n^*) \qquad (4.2)$$

where $\theta_1^* = \theta^*(t_1)$, $\theta_2^* = \theta^*(t_2)$, $\ldots$, $\theta_{n-1}^* = \theta^*(t_{n-1})$, and $\theta_n^* = \theta^*(t_n)$. The random noise $n(t)$ may be represented as

$$\mathbf{n} = \boldsymbol{\theta} - \boldsymbol{\theta}^* = (n_1, n_2, \ldots, n_n) \qquad (4.3)$$

where $n_1 = n(t_1) = \theta_1 - \theta_1^*$, $n_2 = n(t_2) = \theta_2 - \theta_2^*$, $\ldots$, $n_{n-1} = n(t_{n-1}) = \theta_{n-1} - \theta_{n-1}^*$, $n_n = n(t_n) = \theta_n - \theta_n^*$.

The probability density functions of the message signal process and the random noise process are, respectively, expressed as $s(\boldsymbol{\theta}^*)$ and $p(\mathbf{n})$. When the message signal process $\boldsymbol{\theta}^*$ is given, the conditional probability density function of the observed data is denoted by $p(\boldsymbol{\theta} \mid \boldsymbol{\theta}^*)$. According to the second assumption, the probability density function $s(\boldsymbol{\theta}^*)$ of the message signal process is given a priori. In other words, with respect to the information of the message signal, we may immediately use the a priori probability density function as a datum of the decision problem at hand, for example, in a stationary gaussian form. There may also be the situation in which the message signal is mathematically represented by a known function of one or more random parameters $\boldsymbol{\alpha} = (\alpha_1, \alpha_2, \ldots, \alpha_m)$; in this case the probability density function $s(\boldsymbol{\alpha})$ of the message signal parameter is given a priori.

Now we proceed with the decision-making. As already pointed out in the simple example presented in Chapter 3, the decision itself is a function of the observed data and is represented as a conditional probability or a conditional probability density function. That is, a rule of decision-making may be represented by the conditional probability density function of making one decision among several or more possible decisions, $\delta_1, \delta_2, \ldots, \delta_{n-1}, \delta_n$ with a view to the optimal one, when the observed data are given. Therefore, the decision, like the message signal in Eq. (4.1), is described by a vector with n components,

$$\boldsymbol{\delta} = (\delta_1, \delta_2, \ldots, \delta_n), \tag{4.4}$$

and the conditional probability density function representing the decision situation may be denoted by $p_d(\boldsymbol{\delta} \mid \boldsymbol{\theta})$.

Thus the decision is based on the observed data $\boldsymbol{\theta}$. However, no matter what the decision procedure finally adopted, the decision made cannot always be the perfectly correct one, because our observation is always limited to a finite time interval. This fact reveals that we must assign some sort of penalty (loss) to the making of a wrong decision. It is convenient to consider the penalty in two ways. The first concerns mainly the decision procedure itself; that is, a more expensive and complicated procedure than we need is, of course, not desirable, even when a very refined decision-making is being carried out, and flimsy procedure might lead to total failure. The second way of considering the penalty is by assigning numerical costs to the decisions; for instance, procedures in which information is acquired over an unnecessarily long time interval and in very great amount should be avoided. So, a loss is assigned to each combination of the decision $\boldsymbol{\delta}$ and message signal $\boldsymbol{\theta}^*$, as in formula (3.2), and we make some a priori judgement of the relative importances of various correct and incorrect decisions. Since the decision-making itself is mathematically represented by the conditional probability density function, it is natural to represent the penalty by the mathematical expectation of a loss.

4.3   General Formulation of Evaluation Functions in Decision Problems

We shall consider in this section the mathematical expectation of a loss $L(\boldsymbol{\theta}^*, \boldsymbol{\delta})$. This is given by

$$\langle L(\boldsymbol{\theta}^*, \boldsymbol{\delta}) \rangle_{\mathrm{sav}} = \int_{\mathscr{D}_s} \int_{\mathscr{D}_d} L(\boldsymbol{\theta}^*, \boldsymbol{\delta}) p(\boldsymbol{\delta}, \boldsymbol{\theta}^*) \, d\boldsymbol{\theta}^* \, d\boldsymbol{\delta}, \tag{4.5a}$$

where $\mathcal{D}_s$ and $\mathcal{D}_d$ are, respectively, the message signal space and the decision space. Furthermore, $p(\delta, \theta^*)$ in this equation expresses the joint probability density function with respect to the message signal process and the decision process, and, by using Eq. (2.7), this becomes

$$p(\delta, \theta^*) = p(\delta \mid \theta^*)s(\theta^*) = p_d(\delta \mid \theta)p(\theta \mid \theta^*)s(\theta^*) \qquad (4.5b)$$

where $s(\theta^*)$ expresses the a priori probability density function of the message signal, which is assumed to be known. By applying Eq. (4.5b) to Eq. (4.5a), we derive the function

$$R(s, p_d) = \int_{\mathcal{D}_s} d\theta^* \int_{\mathcal{D}_a} d\theta \int_{\mathcal{D}_d} L(\theta^*, \delta)p_d(\delta \mid \theta)p(\theta \mid \theta^*)s(\theta^*) \, d\delta \qquad (4.6)$$

where $\mathcal{D}_a$ expresses the observed data space. This function is called the average risk, and it simultaneously depends upon both the mathematical form of the a priori density function of the message signal $s(\theta^*)$ and the rule of decision-making, that is, the conditional probability density function $p_d(\delta \mid \theta)$ under a certain assignment of loss $L(\theta^*, \delta)$.

If in Eq. (4.6) we let

$$l(\theta^*, p_d) = \int_{\mathcal{D}_a} d\theta \int_{\mathcal{D}_d} L(\theta^*, \delta)p_d(\delta \mid \theta)p(\theta \mid \theta^*) \, d\delta \qquad (4.7)$$

then Eq. (4.6) can be expressed as

$$R(s, p_d) = \langle l(\theta^*, p_d) \rangle_{\text{sav in } \mathcal{D}_s}$$

$$= \int_{\mathcal{D}_s} l(\theta^*, p_d)s(\theta^*) \, d\theta^* \qquad (4.8)$$

The function $l(\theta^*, p_d)$ defined by Eq. (4.7) is called the conditional risk. From Eqs. (4.6) and (4.8) we may say that the average risk $R(s, p_d)$ is defined by taking the statistical average of the conditional risk $l(\theta^*, p_d)$ over the message signal distribution, on condition that the a priori probability density function of the message signal is given. The two functions defined by Eqs. (4.6) and (4.7) are evaluation functions of decision problems.

4.4 Solutions of Decision Problems by the Bayes Criterion

The principal line of attack in decision problems is to minimize the conditional risk or the average risk, having a regard to the optimum. Before we perform the minimization of evaluation functions, we shall define the meaning of the optimum in decision problems for the case in which complete information of the a priori probability density function $s(\theta^*)$ of the message signal is known. We say that a system is better than others if its average risk is smaller on application of the same decision criterion and preassigned loss or cost. Furthermore, we say that the best, or optimal, system is the one so designed by the application of a decision criterion that its average risk is minimal. We call it a Bayes system. More precisely, a Bayes system complies with the decision-making $p_d^*(\delta \mid \theta)$, whose average risk $R(s, p_d)$ is smallest for a given a priori probability density function $s(\theta^*)$ of the message signal. By using Eq. (4.6), this statement may be expressed as

$$R(s, p_d^*) = \min_{p_d} R(s, p_d) \qquad (4.9)$$

where p_d^* is the conditional probability density function of the optimal decision-making giving minimal average risk. The rule of decision-making described by Eq. (4.9) is called the Bayes decision rule for the preassigned loss $L(\theta^*, \delta)$.

When the a priori probability density function of the message signal is not known, a possible criterion of optimization is provided by the Minimax decision rule. Naturally, we may consider various values of the conditional risk $l(\theta^*, p_d)$ with respect to the message signal itself, and a maximal value will certainly be among them. Roughly speaking, the Minimax rule is a rule of decision-making by which the maximal value of the conditional risk is made minimal. The Minimax theorem was originated by von Neumann in the field of game theory. Although detailed descriptions of it are omitted here, the reader should refer to the excellent books of von Neumann and Morgenstern[1] and Middleton.[2]

---

[1] J. von Neumann and O. Morgenstern, "Theory of Games and Economic Behavior." Princeton Univ. Press, Princeton, New Jersey, 1953.
[2] D. Middleton, "An Introduction to Statistical Communication Theory," Chap. 18. McGraw-Hill, New York, 1962.

The essence of decision theory is embodied in Fig. 4.1 and in the descriptions given so far in this chapter.

4.5 Solutions of Binary Detection Problems

We now consider an example of solving decision problems by the Bayes criterion. We shall consider binary detection (introduced in Chapter 3), in which the presence and absence of message signals in random noise are distinguished. Although analytical studies of binary detection problems in terms of statistical decision theory are rather recent (since about 1945), they have been made by many scientists.[3-9]

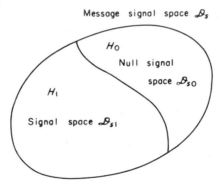

FIG. 4.2. Signal space in the binary detection problem.

[3] D. Middleton and D. Van Meter, Symposium on information theory. *IRE Trans.* **PGIT-4,** Sept. (1954); *J. SIAM* **3** (1955); **4** (1956).

[4] D. Middleton and J. Bussgang, Optimum sequential detection of signals in noise. *IRE Trans.* **PGIT-1,** 5 (1955).

[5] L. A. Zadeh, Optimum nonlinear filters for the extraction and detection of signals in noise. *J. Appl. Phys.* **24,** 396 (1953), and *IRE Conv. Rec.* Pt. 8, 57 (1953).

[6] R. C. Davis, On the detection of sure signals in noise. *J. Appl. Phys.* **25,** 76 (1953).

[7] U. Grenander and M. Rosenblatt, "Statistical Analysis of Stationary Time Series." Wiley, New York, 1957.

[8] W. B. Davenport, Jr., and W. L. Root, "An Introduction to the Theory of Random Signals and Noise." McGraw-Hill, New York, 1960.

[9] C. W. Helstrom, "Statistical Theory of Signal Detection." Pergamon, New York 1960.

Before we obtain the solution of binary detection problems, we must evaluate the average risk. Our first step is to consider the a priori probability density function of the message signals. Since we are considering the binary situation of distinguishing between the presence of message signals in random noise (hypothesis H_1) and the absence of them (hypothesis H_0), the signal space $\mathscr{D}_s$ in Eq. (4.6) may be divided into two spaces, $\mathscr{D}_{s1}$ and $\mathscr{D}_{s0}$, respectively, the message signal space and the null signal space; see Fig. 4.2. Of course, $\mathscr{D}_s = \mathscr{D}_{s0} + \mathscr{D}_{s1}$. The a priori probability density functions of the message signal in the spaces $\mathscr{D}_{s1}$ and $\mathscr{D}_{s0}$ are, respectively, expressed as $s_1(\theta^*)$ and $s_0(\theta^*)$ with the normalized conditions

$$\int_{\mathscr{D}_{s1}} s_1(\theta^*)\, d\theta^* = 1 \qquad (4.10a)$$

$$\int_{\mathscr{D}_{s0}} s_0(\theta^*)\, d\theta^* = 1 \qquad (4.10b)$$

where

$$s_0(\theta^*) = \delta(\theta^* - 0) \qquad (4.10c)$$

If P and $Q = (1 - P)$ express, respectively, the a priori probabilities that the message signals from the spaces $\mathscr{D}_{s1}$ and $\mathscr{D}_{s0}$ occur, the a priori probability with respect to the whole message signal space becomes

$$s(\theta^*)\, d\theta^* = Ps_1(\theta^*)\, d\theta^* + Qs_0(\theta^*)\, d\theta^*$$

That is, by Eq. (4.10c), we have

$$s(\theta^*) = Ps_1(\theta^*) + Qs_0(\theta^*) = Ps_1(\theta^*) + Q\delta(\theta^* - 0) \qquad (4.11)$$

In binary detection problems we must test hypothesis H_0 against hypothesis H_1. This means that the decision space $\mathscr{D}_d$ in Eq. (4.6) can be divided into two spaces, $\mathscr{D}_0$ and $\mathscr{D}_1$, which accept H_0 and H_1, respectively. Then the decision procedures may be expressed by $p_d(\delta_0 \mid \theta)$ and $p_d(\delta_1 \mid \theta)$, respectively, with the relation

$$p_d(\delta \mid \theta) = p_d(\delta_0 \mid \theta)\delta(\delta - \delta_0) + p_d(\delta_1 \mid \theta)\delta(\delta - \delta_1) \qquad (4.12a)$$

where

$$p_d(\delta_0 \mid \theta) + p_d(\delta_1 \mid \theta) = 1 \qquad (4.12b)$$

In our second step we assign a set of loss values to each possible combination of message signal and decision-making. As we saw in the preceding chapter, in detection problems the loss may be generally assigned

TABLE 4.1

THE LOSS MATRIX IN BINARY DETECTION PROBLEMS

Signal space	A priori probability	Loss	
		δ_0	δ_1
$\mathscr{D}_{s0}$	Q	L_{11}	L_{12}
$\mathscr{D}_{s1}$	P	L_{21}	L_{22}

as in Table 4.1, or, mathematically, as

$$
\begin{aligned}
L(\boldsymbol{\theta}^* \in \mathscr{D}_{s0} : \delta_0) &= L_{11} \\
L(\boldsymbol{\theta}^* \in \mathscr{D}_{s0} : \delta_1) &= L_{12} \\
L(\boldsymbol{\theta}^* \in \mathscr{D}_{s1} : \delta_0) &= L_{21} \\
L(\boldsymbol{\theta}^* \in \mathscr{D}_{s1} : \delta_1) &= L_{22}
\end{aligned}
\tag{4.13}
$$

By applying Eqs. (4.11), (4.12), and (4.13) to Eq. (4.6) the average risk can be computed as

$$
\begin{aligned}
R(s, p_d) =& \int_{\mathscr{D}_s} [Ps_1(\boldsymbol{\theta}^*) + Q\delta(\boldsymbol{\theta}^* - 0)]\, d\boldsymbol{\theta}^* \\
&\times \int_{\mathscr{D}_a} p(\boldsymbol{\theta} \mid \boldsymbol{\theta}^*)[L_{11}p_d(\delta_0 \mid \boldsymbol{\theta}) + L_{21}p_d(\delta_0 \mid \boldsymbol{\theta}) \\
&\quad + L_{12}p_d(\delta_1 \mid \boldsymbol{\theta}) + L_{22}p_d(\delta_1 \mid \boldsymbol{\theta})]\, d\boldsymbol{\theta} \\
=& \int_{\mathscr{D}_s} [Ps_1(\theta^*) + Q\delta(\boldsymbol{\theta}^* - 0)]\, d\boldsymbol{\theta}^* \\
&\times \int_{\mathscr{D}_a} [(L_{11} + L_{21})\, p_d(\delta_0 \mid \boldsymbol{\theta})\, p(\boldsymbol{\theta} \mid \boldsymbol{\theta}^*) \\
&\quad + (L_{12} + L_{22})\, p_d(\delta_1 \mid \boldsymbol{\theta})\, p(\boldsymbol{\theta} \mid \boldsymbol{\theta}^*)]\, d\boldsymbol{\theta} \\
=& \int_{\mathscr{D}_a} \{p_d(\delta_0 \mid \boldsymbol{\theta})[QL_{11}p(\boldsymbol{\theta} \mid 0) \\
&+ PL_{21}\int_{\mathscr{D}_{s1}} s_1(\boldsymbol{\theta}^*)p(\boldsymbol{\theta} \mid \boldsymbol{\theta}^*)\, d\boldsymbol{\theta}^*] + p_d(\delta_1 \mid \boldsymbol{\theta})[QL_{12}p(\boldsymbol{\theta} \mid 0) \\
&+ PL_{22}\int_{\mathscr{D}_{s1}} s_1(\boldsymbol{\theta}^*)\, p(\boldsymbol{\theta} \mid \boldsymbol{\theta}^*)\, d\boldsymbol{\theta}^*]\}\, d\boldsymbol{\theta}
\end{aligned}
\tag{4.14}
$$

Now we can consider concretely the two possible classes of errors in the present problem. The error of the first kind is to make the wrong decision, that the message signal is present when in fact noise alone is present. This is defined by

$$\epsilon_1 = \int_{\mathscr{D}_a} p(\mathbf{\theta} \mid 0) p_d(\delta_1 \mid \mathbf{\theta}) \, d\mathbf{\theta} \tag{4.15}$$

The error of the second kind is to make the wrong decision, that random noise alone exists when in fact the message signal is present. This is defined by

$$\epsilon_2 = \int_{\mathscr{D}_{s1}} \int_{\mathscr{D}_a} p(\mathbf{\theta} \mid \mathbf{\theta}^*) p_d(\delta_0 \mid \mathbf{\theta}) s_1(\mathbf{\theta}^*) \, d\mathbf{\theta} \, d\mathbf{\theta}^* \tag{4.16}$$

By means of Eq. (4.12) and the definitions given by Eqs. (4.15) and (4.16) the average risk given by Eq. (4.14) may be expressed compactly as

$$R(s, p_d) = QL_{11} \int_{\mathscr{D}_a} p_d(\delta_0 \mid \mathbf{\theta}) \, p(\mathbf{\theta} \mid 0) \, d\mathbf{\theta}$$

$$+ PL_{21} \int_{\mathscr{G}_a} d\mathbf{\theta} \int_{\mathscr{C}_{s1}} s_1(\mathbf{\theta}^*) \, p_d(\delta_0 \mid \mathbf{\theta}) \, p(\mathbf{\theta} \mid \mathbf{\theta}^*) \, d\mathbf{\theta}^*$$

$$+ QL_{12} \int_{\mathscr{D}_a} p_d(\delta_1 \mid \mathbf{\theta}) \, p(\mathbf{\theta} \mid 0) \, d\mathbf{\theta}$$

$$+ PL_{22} \int_{\mathscr{D}_a} d\mathbf{\theta} \int_{\mathscr{D}_{s1}} s_1(\mathbf{\theta}^*) \, p_d(\delta_1 \mid \mathbf{\theta}) \, p(\mathbf{\theta} \mid \mathbf{\theta}^*) \, d\mathbf{\theta}^* \tag{4.17a}$$

$$= QL_{11} \int_{\mathscr{D}_a} [1 - p_d(\delta_1 \mid \mathbf{\theta})] \, p(\mathbf{\theta} \mid 0) \, d\mathbf{\theta}$$

$$+ PL_{21} \int_{\mathscr{D}_a} d\mathbf{\theta} \int_{\mathscr{D}_{s1}} s_1(\mathbf{\theta}^*) \, p_d(\delta_0 \mid \mathbf{\theta}) \, p(\mathbf{\theta} \mid \mathbf{\theta}^*) \, d\mathbf{\theta}^*$$

$$+ QL_{12} \int_{\mathscr{D}_a} p_d(\delta_1 \mid \mathbf{\theta}) \, p(\mathbf{\theta} \mid 0) \, d\mathbf{\theta}$$

$$+ PL_{22} \int_{\mathscr{D}_a} d\mathbf{\theta} \int_{\mathscr{D}_{s1}} s_1(\mathbf{\theta}^*)[1 - p_d(\delta_0 \mid \mathbf{\theta})] \, p(\mathbf{\theta} \mid \mathbf{\theta}^*) \, d\mathbf{\theta}^* \tag{4.17b}$$

$$= QL_{11} + PL_{22} + Q\epsilon_1(L_{12} - L_{11}) + P\epsilon_2(L_{21} - L_{22}) \tag{4.17c}$$

Our present problem is to obtain $p_d(\delta_0 \mid \boldsymbol{\theta})$ and hence $p_d(\delta_1 \mid \boldsymbol{\theta})$ in such a way that the average risk obtained by Eq. (4.17a) becomes minimal. For this purpose let us rewrite Eq. (4.17a) as

$$
\begin{aligned}
R(s, p_d) = {} & QL_{11} \int_{\mathscr{D}_a} p_d(\delta_0 \mid \boldsymbol{\theta}) p(\boldsymbol{\theta} \mid 0)\, d\boldsymbol{\theta} \\
& + PL_{21} \int_{\mathscr{D}_a} d\boldsymbol{\theta} \int_{\mathscr{D}_{s1}} s_1(\boldsymbol{\theta}^*)\, p_d(\delta_0 \mid \boldsymbol{\theta})\, p(\boldsymbol{\theta} \mid \boldsymbol{\theta}^*)\, d\boldsymbol{\theta}^* \\
& + QL_{12} \int_{\mathscr{D}_a} [1 - p_d(\delta_0 \mid \boldsymbol{\theta})]\, p(\boldsymbol{\theta} \mid 0)\, d\boldsymbol{\theta} \\
& + PL_{22} \int_{\mathscr{D}_a} d\boldsymbol{\theta} \int_{\mathscr{D}_{s1}} s_1(\boldsymbol{\theta}^*)[1 - p_d(\delta_0 \mid \boldsymbol{\theta})]\, p(\boldsymbol{\theta} \mid \boldsymbol{\theta}^*)\, d\boldsymbol{\theta}^* \\
= {} & QL_{12} + PL_{21} + \int_{\mathscr{D}_a} d\boldsymbol{\theta}\, p_d(\delta_0 \mid \boldsymbol{\theta})[P(L_{21} - L_{22}) \\
& \times \int_{\mathscr{D}_{s1}} s_1(\boldsymbol{\theta}^*)\, p(\boldsymbol{\theta} \mid \boldsymbol{\theta}^*)\, d\boldsymbol{\theta}^* - Q(L_{12} - L_{11})\, p(\boldsymbol{\theta} \mid 0)]
\end{aligned}
\tag{4.18}
$$

It is clear that in the right-hand member of Eq. (4.18), when

$$
P(L_{21} - L_{22}) \int_{\mathscr{D}_{s1}} s_1(\boldsymbol{\theta}^*)\, p(\boldsymbol{\theta} \mid \boldsymbol{\theta}^*)\, d\boldsymbol{\theta}^* > Q(L_{12} - L_{11})\, p(\boldsymbol{\theta} \mid 0) \tag{4.19}
$$

the average risk $R(s, p_d)$ becomes minimal if

$$
p_d(\delta_0 \mid \boldsymbol{\theta}) = 0 \tag{4.20a}
$$

and hence, from Eq. (4.12) we have

$$
p_d(\delta_1 \mid \boldsymbol{\theta}) = 1 \tag{4.20b}
$$

Similarly, when

$$
P(L_{21} - L_{22}) \int_{\mathscr{D}_{s1}} s_1(\boldsymbol{\theta}^*)\, p(\boldsymbol{\theta} \mid \boldsymbol{\theta}^*)\, d\boldsymbol{\theta}^* < Q(L_{12} - L_{11})\, p(\boldsymbol{\theta} \mid 0) \tag{4.21}
$$

the average risk becomes minimal if

$$
p_d(\delta_0 \mid \boldsymbol{\theta}) = 1 \tag{4.22a}
$$

and hence we have

$$p_d(\delta_1 \mid \boldsymbol{\theta}) = 0 \tag{4.22b}$$

The rule of decision-making stated above is called the Bayes decision rule. The quantity

$$\Lambda = \frac{P \displaystyle\int_{\mathscr{D}_{s1}} s_1(\boldsymbol{\theta}^*) \, p(\boldsymbol{\theta} \mid \boldsymbol{\theta}^*) \, d\boldsymbol{\theta}^*}{Q \, p(\boldsymbol{\theta} \mid 0)} \tag{4.23}$$

derived from the condition

$$P(L_{21} - L_{22}) \int_{\mathscr{D}_{s1}} s_1(\boldsymbol{\theta}^*) \, p(\boldsymbol{\theta} \mid \boldsymbol{\theta}^*) \, d\boldsymbol{\theta}^* = Q(L_{12} - L_{11}) \, p(\boldsymbol{\theta} \mid 0) \tag{4.24}$$

plays an important role in binary detection problems. The quantity is called the generalized-likelihood ratio, and by means of it an alternative statement of the Bayes decision rule may be written:

$$\begin{aligned} &\text{Choose } \delta_0 \quad \text{when} \quad \Lambda < \gamma. \\ &\text{Choose } \delta_1 \quad \text{when} \quad \Lambda > \gamma. \end{aligned} \tag{4.25}$$

where

$$\gamma = \frac{L_{12} - L_{11}}{L_{21} - L_{22}} \tag{4.26}$$

and γ is called the threshold and depends upon only the preassigned loss values.

4.6   The Neyman-Pearson Detection Rule

We consider here a case in which there is only one nonzero message signal in the entire signal space. This situation of decision-making is called the simple alternative. Since it is enough to consider only one message signal, then instead of Eqs. (4.15) and (4.16), we stipulate two kinds of error, ϵ_1' and ϵ_2', which are, respectively, defined by the following conditional probabilities:

$$\epsilon_1' = \int_{\mathscr{D}_a} p(\boldsymbol{\theta} \mid \boldsymbol{0}) \, p_d(\delta_1 \mid \boldsymbol{\theta}) \, d\boldsymbol{\theta} \equiv \epsilon_1 \qquad (4.27a)$$

$$\epsilon_2' = \int_{\mathscr{D}_a} p(\boldsymbol{\theta} \mid s) \, p_d(\delta_0 \mid \boldsymbol{\theta}) \, d\boldsymbol{\theta} \qquad (4.27b)$$

Here ϵ_2' is derived by letting $s_1(\boldsymbol{\theta}^*) = \delta(\boldsymbol{\theta}^* - s)$ in Eq. (4.16) because the message signal space is constructed with only one element. The Neyman-Pearson detection rule gives the minimization of the error probability of the second type, $P\epsilon_2'$, with the condition that the error probability of the first type, $Q\epsilon_1'$, is fixed. However, we extend this classic approach to a more general situation. Instead of using the error probabilities ϵ_1' and ϵ_1', we shall consider the minimization of the error probability of the second type, $P\epsilon_2$, with the condition that the error probability of the first type, $Q\epsilon_1$, is fixed. This situation implies that

$$R_N^* = \min_{\delta}(P\epsilon_2 + \lambda Q\epsilon_1) \qquad (4.28)$$

where λ is an undetermined multiplier and R_N^* is the minimum value of the total risk $R_N = P\epsilon_2 + \lambda Q\epsilon_1$ with respect to the decision-making δ.

By means of Eqs. (4.12), (4.15), and (4.16), Eq. (4.28) can be expressed as

$$
\begin{aligned}
R_N^* &= \min_{\delta}(P\epsilon_2 + \lambda Q\epsilon_1) \\
&= \min_{\delta}\Bigg\{ P \int_{\mathscr{D}_{s1}} s_1(\boldsymbol{\theta}^*) \, d\boldsymbol{\theta}^* \int_{\mathscr{D}_a} p(\boldsymbol{\theta} \mid \boldsymbol{\theta}^*) \, p_d(\delta_0 \mid \boldsymbol{\theta}) \, d\boldsymbol{\theta} \\
&\qquad\qquad\qquad + \lambda Q \int_{\mathscr{D}_a} p(\boldsymbol{\theta} \mid \boldsymbol{0}) \, p_d(\delta_1 \mid \boldsymbol{\theta}) \, d\boldsymbol{\theta} \Bigg\} \\
&= \min_{\delta}\Bigg\{ \int_{\mathscr{D}_a} p_d(\delta_0 \mid \boldsymbol{\theta}) \, d\boldsymbol{\theta} \Bigg[P \int_{\mathscr{D}_{s1}} p(\boldsymbol{\theta} \mid \boldsymbol{\theta}^*) s_1(\boldsymbol{\theta}^*) \, d\boldsymbol{\theta} \\
&\qquad\qquad\qquad\qquad\qquad - \lambda Q \, p(\boldsymbol{\theta} \mid \boldsymbol{0}) \Bigg] \Bigg\} + \lambda Q \quad (4.29)
\end{aligned}
$$

As in the derivation of the Bayes decision rule, the optimal rule of decision-making in this case is such that, when

$$P \int_{\mathscr{D}_{s1}} p(\boldsymbol{\theta} \mid \boldsymbol{\theta}^*) \, s_1(\boldsymbol{\theta}^*) \, d\boldsymbol{\theta}^* > \lambda Q \, p(\boldsymbol{\theta} \mid \boldsymbol{0}) \qquad (4.30)$$

we choose the decision rules

$$p_d(\delta_0 \,|\, \boldsymbol{\theta}) = 0$$
$$p_d(\delta_1 \,|\, \boldsymbol{\theta}) = 1$$

(4.31)

and, conversely, when

$$P \int_{\mathcal{D}_{s1}} p(\boldsymbol{\theta} \,|\, \boldsymbol{\theta}^*) \, s_1(\boldsymbol{\theta}^*) \, d\boldsymbol{\theta}^* < \lambda Q \, p(\boldsymbol{\theta} \,|\, 0)$$

(4.32)

we choose the decision rules

$$p_d(\delta_0 \,|\, \boldsymbol{\theta}) = 1$$
$$p_d(\delta_1 \,|\, \boldsymbol{\theta}) = 0$$

(4.33)

With the use of the quantity Λ defined by Eq. (4.23) the decision rule given by Eq. (4.25) may alternatively be stated:

$$\text{Choose } \delta_0 \quad \text{when} \quad \Lambda < \lambda.$$
$$\text{Choose } \delta_1 \quad \text{when} \quad \Lambda > \lambda.$$

(4.34)

A comparison of Eqs. (4.25) and (4.34) shows that the undetermined multiplier λ plays a role equivalent to that of the threshold γ, defined by Eq. (4.26). The value of λ must be determined by the constraint of a preassigned value of the error of the first kind, ϵ_1.

We shall not treat here of the Ideal Observer test,[10] because its theoretical aspects are easily understood without the help of any new concepts, the notions contained in it being a modification of the Bayes decision rule. Some of useful information concerning problems of the Ideal Observer test in control engineering will be introduced in the next chapter.

[10] See Ref. 2.

CHAPTER 5

Statistical Decision Concept in Control Processes

5.1 Introductory Remarks

We repeat the three essential problems in decision adaptive control systems:

1. Identification problems.
2. Decision problems.
3. Modification problems.

The key problem is that of identification, because solving both decision and modification problems depends solely on continuous measurements of information concerning the system dynamics. A fundamental difficulty in identification problems is the fact that, because of the inevitable factors mentioned in Chapter 1, the measurement schemes proposed by many investigators can only be approximate. It is very important, therefore, to reduce as much as possible the effect of error in identification procedures.

To open the door to the combination of the decision concept and control theory we consider here a simple configuration of an adaptive control system, shown in Fig. 5.1. Let an unknown parameter in the controlled element be expressed by $\theta^*(t)$. The measuring device identifies this parameter. As stated previously, in the process of carrying out a measurement or observation some error or inaccuracy may always be observed at the output of the measuring device; therefore, the device gives an imperfect measurement $\theta(t)$ of the parameter $\theta^*(t)$, so that

$$\theta(t) = \theta^*(t) + n(t) \tag{5.1}$$

where $n(t)$ is considered an equivalent additive noise. The known quantity is, of course, only the observed data $\theta(t)$ contaminated with random noise $n(t)$, and the true value $\theta^*(t)$ must be inferred from it. Thus, the central problem of identification in adaptive control systems is to determine a true value on the basis of incomplete information. Optimal control performance is realized by changing the control parameters on the basis of determining the true value $\theta^*(t)$, and this is done by making a choice among various combinations of controlled elements, characterized by parameters $\theta^*(t)$, and controller parameters. The effective technique is statistical inference; this suggests the application of statistical decision

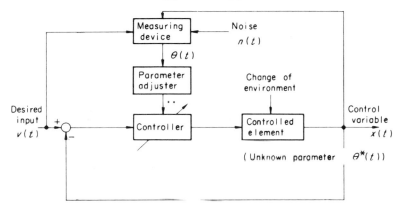

FIG. 5.1. Configuration of a simple adaptive control system.

theory, which in fact provides a very general method for statistical inference and, hence, for the design of an adaptive loop.

To illustrate the way in which the best statistical decision procedure is established we consider a simple example. The block diagram of the system to be considered here is given in Fig. 5.2, this is a practical example of the adaptive control system shown in Fig. 5.1. The controlled element (an industrial plant) contains the unknown parameter $\theta^*(t)$, which is quantized by N different values θ_i^* $(i = 1, 2, \ldots, N)$ and is to be found by the decision device. The controller is operated by a switching element through the use of decision logic, so as to produce an optimal output through an appropriate choice of controller parameters K_i $(i = 1, 2, \ldots, N)$.[1] The problem is to choose one of the controller parameters K_i by divining the true value θ_i^* from the observed value

[1] J. G. Truxal and J. J. Padalino, Decision theory. *In* "Adaptive Control Systems" (E. Mishkin and L. Brown, eds.), Chap. 15. McGraw-Hill, New York, 1960.

$\theta(t)$, the aim being to construct a device that will statistically minimize losses. For convenience we shall confine ourselves to the case in which the value of the observed data $\theta(t)$ also is quantized by N different values $\theta_i\ (i = 1, 2, \ldots, N)$.

Let us state it concretely. When the true value $\theta^*(t)$ takes a quantized value θ_i^*, the corresponding optimal gain K should be K_i with respect to control performance. We introduce here the average risk to be minimized by an appropriate choice of decision δ_i, which means the adjustment of

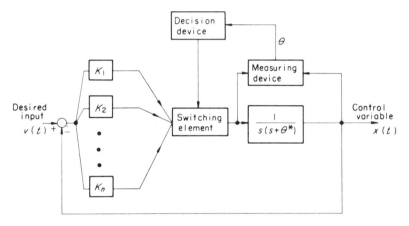

FIG. 5.2. Servo system containing a decision logic.

gain K_i. As mentioned in Chapter 4, each of the possible values θ_i^* may be expected to occur with a priori probability density $s(\theta_i^*)$. We assign the loss function $L(\theta_i^*, \delta_k)$ to the decision δ_k when θ_i^* is true. Furthermore, $P(\theta_j \mid \theta_i^*)$ is the conditional probability of the observed value θ_j when θ_i^* is given. Since the a priori probability density function is given with respect to a discrete form of $\theta_i^*(i = 1, 2, \ldots, N)$, then with the use of Eq. (2.55), the integral over the signal space $\mathscr{D}_s$ in Eq. (4.8) is replaced with the sum

$$\sum_{i=1}^{N} s(\theta_i^*)\, \delta(\boldsymbol{\theta}^* - \theta_i^*)$$

and the average risk introduced here is expressed as

$$R_k = \sum_{i=1}^{N} L(\theta_i^*, \delta_k)\, P(\theta_j \mid \theta_i^*)\, s(\theta_i^*) \tag{5.2}$$

or, more compactly,

$$R_k = \sum_{i=1}^{N} L_{ik} P_{ij} s_i \qquad (5.3)$$

where $L_{ik} = L(\theta_i^*, \delta_k)$, $P_{ij} = P(\theta_j \mid \theta_i^*)$, and $s_i = s(\theta_i^*)$.

To proceed with a specific numerical example, using Fig. 5.3, we consider the case in which $i = 1, 2,$ and 3, and we assume that the param-

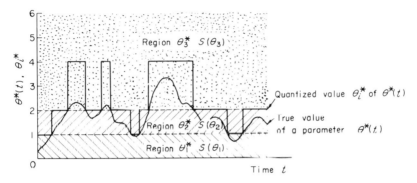

FIG. 5.3. The true value of a parameter $\theta^*(t)$ and its quantized processing θ_i^* ($i = 1, 2, 3$), where $s(\theta_i^*)$ is the a priori probability density function.

eter θ^* takes a quantized value among $\theta_1^* = 1$, $\theta_2^* = 2$, and $\theta_3^* = 4$ with a change in environmental conditions.

As the first step mentioned in Chapter 3, the a priori probabilities $s(\theta_i^*)$ are assumed to be

$$s(\theta_1^*) = 0.3$$

$$s(\theta_2^*) = 0.5 \qquad (5.4)$$

$$s(\theta_3^*) = 0.2$$

The measurement error (equivalent noise) makes the measured value θ_i differ from the true value θ_i^*. However, if we know the probability of the measurement error, we can assume the conditional probability P_{ij}, which may be presented in the form of a matrix. So from formula (3.1), the following array is constructed as the second step:

quantized true value of parameter	quantized value of observations		
	$\theta_1 = 1$	$\theta_2 = 2$	$\theta_3 = 4$
$\theta_1^* = 1$	$P_{11} = 0.6$	$P_{12} = 0.2$	$P_{13} = 0.2$
$\theta_2^* = 2$	$P_{21} = 0.1$	$P_{22} = 0.6$	$P_{23} = 0.3$
$\theta_3^* = 4$	$P_{31} = 0$	$P_{32} = 0.4$	$P_{33} = 0.6$

$$(5.5a)$$

Here, for example, $P_{21} = 0.1$ is the probability that the result of the observation, θ, will be equal to 1 when the actual value, θ^*, is equal to 2. In other words, the probabilities P_{ij} depend only upon the probability distribution of the equivalent nose and actually constitute a quantitative description of it.

Finally, a reasonable set of loss functions may be assigned*:

quantized true value of parameter	decisions		
	$\delta_1 = K_1$	$\delta_2 = K_2$	$\delta_3 = K_3$
$\theta_1^* = 1$	$L_{11} = 2.4$	$L_{12} = 6.0$	$L_{13} = 7.2$
$\theta_2^* = 2$	$L_{21} = 4.6$	$L_{22} = 1.2$	$L_{23} = 2.7$
$\theta_3^* = 4$	$L_{31} = 10.8$	$L_{32} = 2.3$	$L_{33} = 0.6$

$$(5.5b)$$

In this example the technique of making an optimal decision is rather straightforward. We simply assume δ_1, δ_2, and δ_3 in turn, calculate Eq. (5.3) for each case, and select the decision δ_j yielding the minimal cost. We compute the respective average losses associated with each of the three decisions by applying Eqs. (5.4) and (5.5) to Eq. (5.2).

First, if the observed value $\theta(t)$ of the parameter is equal to 1, that is, $\theta = 1 = \theta_1$, the average risk is found as follows. When the rule of

---

* Truxal and Padalino (*op. cit.*) have specified this loss function on the basis of specific control performance.

decision-making $\delta_1 = K_1$ is chosen, we have

$$R_1 = L_{11}P_{11}S_1 + L_{21}P_{21}S_2 + L_{31}P_{31}S_3$$

$$= 2.4 \times 0.6 \times 0.3 + 4.6 \times 0.1 \times 0.5 + 10.8 \times 0 \times 0.2$$

$$= 0.432 + 0.23 = 0.662 \tag{5.6a}$$

When the rule $\delta_2 = K_2$ is chosen, we have

$$R_2 = L_{12}P_{11}S_1 + L_{22}P_{21}S_2 + L_{32}P_{31}S_3$$

$$= 6.0 \times 0.6 \times 0.3 + 1.2 \times 0.1 \times 0.5 + 2.3 \times 0 \times 0.2$$

$$= 1.08 + 0.06 = 1.14 \tag{5.6b}$$

When $\delta_3 = K_3$ is chosen, we have

$$R_3 = L_{13}P_{11}S_1 + L_{23}P_{21}S_2 + L_{33}P_{31}S_3$$

$$= 7.2 \times 0.6 \times 0.3 + 2.7 \times 0.1 \times 0.5 + 0.6 \times 0 \times 0.2$$

$$= 1.296 + 0.135 = 1.431 \tag{5.6c}$$

With a similar computation for $\theta = 2$ and $\theta = 4$ we obtain the following.

decisions	quantized observed data		
	$\theta_1 = 1$	$\theta_2 = 2$	$\theta_3 = 4$
$\delta_1 = K_1$	0.662	2.388	2.130
$\delta_2 = K_2$	1.140	0.904	0.816
$\delta_3 = K_3$	1.431	1.190	0.909

$$\text{Optimal decision} \quad \delta_1 = K_1 \quad \delta_2 = K_2 \quad \delta_2 = K_2 \tag{5.7}$$

Thus we achieve, on the basis of the statistical characteristics of the measurements and the specific control performance, a design that will allow the decision adaptive controller to make the best decision. Since this example presents only the fundamental concept, the results are too brief to be of use in the practical analysis and synthesis of adaptive control systems; however, Truxal and Padalino[2] have given an excellent review of how statistical decision theory may be applied to adaptive control problems, and a valuable discussion may be found in the work of Hsu and Meserve.[3]

5.2 Decision Adaptive Control Systems under Preassigned Error Probabilities

As has been stated, the problem in adaptive control is to estimate or test the true value of a parameter θ^* from the observed value θ, and the mathematical tools for doing so are obtained from the discipline of

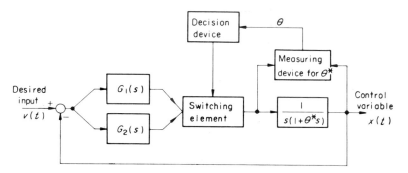

FIG. 5.4. Block diagram of an adaptive servo system containing a binary decision logic.

statistical inference or, more generally, statistical decision theory. A rather intuitive example, the control system shown in Fig. 5.4, will now be considered. The situation described in the previous section is converted into a more practical one, in which the time constant θ^* of the controlled element with transfer function $G_0(s) = 1/s(1 + \theta^*s)$ slowly changes with time, in some unpredictable fashion, from its preassigned value $\theta_1^* = 0.07$ to the value $\theta_2^* = 0.16$.

[2] J. G. Truxal and J. J. Padalino, *op. cit.*
[3] J. C. Hsu and W. E. Meserve, Decision-making adaptive control systems. *IRE Trans. Automatic Control* **AC-7** (No. 1), 24 (1962).

We consider two procedures of data acquisition. The first has a continuous form and the second a discrete one. For the convenience of analysis, we shall consider the discrete form of data acquisition. It is assumed that the value of parameter $\theta*$ is measured at a sampling interval of T seconds, so that the measured value θ is essentially a sequence of sample values $\theta_i = \theta(iT)$, where $i = 1, 2, \ldots, n$.

In the present example the range of parameter variation $\theta*(t)$ is separated into two regions with the value $\theta_0^* = 0.116$ as the boundary. In the region C_1, where $\theta* < \theta_0^*$, the controller with its transfer function $G_1(s)$ is required; in the region C_2, where $\theta* > \theta_0^*$, the controller with its transfer function $G_2(s)$ is required. The problem is as follows. At the end of each interval nT it must be inferred from the observed value θ whether $\theta*$ lies in C_1 or not. From the result either of the transfer functions $G_i(s)$, where $i = 1, 2$, is chosen through one of two decisions δ_i ($i = 1, 2$), where δ_1 and δ_2 correspond to the choice of transfer functions $G_1(s)$ and $G_2(s)$, respectively. The problem is, therefore, to make decision δ_1 or δ_2 with respect to a certain statistical criterion. Since the known quantity is only the observed data θ, the problem is solved when the boundary D can be found. Then, at the end of an interval nT:

$$\text{If } f(\boldsymbol{\theta}) < D \quad \text{or} \quad f(\theta_1, \theta_2, \ldots, \theta_n) < D, \qquad \text{choose } \delta_1.$$
$$\text{If } f(\boldsymbol{\theta}) > D \quad \text{or} \quad f(\theta_1, \theta_2, \ldots, \theta_n) > D, \qquad \text{choose } \delta_2.$$

Here $f(\boldsymbol{\theta})$ or $f(\theta_1, \theta_2, \ldots, \theta_n)$ expresses the form of processing the $\boldsymbol{\theta}(t)$, or $\theta_1, \theta_2, \ldots, \theta_{n-1}, \theta_n$. Thus, the problem is equivalent to testing hypothesis H_1, in which $\theta* \in C_1$, against hypothesis H_2, in which $\theta* \in C_2$ (cf. Chapter 4). Figure 5.5 shows the basic notion of decision adaptive control described here. In this figure our test requires that the observed data space be divided into two subspaces, one of them associated with decision δ_1 and the other with decision δ_2. Consequently, in this case the two possible types of error given by Eqs. (4.15) and (4.16) may, respectively, be modified as follows:

1. Error α, that of switching to controller $G_2(s)$ when in reality $\theta*$ belongs to region C_1.
2. Error β, that of not switching to controller $G_2(s)$ although actually $\theta*$ belongs to region C_2.

It is the present problem to construct a decision device such that α and β are jointly minimized on the basis of a finite number n of observed data at our disposal. Three situations will be considered in the following sections:

1. Both the values of α and β are fixed; then the number n is adjusted. This is the sequential test.

2. The values of α and n are simultaneously fixed; then β is minimized. This is the Neyman-Pearson test mentioned in Chapter 4.

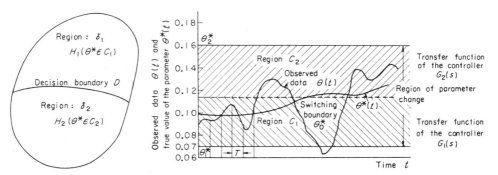

FIG. 5.5. The basic notion of the binary decision adaptive control: (left) decision space; (right) observed data $\theta(t)$ and true value $\theta^*(t)$ of the parameter of a controlled element.

3. The number n is fixed; then the probability of an incorrect decision is minimized; that is, the total error probability, $\alpha + \beta$, is minimized. This is the ideal observer.

5.3 Binary Decision Adaptive Control Systems Based on the Concept of the Sequential Test

We turn to a specific example of the procedure in sequential testing. We consider first the decision approach to the analog form of data acquisition and assume here that both the true value θ^* and the additive random noise are gaussian. It is, therefore, apparent that the process $\theta = \theta^* + n$ also is gaussian.[4] Since the conditional probability density

[4] J. L. Doob, "Stochastic Processes." Wiley, New York, 1953.

function $p(\theta \mid \theta^*)$ is concerned with the occurrence of the observed value θ when the true value θ^* is given, the latter may be considered the mean value of the former. Furthermore, the variance of θ is that of the random noise $n(t)$, which is expressed by σ_n^2, where σ_n is the standard deviation of the random noise $n(t)$. Thus, with the help of Eq. (2.97) we may express the conditional probability density function as

$$p(\theta \mid \theta^*) = \frac{1}{(2\pi)^{1/2}\sigma_n} \exp\left(-\frac{(\theta - \theta^*)^2}{2\sigma_n^2}\right) \tag{5.8}$$

where we assume $\sigma_n = 0.02$ for the convenience of numerical illustrations.

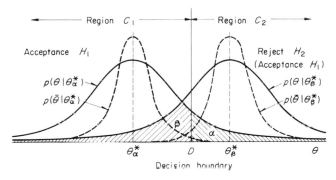

FIG. 5.6. Error probabilities α and β.

We shall mathematically assign the two kinds of error probabilities, α and β. Error probability α may mathematically be expressed as

$$\alpha(D, \theta^*) = \int_D^\infty p(\theta \mid \theta^*)\, d\theta, \qquad \text{for} \quad \theta^* \in C_1 \tag{5.9a}$$
$$= 0 \qquad \text{for} \quad \theta^* \in C_2$$

where D is the decision threshold. Similarly, the error probability β is

$$\beta(D, \theta^*) = \int_{-\infty}^D p(\theta \mid \theta^*)\, d\theta, \qquad \text{for} \quad \theta^* \in C_2 \tag{5.9b}$$
$$= 0 \qquad \text{for} \quad \theta^* \in C_1$$

Figure 5.6 depicts the basic notion of these equations. In this figure two possible peaks of $p(\theta \mid \theta^*)$, the $\theta^* = \theta_\alpha^*$ in $\theta^* \in C_1$ and the $\theta^* = \theta_\beta^*$ in $\theta^* \in C_2$, are assumed. We observe that the figures of α and β with the respective parameters $\theta^* = \theta_\alpha^*$ and $\theta^* = \theta_\beta^*$ show contradictory trends with respect to the value of D; see Fig. 5.7. To make the decision is thus to seek the decision boundary D by fixing the values of α and β, then:

If $D > 0$, accept H_1.

If $D < 0$, reject H_1 (accept H_2).

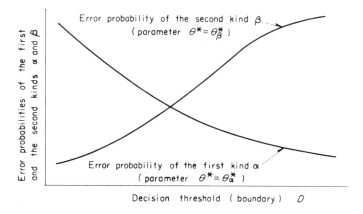

FIG. 5.7. The two kinds of error probabilities α and β plotted against the decision threshold D.

To fix the values of α and β we shall consider once again the fundamental schemata of the error probabilities α and β. Let us take the case in which $\theta_\alpha^* = 0.1$ and $\theta_\beta^* = 0.123$. In this case, by a computation similar to that of Eq. (2.98), using the relation $\theta^* = \theta_\alpha^*$ and substituting Eq. (5.8) into Eq. (5.9a) we obtain the expression

$$\alpha(D, \theta_\alpha^*) = \frac{1}{(2\pi)^{1/2}\sigma_n} \int_D^\infty \exp\left[-\frac{(\theta - \theta_\alpha^*)^2}{2\sigma_n^2}\right] d\theta$$

$$= \frac{1}{2}\left[1 - \mathrm{erf}\left(\frac{D - \theta_\alpha^*}{2^{1/2}\sigma_n}\right)\right] \tag{5.10a}$$

Similarly, from Eqs. (5.8) and (5.9b), we obtain

$$\beta(D, \theta_\beta^*) = \frac{1}{(2\pi)^{\frac{1}{2}}\sigma_n} \int_{-\infty}^{D} \exp\left[-\frac{(\theta - \theta_\beta^*)^2}{2\sigma_n^2}\right] d\theta$$

$$= \frac{1}{2}\left[1 + \mathrm{erf}\left(\frac{D - \theta_\beta^*}{2^{\frac{1}{2}}\sigma_n}\right)\right] \qquad (5.10b)$$

The two error probabilities $\alpha(D; \theta_\alpha^* = 0.1)$ and $\beta(D; \theta_\beta^* = 0.123)$ may each be computed with respect to the value of D as a variable, as shown

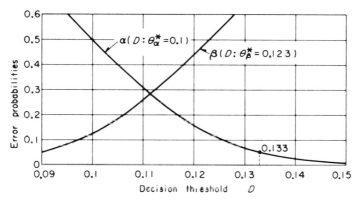

FIG. 5.8. Numerical example of the error probabilities α and β plotted against decision threshold D.

in Fig. 5.8. We stipulate here two specifications which, with the help of Fig. 5.6, may be given as follows.

1. We consider that $\theta^* = 0.1 = \theta_\alpha^*$ in region C_1. The value of α should be smaller than the value of $\alpha_1 = (\alpha$ at $\theta_\alpha^* = D = 0.1)$, the case in which the value of D is equal to the value of θ_α^*.

2. We consider that $\theta^* = 0.123 = \theta_\beta^*$ in region C_2. The value of β should be smaller than the value of $\beta_1 = (\beta$ at $\theta_\beta^* = D = 0.123)$, the case in which the value of D is equal to the value of θ_β^*.

If the value of the penalty is $\alpha(D; \theta_\alpha^* = 0.1) = 0.05$, then the value of the decision threshold is $D = 0.133$, when Eq. (5.10a) is solved with respect to D. On the other hand, if the penalty is $\beta(D; \beta_\alpha^* = 0.123) = 0.05$, then $D = 0.09$. However, when we take $D = 0.133$, the value of β_1 exceeds the preassigned limitation, because $D > \theta_\beta^*$. Similarly, when $D = 0.09$, the value of α_1 exceeds the preassigned limitation. It is thus apparent that it is impossible to realize the system under the specification $\alpha_1 = \beta_1 = 0.05$ by the method mentioned above. Although only the value $D = 0.115$ gives equal values for the two penalties (that is, $\alpha_1 = \beta_1$), the penalty in this case is larger than in the case of $\alpha_1 = \beta_1 = 0.05$. This fact suggests that there is a need to introduce a certain statistical treatment.

We now consider data acquisition in a discrete form. An effective approach is an averaging process with the observed data. The arithmetical mean of the observed data, $\bar\theta = \sum_{i=1}^n \theta_i/n$, is used for making the decision instead of each value of the observed data. In the averaging process the conditional probability density function $p(\theta \mid \theta^*)$ becomes slender in shape near the value of θ^*, as shown by the dotted line in Fig. 5.6. This is a welcome trend in the present situation. The decision situation stated in Eq. (5.7) is now changed:

$$\text{If } f(\theta_1, \theta_2, \ldots, \theta_n) = \sum_{i=1}^n \frac{\theta_i}{n} = \bar\theta < D, \qquad \text{choose } \delta_1.$$

$$\text{If } f(\theta_1, \theta_2, \ldots, \theta_n) = \sum_{i=1}^n \frac{\theta_i}{n} = \bar\theta > D, \qquad \text{choose } \delta_2.$$

(5.11)

If the successive values of θ_i may be assumed mutually independent, then the conditional probability density function $p(\bar\theta \mid \theta^*)$ becomes gaussian with mean value θ^* and variance σ_n^2/n.[5] Consequently, Eqs. (5.10) may, respectively, be expressed as

$$\alpha_{\bar\theta}(D, \theta_\alpha^*) = \frac{1}{2}\left[1 - \text{erf}\left(\frac{D - \theta_\alpha^*}{2^{1/2}\sigma_n/n^{1/2}}\right)\right] \qquad (5.12a)$$

$$\beta_{\bar\theta}(D, \theta_\beta^*) = \frac{1}{2}\left[1 + \text{erf}\left(\frac{D - \theta_\beta^*}{2^{1/2}\sigma_n/n^{1/2}}\right)\right] \qquad (5.12b)$$

where the left-hand sides of the equations correspond respectively to $\alpha(D, \theta_\alpha^*)$ and $\beta(D, \theta_\beta^*)$ with the substitution of $\theta = \bar\theta$ in Eqs. (5.10). By means of the numerical table of the error function and Eqs. (5.12) the values of the decision threshold satisfying the preassigned specifications

[5] Y. W. Lee, "Statistical Theory of Communication," p. 278. Wiley, New York, 1960,

$\alpha = 0.05$ and $\beta = 0.05$ are respectively obtained as

$$D = \theta_\alpha^* + 1.163\left(\frac{2}{n}\right)^{\frac{1}{2}}\sigma_n \tag{5.13a}$$

$$D = \theta_\beta^* - 1.163\left(\frac{2}{n}\right)^{\frac{1}{2}}\sigma_n \tag{5.13b}$$

If the value of the standard deviation δ of the observed data is 0.02, the sampled number may be determined by solving Eqs. (5.13) simultaneously:

$$n^{\frac{1}{2}} = \frac{2 \times 1.163}{\theta_\beta^* - \theta_\alpha^*} 2^{\frac{1}{2}}\sigma_n \simeq 2.86 \tag{5.14}$$

That is,

$$n = 9 \tag{5.15}$$

Then

$$D = 0.1 + 1.163\frac{1.41 \times 0.02}{3}$$
$$= 0.111 \tag{5.16}$$

This result reveals that, if we use the arithmetically averaged value $\bar{\theta}$ computed by successively storing nine values θ_i instead of instantaneously storing them, then the value of the decision boundary D becomes 0.111, and this is a useful conclusion satisfying the preassigned limitation. As we can observe in Fig. 5.6, the introduction of this kind of data-processing contributes to changing the conditional probability density function $p(\theta \mid \theta^*)$.

5.4   Decision Adaptive Control Systems Based on the Neyman-Pearson Test

We have invoked a technique of data-processing by means of the arithmetical average of the observed data. To emphasize the importance of taking the arithmetical average, we shall now discuss the Neyman-Pearson test mentioned in Sect. 5.2.

We assume first that the conditional probability density function of a sampled value θ_i of the observed data, when θ^* is given, may be represented by

$$p(\theta_i \mid \theta^*) = \frac{1}{(2\pi)^{\frac{1}{2}}\sigma_n} \exp\left[-\frac{(\theta_i - \theta^*)^2}{2\sigma_n^2}\right], \qquad i = 1, 2, \ldots, n \quad (5.17)$$

If the additive random noise may be assumed to be a gaussian white-noise random process, then the values of successive measurements θ_i are mutually independent, and the conditional probability density function of the vector process $\boldsymbol{\theta} = (\theta_1, \theta_2, \ldots, \theta_n)$, when θ^* is given, becomes

$$p(\boldsymbol{\theta} \mid \theta^*) = (2\pi)^{-n/2}\sigma_n^{-n} \exp\left[-\frac{1}{2\sigma_n^2}\sum_{i=1}^{n}(\theta_i - \theta^*)^2\right] \qquad (5.18)$$

Now we shall test hypothesis H_1, that $\theta^* = \theta_\alpha^*$, against hypothesis H_2, that $\theta^* = \theta_\beta^*$, as shown in Fig. 5.6. According to the Neyman-Pearson test, and as mentioned in Chapter 4, we have a choice:

$$\begin{aligned} &\text{If} \quad \Lambda(\boldsymbol{\theta}) < \lambda, \qquad \text{accept } H_1. \\ &\text{If} \quad \Lambda(\boldsymbol{\theta}) > \lambda, \qquad \text{reject } H_1. \end{aligned} \qquad (5.19)$$

Here $\Lambda(\boldsymbol{\theta})$ is the generalized-likelihood ratio, which in this case is given by

$$\Lambda(\boldsymbol{\theta}) = \frac{P p(\boldsymbol{\theta} \mid \theta_\beta^*)}{Q p(\boldsymbol{\theta} \mid \theta_\alpha^*)} \qquad (5.20)$$

In this equation P and Q are the a priori probabilities that θ_β^* and θ_α^* occur in regions C_1 and C_2, respectively; see Fig. 5.6. Substituting Eq. (5.18) into Eq. (5.20), and letting $P = Q$ without loss of generality, we get

$$\begin{aligned} \Lambda(\boldsymbol{\theta}) &= \exp\left[-\frac{1}{2\sigma_n^2}\sum_{i=1}^{n}(\theta_i - \theta_\beta^*)^2 + \frac{1}{2\sigma_n^2}\sum_{i=1}^{n}(\theta_i - \theta_\alpha^*)^2\right] \\ &= \exp\left[\frac{1}{\sigma_n^2}\sum_{i=1}^{n}(\theta_\beta^* - \theta_\alpha^*)\theta_i - \frac{n}{2\sigma_n^2}(\theta_\beta^{*2} - \theta_\alpha^{*2})\right] \qquad (5.21) \end{aligned}$$

From this equation the logarithmic form of the relation $\Lambda(\boldsymbol{\theta}) = \lambda$ becomes

$$\sum_{i=1}^{n} \frac{\theta_i}{n} = \frac{\sigma_n^2}{n} \cdot \frac{\log \lambda}{\theta_\beta^* - \theta_\alpha^*} + \frac{\theta_\alpha^* + \theta_\beta^*}{2} \tag{5.22}$$

Since the left-hand member is equal to $\bar{\theta}$, this may compactly be expressed as

$$\bar{\theta} = \frac{\sigma_n^2}{n} \cdot \frac{\log \lambda}{\theta_\beta^* - \theta_\alpha^*} + \frac{\theta_\alpha^* + \theta_\beta^*}{2} \equiv \lambda' \tag{5.23}$$

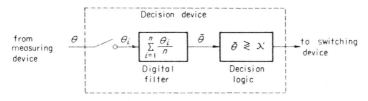

FIG. 5.9. Block diagram of the decision device of the system shown in Fig. 5.4.

Equation (5.19) can, therefore, be rewritten:

$$\begin{array}{lll} \text{If} & \bar{\theta} < \lambda', & \text{accept } H_1. \\ \text{If} & \bar{\theta} > \lambda', & \text{reject } H_1. \end{array} \tag{5.24}$$

Here the threshold λ' can be assigned by using the values of the variance σ_n^2 of the additive random noise and the sample size n and by setting the values of θ_α^*, θ_β^*, and λ. The value of λ, which plays the role of Lagrangian multiplier, can be assigned the minimization of the total error probability $\alpha + \beta$, as shown in Eq. (4.28). In this case the error probabilities of the first and second kinds are defined by

$$\alpha = \int_{C_2} p(\boldsymbol{\theta} \mid \theta^*) \, d\boldsymbol{\theta}, \qquad \text{when in reality } \theta^* \in C_1 \tag{5.25a}$$

$$\beta = \int_{C_1} p(\boldsymbol{\theta} \mid \theta^*) \, d\boldsymbol{\theta}, \qquad \text{when in reality } \theta^* \in C_1 \tag{5.25b}$$

where C_1 is the acceptance region of H_1 and C_2 its rejection region. We see that the arithmetical averaging procedure is an essential requirement of testing the hypothesis; in other words, it may be introduced naturally as a form of hypothesis testing. With the help of Eq. (5.24) the decision device shown in Fig. 5.9 can be constructed.

5.5 Ideal-Observer Decision-Making

In practice we frequently observe the fact, illustrated in Fig. 5.10, that the true value θ^* of the parameter of the controlled element appears around a particular value θ_1^* in C_1 and around a particular value θ_2^* in C_2.

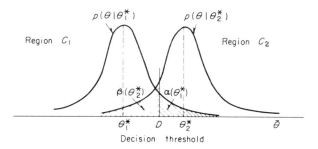

FIG. 5.10. Conditional probability density function.

The fact that there are only two regions makes decision-making easy. However, an incorrect decision δ_1 or δ_2, when in reality $\theta^* \in C_2$ or $\theta^* \in C_1$, may lead to the worst control condition. In Fig. 5.10 the conditional probability density function $p(\theta \mid \theta^*)$ shows steep peaks, $p(\theta \mid \theta_1^*)$ and $p(\theta \mid \theta_2^*)$, within the regions C_1 and C_2, respectively. Therefore,

$$\max_{\theta^*} \alpha(\theta^*) = \alpha(\theta_1^*) \quad \text{in } C_1$$

$$\max_{\theta^*} \beta(\theta^*) = \beta(\theta_2^*) \quad \text{in } C_2$$

A method of minimizing the maximal average risk indicated by the maximal error probabilities and their loss values is an effective approach to designing adaptive decision control systems. Now, let us assign the loss function $L(\theta_i^*, \delta_j) = L_{ij}$ as the cost of making decision δ_j when θ_i^* is the true value of a parameter of the controlled element. In the present example, as in that given in Table 4.1, there are four possible losses, L_{11}, L_{22}, L_{12}, and L_{21}.

We further consider that $L_{11} = L_{22} = 0$. This reflects that there is no loss associated with a correct decision. Since only relative values of L_{12} and L_{21} are of interest, the loss assignment is performed in an arbitrary normalized way; see Table 5.1, where C is an arbitrary constant.

TABLE 5.1

Loss Assignment

True value of parameter	Loss	
	δ_1	δ_2
θ_1^*	$L_{11} = 0$	$L_{12} = C$
θ_2^*	$L_{21} = 1$	$L_{22} = 0$

The total probability of error is considered the average risk; that is,

$$R(D) = C\alpha(\theta_1^*) + \beta(\theta_2^*) \qquad (5.26)$$

where

$$\alpha(\theta_1^*) = \int_D^{\infty} p(\theta \mid \theta_1^*)\, d\theta$$

$$\beta(\theta_2^*) = \int_{-\infty}^{D} p(\theta \mid \theta_2^*)\, d\theta \qquad (5.27)$$

Hence Eq. (5.26) becomes

$$R(D) = C\int_D^{\infty} p(\theta \mid \theta_1^*)\, d\theta + \int_{-\infty}^{D} p(\theta \mid \theta_2^*)\, d\theta \qquad (5.28)$$

The central problem is to find the boundary D such that the average risk described by this equation becomes minimal. When Eq. (5.28) is differentiated with respect to the variable D and the result is set equal to zero,

$$p(D \mid \theta_2^*) = C p(D \mid \theta_1^*) \qquad (5.29)$$

Then, since the value of D is simply the point where the value of $p(\theta \mid \theta_2^*)$ is C times greater than that of $p(\theta \mid \theta_1^*)$, it may be readily determined from a graph, such as that of Fig. 5.11. In particular, when $C = 1$, the sum $\alpha + \beta$ is to be minimized. This is often called an ideal observer in the field of communications.

This idea suggests that there exists another way of improving the decision-making. We may slightly modify the problem of minimizing

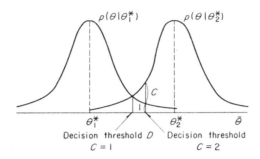

FIG. 5.11. Graphical determination of the decision threshold D for the Ideal Observer test.

the maximal average risk by replacing θ with $\bar{\theta}$, provided that a proper configuration of digital filter is chosen for realizing $\bar{\theta}$. In such a case the switching boundary D is to be so determined that

$$R(D) = C \int_D^\infty p(\bar{\theta} \mid \theta_1^*)\, d\theta + \int_{-\infty}^D p(\bar{\theta} \mid \theta_2^*)\, d\theta \qquad (5.30)$$

becomes minimal. Then, again by means of a graph, the value of D is obtained as the point where $p(\bar{\theta} \mid \theta_2^*)$ is C times greater than $p(\bar{\theta} \mid \theta_1^*)$. This graphical procedure can generally be used for finding the boundary D. It should be noted that the idea of minimizing the maximal average risk is based upon the assumption that the conditional probability density function $p(\theta \mid \theta^*)$ is of the shape having two peaks, one each for the values θ_1^* and θ_2^*.

CHAPTER 6

Nonsequential Decision Approaches in Adaptive Control Systems

6.1 Introductory Remarks

In a fairly large number of control systems, as has already been pointed out, the major difficulty lies in the fact that the dynamic characteristics of a controlled element are described or approximated by an ordinary differential equation, transfer function, or impulse response function, the exact values of whose parameters are seldom known because of environmental changes. The adjustment of controller parameters is to be carried out automatically, provided that an observation of parameter variation in some parts of the system is performed. In Chapter 5 simple but fundamental examples were considered for the purpose of illustrating the decision situation in adaptive control. They were mainly concerned with the concept of binary detection, attention being focused on the measurement of unknown parameters with a finite amount of incorrect information.

The concept of binary detection in adaptive control implies choosing among pairs consisting of a dynamic characteristic of a controlled element and the corresponding desired transfer functions of the controller. However, in practice, since the dynamic characteristics of a controlled element show wide variations because of environmental changes, we must prepare combinations of more than two pairs. We shall once again approach decision adaptive control from the practical viewpoint of control engineering. In particular, assuming that the true value of a parameter does not change with time during a preassigned observation interval, we try to establish the decision-making in system identification with gaussian random noise.

91

6.2   Extension of the Binary Detection Concept to N-ary Decision Problems

To infer the true value of a parameter $\theta^*(t)$ from the observed value $\theta(t) = \theta^*(t) + n(t)$, as shown in Eq. (5.1), the range of parameter variation is divided into N regions respectively denoted $C_1, C_2, \ldots, C_{N-1}, C_N$,

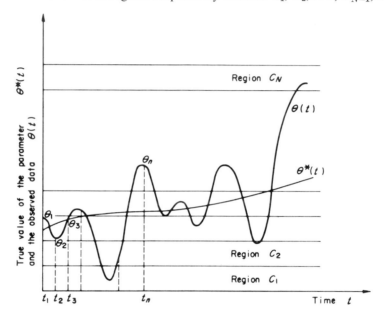

FIG. 6.1. Quantization of the true value of the parameter $\theta^*(t)$ and the observed data $\theta(t)$.

as shown in Fig. 6.1. Our present problem is to determine in which region the true value $\theta^*(t)$ lies. There is no need to say that this is the most important problem in designing not only adaptive control systems but also a large number of industrial process control systems. We shall attack this problem with statistical decision theory.

Now, a vector process $\boldsymbol{\theta} = (\theta_1, \theta_2, \ldots, \theta_n)$ in the n-dimensional observed space $\mathscr{D}_a$ is introduced, and the components of $\boldsymbol{\theta}$ are ordered in time, as shown by the subscript labels in Fig. 6.1. As in Chapter 5, we assume that the true value $\theta^*(t)$ of the parameter does not change during the time interval ending with the observed value θ_n. The number n determining the sample size considered here has a fixed preassigned value throughout the discussion in this chapter. This means a nonsequential situation. We consider the N-dimensional observed data space $\mathcal{D}_a$, which is separated into N subsets $L_1, L_2, \ldots, L_{N-1}, L_N$ in accordance with the N subsets $C_1, C_2, \ldots, C_{N-1}, C_N$ of the set $\mathcal{D}_s$, as shown in Fig. 6.2. It

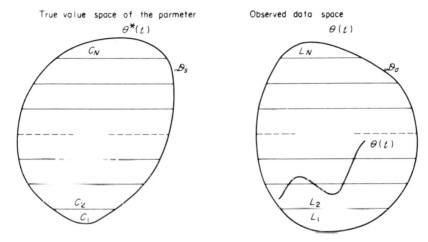

FIG. 6.2. The spaces $\mathcal{D}_a$ and $\mathcal{D}_s$.

can easily be seen that the spaces $\mathcal{D}_a$ and $\mathcal{D}_s$ correspond respectively to the observed data space and the message signal space of Chapter 4. The present situation is described as follows. The hypothesis H_i that the true value of $\theta^*(t)$ lies in the region C_i, where $i = 1, 2, \ldots, N$, is accepted when the observed vector $\boldsymbol{\theta}$ belongs to the region L_i, where $i = 1, 2, \ldots, N$. The acceptance is denoted by the decision δ_i, where $i = 1, 2, \ldots, N - 1, N$. Here we introduce the loss function $L_{ij} = L(C_i, \delta_j)$ for the error of making a decision δ_j when in actuality $\theta^*(t) \in C_i$. The function $L(C_i, \delta_j)$ is a prescribed nonnegative function, where $j = 1, 2, \ldots, N - 1, N$. Furthermore, the following two groups of notations are introduced.

I. ξ_i The a priori probability that the true value $\theta^*(t)$ of the parameter occurs in the region C_i, where $i = 1, 2, \ldots, N - 1, N$.

$s(\boldsymbol{\theta}_i^*)$ The probability density function of $\theta^*(t)$ when the state $\theta^*(t) \in C_i$ occurs; this satisfies the relations

$$\sum_{i=1}^{N} \int_{C_i} \xi_i s_i(\theta^*) \, d\theta^* = 1$$

$$\xi_i s_i(\theta^*) \geq 0$$

II. $p_d(\boldsymbol{\delta} \mid \boldsymbol{\theta})$ The probability that the decision δ_j will be made for the given observed vector $\boldsymbol{\theta}$, so that

$$\sum_{j=1}^{N} p_d(\delta_j \mid \boldsymbol{\theta}) \, d\boldsymbol{\theta} = 1 \quad\text{and}\quad p_d(\delta_j \mid \boldsymbol{\theta}) \geq 0$$

Since the integration over the decision space $\mathcal{D}_d$ in Eq. (4.6) may be replaced by an appropriate summation, the average risk is expressed as

$$R(\boldsymbol{\xi s}, p_d) = \sum_{i=1}^{N} \sum_{j=1}^{N} \xi_i \int_{L_i} p_d(\delta_j \mid \boldsymbol{\theta}) L(C_i, \delta_j) \, d\boldsymbol{\theta} \int_{C_i} p(\boldsymbol{\theta} \mid C_i) s(\boldsymbol{\theta}_i^*) \, d\boldsymbol{\theta}_i^* \quad (6.1)$$

where $p(\boldsymbol{\theta} \mid C_i)$ represents the conditional probability density function of the observed vector $\boldsymbol{\theta}$, when $\theta^*(t) \in C_i$ is the true state, and corresponds to $p(\boldsymbol{\theta} \mid \boldsymbol{\theta}^*)$ in Eq. (4.6). We express the second integral in Eq. (6.1) by

$$q_i(\boldsymbol{\theta}) = \int_{C_i} p(\boldsymbol{\theta} \mid C_i) s(\boldsymbol{\theta}_i^*) \, d\boldsymbol{\theta}_i^* \quad (6.2)$$

Equation (6.1) may then be rewritten as

$$R(\boldsymbol{\xi s}, p_d) = \sum_{i=1}^{N} \sum_{j=1}^{N} \int_{L_i} p_d(\delta_j \mid \boldsymbol{\theta}) \xi_i L(C_i, \delta_j) q_i(\boldsymbol{\theta}) \, d\boldsymbol{\theta} \quad (6.3)$$

The problem is now reduced to the determination of a decision rule p_d for minimizing the average risk given by Eq. (6.3). As stated in Sect. 4.4, the optimal decision rule p_d^* is called the Bayes solution; it satisfies

$$R(\boldsymbol{\xi s}, p_d^*) \leq R(\boldsymbol{\xi s}, p_d), \quad\text{for all}\quad p_d(\delta_j \mid \boldsymbol{\theta}) \quad (6.4)$$

6.3   Derivation of the Bayesian System

To determine the Bayes solution given by Eq. (6.4) we first introduce the notion of the a posteriori risk with the help of the Bayes formula given by Eq. (2.17).

The a posteriori probability ζ_i that $\theta^*(t) = \theta_i^*$, expressing the fact that $\theta^*(t) \in C_i$ is the true state when the value of the observed data θ is given, may be expressed as

$$\zeta_i = \Pr(\theta_i^* \mid \theta) = \frac{\Pr(\theta_i^*)\,\Pr(\theta \mid \theta_i^*)}{\sum_{k=1}^{N}\Pr(\theta_k^*)\,\Pr(\theta \mid \theta_k^*)}$$

$$= \frac{\xi_i q_i(\theta)}{\sum_{k=1}^{N}\xi_k q_k(\theta)}, \quad k = 1, 2, \ldots, i, \ldots, n \quad (6.5)$$

The a posteriori average risk can, therefore, be defined by

$$r_j(\theta) = \sum_{i=1}^{N} \zeta_i L_{ij}$$

$$= \frac{\sum_{i=1}^{N} \xi_i q_i(\theta) L_{ij}}{\sum_{k=1}^{N} \xi_k q_k(\theta)} \equiv \frac{V_j(\theta)}{\sum_{k=1}^{N} \xi_k q_k(\theta)} \quad (6.6)$$

where

$$V_j(\theta) = \sum_{i=1}^{N} \xi_i L_{ij} q_i(\theta) \quad (6.7)$$

From a consideration of the a posteriori average risk $r_j(\theta)$ defined by Eq. (6.6) Wald's theorem has been stated as follows[1]:

THEOREM.   A necessary and sufficient condition for a decision function p_d to be a Bayes solution relative to a given a priori probability measure is that

$$p_d(\delta_j \mid \theta) = 0$$

[1] A. Wald, "Statistical Decision Function." Wiley, New York, 1950. It is not difficult to prove this theorem. See also Sect. 4 of this chapter.

for any observed value $\boldsymbol{\theta}$ and for any j for which

$$r_j(\boldsymbol{\theta}) > \min_k [r_k(\boldsymbol{\theta})]$$

where $r_k(\boldsymbol{\theta})$ is the a posteriori average risk.

This theorem states the decision rule that all decision rules $p_d(\delta_j \mid \boldsymbol{\theta})$ should be zero except for one, $p_d(\delta_k \mid \boldsymbol{\theta})$, in which the a posteriori average risk $r_k(\boldsymbol{\theta})$ becomes minimal. From Eq. (6.6), since the a posteriori average risk function $r_j(\boldsymbol{\theta})$ is proportional to the function $V_j(\boldsymbol{\theta})$ given by Eq. (6.7), we may consider henceforth the latter instead of the former. Bayes solution determined by Wald's theorem is obtained as

$$p_d^*(\delta_j \mid \boldsymbol{\theta}) = 1, \qquad j = k$$
$$= 0, \qquad j \neq k \quad (6.8)$$

whenever

$$V_k(\boldsymbol{\theta}) = \min_j [V_j(\boldsymbol{\theta})] \quad (6.9)$$

From Eq. (6.3) and with the use of Eqs. (6.7) and (6.8), the minimal average risk becomes

$$R(\boldsymbol{\xi}\mathbf{s}, p_d^*) = \sum_{i=1}^{N} \int_{L_i} \xi_i L(C_i, \delta_k) q_i(\boldsymbol{\theta}) \, d\boldsymbol{\theta}$$

$$= \int_{L_k} V_k(\boldsymbol{\theta}) \, d\boldsymbol{\theta}$$

$$= \int_{L_k} \min_j [V_j(\boldsymbol{\theta})] \, d\boldsymbol{\theta} \quad (6.10)$$

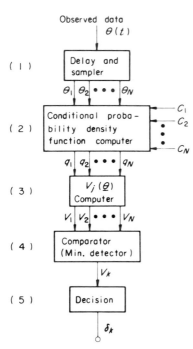

FIG. 6.3. Construction of N-ary Bayesian optimal decision device.

From these results the decision system shown in Fig. 6.3 can be constructed. This figure shows that Eqs. (6.8) and (6.9) reveal decision system to be constructed by the following five devices:

1. Discrete acquisition of observed data $\boldsymbol{\theta}$.
2. Computation of conditional probability density function $q_i(\boldsymbol{\theta})$.
3. Computation of function $V_j(\boldsymbol{\theta})$.
4. Detection of smallest value among $V_j(\boldsymbol{\theta})$.
5. Acceptance of decision δ_j.

Figure 6.4 shows the configuration of an adaptive control system with the N-ary decision device shown in Fig. 6.3.   The system in Fig. 6.3 requires a rather complicated configuration for the performance of the

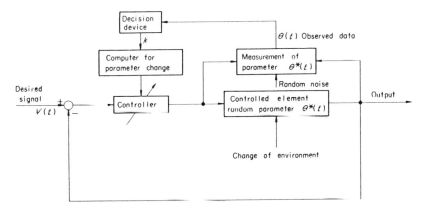

FIG. 6.4. Example of application of N-ary decision device to adaptive control.

mathematical computation, so a simplified system is constructed, in which the loss function is assigned.

Let the loss function be

$$L_{ij} = 1, \qquad \text{for} \quad i \neq j$$
$$= 0, \qquad \text{for} \quad i = j \qquad (6.11)$$

where L_{ii} is the loss due to a correct decision and $L_{ij}\ (i \neq j)$ is the loss due to an incorrect decision that decides the jth state, that is, $\theta^*(t) \in C_j$ when in reality $\theta^*(t) \in C_i$.   In this case the average risk is given by

$$R(C_i, p_d) = \sum_{j=1}^{N}{}' \xi_i \int_{L_i} p_d(\delta_j \mid \boldsymbol{\theta}) q_i(\boldsymbol{\theta})\, d\boldsymbol{\theta} \qquad (6.12)$$

which represents the conditional probability of making an incorrect decision when $\theta^*(t) \in C_i$ is the true state and when p_d is the decision rule adopted.[2] The symbol Σ'_i means the summation of all j except those of a correct decision, in which latter case $i = j$.

Our attention is now directed to the quantity $\xi_i q_i(\theta)$ in the right-hand member of Eq. (6.12). If the definition of ξ_i is recalled, it is easy to see from this equation that the quantity $\xi_j q_j(\theta)$ is the error probability when $i \neq j$ and that, if and only if $i = j$, the quantity $\xi_j q_j(\theta)$ expresses the probability of a correct decision with zero error probability. Therefore, we may expect to improve the configuration of the decision device with the help of the new principle, that the zero error probability $\xi_i q_i(\theta) = \lambda_i(\theta)$ becomes maximal. Since the contrary of this statement is that the zero error probability becomes minimal, the Bayes solution, minimizing the error probability based on an incorrect decision is determined as[3]

$$p_d^*(\delta_j \mid \theta) = 1, \qquad \text{for} \quad j = k$$

$$= 0 \qquad \text{for} \quad j \neq k \qquad (6.13)$$

whenever

$$\lambda_k(\theta) = \max_j [\lambda_j(\theta)] \qquad (6.14)$$

where, by means of Eq. (6.2), $\lambda_j(\theta)$ is given by

$$\lambda_j(\theta) = \xi_j q_j(\theta) \qquad (6.15)$$

Then the decision system of Fig. 6.5 can be constructed. It is obvious from the foregoing discussion that the decision system is also a computer and that its detailed structure depends on the statistical properties of the background noise. For a concrete example of the configuration of the decision device mathematically established here our attention is directed to the maximum detector of $\lambda_j(\theta^*)$.

We introduce the generalized-likelihood ratio defined by Eq. (4.23). From Eqs. (4.23) and (6.2) and with the introduction of the a priori probability ξ_0 that the true value $\theta^*(t)$ of the parameter occurs from the

[2] C. K. Chow, Optimum character recognition system using decision function. *IRE WESCON Conv. Rec.* Pt. 4, 121 (1957).
[3] A. Wald, *op. cit.*

null signal space—that is, that $\theta^*(t)$ does not appear from any quantized region C_i—an expression of the generalized-likelihood ratio for the case of binary detection may be extended to N-ary detection and expressed as

$$\lambda_j'(\boldsymbol{\theta}) = \frac{\xi_j q_j(\boldsymbol{\theta})}{q_0(\boldsymbol{\theta})} \qquad (6.16)$$

where

$$q_0(\boldsymbol{\theta}) = p(\boldsymbol{\theta} \mid 0) \qquad (6.17)$$

For convenience the logarithmic form of Eq. (6.16) is taken, and the following function is derived:

$$\log \lambda_j'(\boldsymbol{\theta}) = \log \frac{\xi_j q_j(\boldsymbol{\theta})}{q_0(\boldsymbol{\theta})} \equiv \Lambda_j(\boldsymbol{\theta}) \qquad (6.18)$$

Bayes' solution may compactly be stated as

$$\text{When} \quad \Lambda_k(\boldsymbol{\theta}) = \max_j [\Lambda_j(\boldsymbol{\theta})], \qquad \text{decide } \delta_k.$$

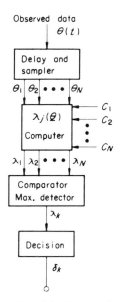

FIG. 6.5. Improved construction of N-ary decision device.

This means that the maximum detector must produce the output corresponding to the decision threshold given by Eq. (6.18).

It must be noted that some available information on $\boldsymbol{\theta}$ is usually assumed beforehand. In practice, however, a reliable estimation of this information is not easily obtained. It is especially difficult to obtain the a priori probability of $\theta^*(t)$ and, hence, $q_i(\boldsymbol{\theta})$; when the a priori probability is not known or only incompletely given, a possible criterion of optimization is provided by a Minimax decision rule. It must further be noted that the a priori probability $s(\boldsymbol{\theta}^*)$ should, in practice, be treated as a weighting function in the computation of $q_i(\boldsymbol{\theta})$ in Eq. (6.2). For example, if a point $\boldsymbol{\theta}_i^*$ in the region C_i occurs with probability 1, then it follows that

$$s(\theta^*) = \delta(\boldsymbol{\theta}^* - \boldsymbol{\theta}_i^*) \qquad (6.19)$$

Thus, from Eq. (6.2) we have

$$q_i(\boldsymbol{\theta}) = p(\boldsymbol{\theta} \mid \boldsymbol{\theta}_i^*) \qquad (6.20)$$

6.4   Construction of a Decision System Subjected to Gaussian Random Noise

In the previous section the Bayes solution of N-ary decision problems in control systems was outlined, and the configuration of the decision system was schematically given. For an interpretation of the analytical version of the decision rule in terms of physically realizable elements our attention is directed to the calculation of Eq. (6.18). We assume here that the additive random noise is a gaussian random process. Under this assumption we calculate Eq. (6.18) by using Eq. (6.20). Equation (2.108) shows that joint statistics of the random noise $n(t)$ are given by the n-dimensional gaussian probability density function of the form

$$p(\mathbf{n}) = p(n_1, n_2, \ldots, n_n) = (2\pi)^{-n/2} |\mathbf{M}|^{-\frac{1}{2}} \exp\left(-\tfrac{1}{2}\mathbf{n}'\mathbf{M}^{-1}\mathbf{n}\right) \quad (6.21a)$$

where the prime on the vector indicates that it is a transposed vector and $\mathbf{M}$ is the covariance matrix. Thus,

$$\mathbf{M} = \|m_{ij}\|$$
$$m_{ij} = \langle n_i n_j \rangle_{\mathrm{sav}} \quad\quad\quad (6.21b)$$

where $n_i = n(t_i)$ and $n_j = n(t_j)$. When a similar consideration is applied to Eq. (5.8), Eq. (6.20) yields

$$q_i(\boldsymbol{\theta}) = (2\pi)^{-n/2} |\mathbf{M}|^{-\frac{1}{2}} \exp\left[-\tfrac{1}{2}(\boldsymbol{\theta} - \boldsymbol{\theta}_i^*)'\mathbf{M}^{-1}(\boldsymbol{\theta} - \boldsymbol{\theta}_i^*)\right] \quad (6.22a)$$

Similarly, Eq. (6.17) may be expressed as

$$q_0(\boldsymbol{\theta}) = (2\pi)^{-n/2} |\mathbf{M}|^{-\frac{1}{2}} \exp\left[-\tfrac{1}{2}\boldsymbol{\theta}'\mathbf{M}^{-1}\boldsymbol{\theta}\right] \quad (6.22b)$$

From the use of Eqs. (6.22) it follows that

$$\frac{\xi_i q_i(\boldsymbol{\theta})}{q_0(\boldsymbol{\theta})} = \xi_i \exp\{[-\tfrac{1}{2}(\boldsymbol{\theta} - \boldsymbol{\theta}_i^*)'\mathbf{M}^{-1}(\boldsymbol{\theta} - \boldsymbol{\theta}_i^*)] + \tfrac{1}{2}\boldsymbol{\theta}'\mathbf{M}^{-1}\boldsymbol{\theta}\} \quad (6.23)$$

Therefore Eq. (6.18) can be expressed as

$$\Lambda_i(\boldsymbol{\theta}) = \mu_i + \boldsymbol{\theta}_i^* \mathbf{M}^{-1} \boldsymbol{\theta} \qquad (6.24a)$$

where

$$\mu_i = \log \xi_i - \tfrac{1}{2} \boldsymbol{\theta}_i^* \mathbf{M}^{-1} \boldsymbol{\theta}_i^* \qquad (6.24b)$$

which is independent of the observed data vector $\boldsymbol{\theta}$. Since only the second term of the right-hand member in Eq. (6.24a) depends upon the value of

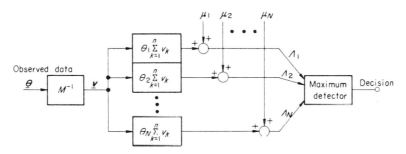

FIG. 6.6. Configuration of the decision system subjected to gaussian random noise.

$\boldsymbol{\theta}$, the decision system can be constructed only from this term, while the term μ_i may play a role on the constant bias level. The configuration of a practical system can be achieved by matrix manipulation. Let

$$\mathbf{v} - \mathbf{M}^{-1} \boldsymbol{\theta} \qquad (6.25)$$

be a matrix, and let the kth component of $\mathbf{v}$ be expressed by v_k; then Eq. (6.24a) yields

$$\Lambda_i(\boldsymbol{\theta}) = \mu_i + \boldsymbol{\theta}_i^* \sum_{k=1}^{n} v_k$$

Figure 6.6 shows the schematic representation of the decision system derived from Eq. (6.24); this may be substituted for parts 2, 3, and 4 of Fig. 6.3.

The construction given in Fig. 6.6 is not yet practical because the symbolic element $\mathbf{M}^{-1}$ makes no contribution to the design. Therefore, we shall go a step further in our analytical consideration. We assume the following, where the function $h(t - \tau)$ is the weighting function of a filter whose input and output are, respectively, $\theta(t)$ and $\eta(t)$:

$$\mathbf{z} = \mathbf{M}^{-1}\boldsymbol{\theta}_i^*$$

$$= \boldsymbol{\theta}_i^* \| h(T - t_j) \Delta t \| \tag{6.26}$$

From Eq. (6.24a), since $\boldsymbol{\theta}_i^* \mathbf{M}^{-1} \boldsymbol{\theta} = \boldsymbol{\theta}' \mathbf{M}^{-1} \boldsymbol{\theta}_i^*$, by setting $t_k = kT/n$ and $\Delta t = T/n$, we have

$$\Lambda_i(\boldsymbol{\theta}) = \mu_i + \boldsymbol{\theta}' \mathbf{z}$$

$$= \mu_i + \boldsymbol{\theta}_i^* \sum_{k=1}^{n} \theta(t_k) h(T - t_k) \Delta t \tag{6.27}$$

By letting $n \to \infty$ and $\Delta t \to 0$ in the continuous case, Eq. (6.27) may be expressed as

$$\lim_{n \to \infty} \Lambda_i(\boldsymbol{\theta}) \equiv \Lambda_T(\boldsymbol{\theta})$$

$$= \hat{\mu}_i + \boldsymbol{\theta}_i^* \int_0^T h(T - \tau)\, \theta(\tau)\, d\tau$$

$$= \hat{\mu}_i + \boldsymbol{\theta}_i^* \eta(t)\big|_{t=T} \tag{6.28}$$

where with the help of Eqs. (6.24b) and (6.26) we have

$$\mu_i = \log \xi_i - \tfrac{1}{2}\boldsymbol{\theta}_i^* \mathbf{z} = \log \xi_i - \tfrac{1}{2}\theta_i^{*2} \sum_{k=1}^{n} h(T - t_k) \Delta t$$

By letting $n \to \infty$ and $\Delta t \to 0$ we have

$$\hat{\mu}_i = \lim_{n \to \infty} \mu_i$$

$$= \log \xi_i - \tfrac{1}{2}\theta_i^{*2} \int_0^T h(T - \tau)\, d\tau \tag{6.29}$$

Furthermore, $\eta(t)$ in Eq. (6.28) is expressed as

$$\eta(t) = \int_0^t h(t - \tau)\, \theta(\tau)\, d\tau \tag{6.30}$$

Now Eq. (6.28) reveals that the decision system can be constructed as shown in Fig. 6.7, where the weighting function $h(t - \tau)$ of the filter still remains to be determined.

From Eq. (6.26), it follows that

$$\boldsymbol{\theta}_i^* = \mathbf{Mz} \tag{6.31}$$

From Eq. (6.26) and by taking θ_i^* as $\boldsymbol{\theta}_i^*$, whose components are equal to

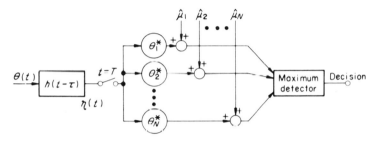

FIG. 6.7. Analogue scheme of the decision device given by Eq. (6.28).

θ_i^*, the jth elements of both sides of Eq. (6.31) are put into the relation

$$(\boldsymbol{\theta}_i^*)_j = \sum_{k=1}^{n} m_{jk}\theta_i^* h(T - t_k)\,\Delta t \tag{6.32}$$

Since $m_{jk} = \langle n(t_j)\, n(t_k)\rangle_{\mathrm{av}} = \phi_n(t_j - t_k)$ in Eq. (6.32), for the stationary gaussian random noise, and by letting $n \to \infty$, this equation becomes

$$\int_0^T m(t - \tau)\, h(T - \tau)\, d\tau = 1 \tag{6.33a}$$

where, since $(\boldsymbol{\theta}_i^*)_j = \theta_i^*$, the suffix j is omitted. Instead of solving this equation we obtain another form of the weighting function $w(\sigma)$ by solving

$$\int_0^T m(t - \sigma)\, w(\sigma)\, d\sigma = 1 \tag{6.33b}$$

The function $h(\tau)$ can be obtained as follows*:

$$h(\tau) = w(T - \tau) \tag{6.33c}$$

6.5 Decision-Making in System Identification

The previous section was limited to the extension of the binary detection concept to the N-ary situation. This section describes the use of N-ary detection in an approach to a practical and important problem of system identification.

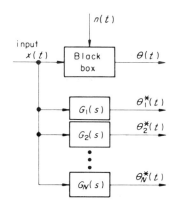

FIG. 6.8. Basic notion of system identification.

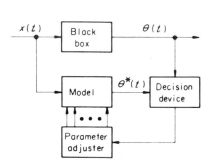

FIG. 6.9. System identification as the parameter adjustment of the model.

We shall consider the construction of a model that simulates the cause-effect relationship of the controlled element (an industrial plant) treated as a blackbox rather than a detailed structure. The present problem is schematically illustrated in Fig. 6.8. The controlled element is subjected to a random input $x(t)$ in the presence of random noise $n(t)$

---

* This is closely related to the theory of matched filters. Detailed descriptions of the solution of Eq. (6.33a) may be found in Middleton[4] and in Helstrom.[5]

[4] D. Middleton, "An Introduction to Statistical Communication Theory." McGraw-Hill, New York, 1961.

[5] C. W. Helstrom, "Statistical Theory of Signal Detection." Pergamon Press, N.Y. (1960).

and produces the output $\theta(t)$. In a feedback control loop the input $x(t)$ to the controlled element may be the manipulating signal, and the output $\theta(t)$ may correspond to the controlled variable. Since the dynamic characteristics of the controlled element are completely unknown, then, by regarding it as a blackbox we preassign its N mathematically linear models, with respective transfer functions $G_1(s)$, $G_2(s)$, ..., $G_{N-1}(s)$, $G_N(s)$, and assume that its characteristics can be approximately represented by one of them having the transfer function $G_i(s)$, where $i = 1$, $2, \ldots, N$, during a certain time interval. Therefore, N output signals $\theta_1^*(t)$, $\theta_2^*(t)$, ..., $\theta_{N-1}^*(t)$, $\theta_N^*(t)$ correspond to the message signals in an ordinary decision situation. As Fig. 6.8 shows, our object is to select the optimal model with transfer function from among the preassigned models through an optimal choice of $\theta_i^*(t)$ by observing the output $\theta(t)$ of the blackbox. Alternatively, by considering the parameter adjustment of the transfer functions of models, the notion embodies in Fig. 6.8 may be expressed as Fig. 6.9. Again there arises the need of the statistical decision concept because of the existence of random noise and the incompleteness of the simulation. Although the present problem is very similar to that described in Sect. 6.2, a group of new symbols will be used for the purpose of exploring identification problems:

ξ_i	The a priori probability of the occurrence of $G_i(s)$.
$\boldsymbol{\theta}$	The n-dimensional observed vector representation of the output $\theta(t)$ of a plant whose elements θ_1, $\theta_2, \ldots, \theta_{n-1}, \theta_n$ are the sampled values arranged in order of increasing time, $t_1 < t_2 < \cdots < t_{n-1} < t_n$; that is, $\theta_1 = \theta(t_1)$, $\theta_2 = \theta(t_2)$, ..., $\theta_{n-1} = \theta(t_{n-1})$, $\theta_n = \theta(t_n)$.
$\boldsymbol{\theta}_i^*$	The n-dimensional vector representation of the output $\theta_i^*(t)$ of the ith models whose elements $\theta_{i,1}^*$, $\theta_{i,2}^*$, ..., $\theta_{i,n-1}^*$, $\theta_{i,n}^*$ are the sampled values arranged in order of increasing time, $t_1 < t_2 < \cdots < t_{n-1} < t_n$; that is, $\theta_{i,1}^* = \theta_i^*(t_1)$, $\theta_{i,2}^* = \theta_i^*(t_2)$, ..., $\theta_{i,n-1}^* = \theta_i^*(t_{n-1})$, $\theta_{i,n}^* = \theta_i^*(t_n)$.
$s(\boldsymbol{\theta}_i^*)$	The a priori probability density function of $\boldsymbol{\theta}_i^*$.
δ_i	The decision that the system should be represented by the model with transfer function $G_i(s)$.

$L_{ij} = L[\delta_j, \theta_i^*(t)]$ The loss function associated with decision δ_j when $G_i(s)$ is the true characteristic of the controlled element.

$p_d(\delta_j \mid \theta)$ The conditional probability that the decision δ_j will be made for a given observed vector θ.

$p(\theta \mid \theta^*)$ The conditional probability density function of the observed vector θ for a given θ_i^*.

If the output signal $\theta_i^*(t)$ of the model with transfer function $G_i(s)$ does not change during the observation, then, by Eq. (6.3), the average risk is given by

$$R(\xi, p_d) = \sum_{i=1}^{N} \sum_{j=1}^{N} \int_L p_d(\delta_j \mid \theta) \xi_i L_{ij} p(\theta \mid \theta_i^*) \, d\theta \qquad (6.34)$$

This equation may readily be rewritten as

$$R(\xi, p_d) = \int_L \sum_{j=1}^{N} p_d(\delta_j \mid \theta) \sum_{i=1}^{N} \xi_i L_{ij} p(\theta \mid \theta_i^*) \, d\theta$$

$$= \int_L \sum_{j=1}^{N} p_d(\delta_j \mid \theta) V_j(\theta) \, d\theta \qquad (6.35)$$

where

$$V_j(\theta) = \sum_{i=1}^{N} \xi_i L_{ij} p(\theta \mid \theta_i^*) \qquad (6.36)$$

By using the minimal value of $V_j(\theta)$ we may express Eq. (6.35) as

$$R(\xi, p_d) \geq \int_{L_i} \sum_{j=1}^{N} p_d(\delta_j \mid \theta) \min_j [V_j(\theta)] \, d\theta \geq \int_{L_i} \min_j [V_j(\theta)] \, d\theta \qquad (6.37)$$

The Bayes solution is, therefore, obtained as

$$p_d^*(\delta_j \mid \theta) = 1, \qquad \text{for } j = k$$
$$= 0 \qquad \text{for } j \neq k \qquad (6.38)$$

whenever

$$V_k(\theta) = \min_j [V_j(\theta)] \qquad (6.39)$$

The configuration of a control system containing the identification concept shown in Fig. 6.8 is shown in Fig. 6.10.

For the more general case, in which the output signal $\theta_i^*(t)$ of the mode is a random process, the formulation should be slightly modified. Since $\theta(t)$ is, of course, a random process, the average risk must be evaluated as

$$R(\xi, p_d) = \sum_{i=1}^{N} \sum_{j=1}^{N} \int_{L_i} p_d(\delta_j \mid \theta) L_{ij} \xi_i \, d\theta \int_{C_i} p(\theta \mid \theta_i^*) s(\theta_i^*) \, d\theta_i^* \quad (6.40)$$

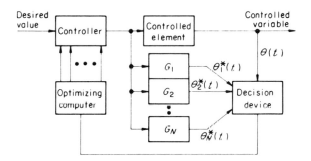

FIG. 6.10. Example of adaptive control system containing the concept of system identification.

In this case the Bayes solution is described as

$$p_d^*(\delta_j \mid \theta) = 1, \qquad \text{for } j = k$$
$$= 0 \qquad \text{for } j \neq k \quad (6.41)$$

whenever

$$U_k(\theta) = \min_j [U_j(\theta)] \quad (6.42)$$

where, from Eq. (6.36), we have

$$U_j(\theta) = \langle V_j(\theta) \rangle_{\text{s. av.}}$$
$$= \sum_{i=1}^{N} \xi_i \int_{C_i} L_{ij} \, p(\theta \mid \theta_i^*) s(\theta_i^*) \, d\theta_i^* \quad (6.43)$$

In a case of simple loss values, in which $L_{ii} = 0$ and $L_{ij} = 1$ ($i \neq j$), according to the considerations given by Eqs. (6.11) to (6.15), the following must replace Eq. (6.42):

$$\lambda_k(\boldsymbol{\theta}) = \max_j[\lambda_j(\boldsymbol{\theta})] \tag{6.44}$$

$$\lambda_i(\boldsymbol{\theta}) = \xi_i \int_{C_i} p(\boldsymbol{\theta} \mid \boldsymbol{\theta}_i^*) s(\boldsymbol{\theta}_i^*) \, d\boldsymbol{\theta}_i^* \tag{6.45}$$

It is, however, not feasible to obtain much beyond these results without specifying the form of the statistical characteristics.

6.6   Decision-Making in System Identification with Gaussian Random Noise

In a specific example, in which both the additive random noise $n(t)$ and true output $\theta_i^*(t)$ of the ith model may, respectively, be assumed gaussian, we have

$$p(\mathbf{n}) = (2\pi)^{-n/2} |\mathbf{M}_n|^{-\frac{1}{2}} \exp(-\tfrac{1}{2}\mathbf{n}'\mathbf{M}_n^{-1}\mathbf{n}) \tag{6.46}$$

$$s(\boldsymbol{\theta}_i^*) = (2\pi)^{-n/2} |\mathbf{M}_s|^{-\frac{1}{2}} \exp(-\tfrac{1}{2}\boldsymbol{\theta}_i^{*'}\mathbf{M}_s^{-1}\boldsymbol{\theta}_i^*) \tag{6.47}$$

and so the conditional probability density function $p(\boldsymbol{\theta} \mid \boldsymbol{\theta}_i^*)$ becomes

$$p(\boldsymbol{\theta} \mid \boldsymbol{\theta}_i^*) = p(\boldsymbol{\theta} - \boldsymbol{\theta}_i^*) = (2\pi)^{-n/2} |\mathbf{M}_n|^{-\frac{1}{2}}$$
$$\times \exp[-\tfrac{1}{2}(\boldsymbol{\theta} - \boldsymbol{\theta}_i^*)'\mathbf{M}_n^{-1}(\boldsymbol{\theta} - \boldsymbol{\theta}_i^*)] \tag{6.48}$$

provided that $n(t)$ and $\theta_i^*(t)$ are mutually independent. $\mathbf{M}_s$ and $\mathbf{M}_n$ are respectively the moment matrices of the output signal and the additive random noise. Consequently, from Eqs. (6.47) and (6.48):

$$\int_{C_i} p(\boldsymbol{\theta} \mid \boldsymbol{\theta}_i^*) s(\boldsymbol{\theta}_i^*) \, d\boldsymbol{\theta}_i^* = \int_{C_i} p(\boldsymbol{\theta}, \boldsymbol{\theta}_i^*) \, d\boldsymbol{\theta}_i^*$$
$$= p(\boldsymbol{\theta})$$
$$= (2\pi)^{-n/2} |\mathbf{M}_s + \mathbf{M}_n|^{-\frac{1}{2}}$$
$$\times \exp[-\tfrac{1}{2}\boldsymbol{\theta}'(\mathbf{M}_s + \mathbf{M}_n)^{-1}\boldsymbol{\theta}] \tag{6.49}$$

To determine concretely the decision threshold given by Eq. (6.44) both the moment matrices $\mathbf{M}_n$ and $\mathbf{M}_s$ must be determined from Eq. (6.49). We shall consider several specific cases in detail, to show how this is done.

6.6-1 The case of independent sampling.

We consider a very special case, in which successive sampled values of $\theta(t)$ and $\theta_i^*(t)$ may be assumed mutually independent. Since

$$\mathbf{M}_s = \|\psi_s \delta_{ij}\| \tag{6.50a}$$

$$\mathbf{M}_n = \|\psi_n \delta_{ij}\| \tag{6.50b}$$

in Eq. (6.49) where δ_{ij} is Kronecker's delta (that is, $\delta_{ij} = 1$ for $i = j$ and $\delta_{ij} = 0$ for $i \neq j$), the equation becomes

$$\int_{U_i} p(\boldsymbol{\theta} \mid \boldsymbol{\theta}_i^*) s(\boldsymbol{\theta}_i^*) \, d\boldsymbol{\theta}_i^* = (2\pi)^{-n/2} |\psi_s \mathbf{I} + \psi_n \mathbf{I}|^{-\frac{1}{2}}$$

$$\times \exp[-\tfrac{1}{2}\boldsymbol{\theta}'(\psi_s \mathbf{I} + \psi_n \mathbf{I})^{-1}\boldsymbol{\theta}]$$

$$= (2\pi)^{-n/2} (\psi_{ns})^{-n/2} \exp\left[-\frac{1}{2}\sum_{j=1}^{n}\left(\frac{\theta_j}{\psi_{ns}^{1/2}}\right)^2\right] \tag{6.51}$$

where $\mathbf{I}$ is a unit matrix and

$$\psi_{ns} = \psi_n + \psi_s \tag{6.52}$$

Then Eq. (6.45) becomes, by means of Eq. (6.51),

$$\lambda_i(\boldsymbol{\theta}) = \xi_i (2\pi)^{-n/2} (\psi_{ns})^{-n/2} \exp\left[-\frac{1}{2}\sum_{j=1}^{n}\left(\frac{\theta_j}{\psi_{ns}^{1/2}}\right)^2\right]$$

$$= \xi_i (2\pi)^{-n/2}[\psi_n(1 + \gamma_i^2)]^{-n/2} \exp\left[-\frac{1}{2}\sum_{j=1}^{n}\left(\frac{\theta_j}{\psi_n^{1/2}}\right)^2\right] \tag{6.53}$$

where γ_i^2 represents the signal-to-noise ratio (or signal-to-noise power ratio); that is

$$\gamma_i^2 = \psi_s/\psi_n \tag{6.54}$$

For the sake of convenience let us introduce the quantity

$$\Lambda_i(\boldsymbol{\theta}) = \log[\lambda_i(\boldsymbol{\theta})/\lambda_0(\boldsymbol{\theta})], \qquad i = 1, 2, \ldots, N \qquad (6.55)$$

where, from Eq. (6.53), it can easily be shown that

$$\lambda_0(\boldsymbol{\theta}) = (1/(2\pi\psi_n)^{1/2})^n \exp\left(-\frac{1}{2\psi_n}\sum_{j=1}^{n}\theta_j^2\right) \qquad (6.56)$$

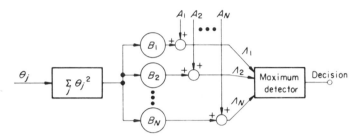

FIG. 6.11. Decision system for system identification in the case of independent sampling.

Hence we have the expression

$$\Lambda_i(\boldsymbol{\theta}) = A_i + B_i\sum_{j=1}^{n}\theta_j^2, \qquad i = 1, 2, \ldots, N \qquad (6.57)$$

where

$$A_i = \log \xi_i - \tfrac{1}{2}n \log(1 + \gamma_i^2)$$

$$B_i = \frac{\gamma_i^2}{2\psi_n(1 + \gamma_i^2)} \qquad (6.58)$$

It is noted that both A_i and B_i are independent of the observed value $\boldsymbol{\theta}$ but are dependent on the signal-to-noise ratio γ_i^2. Therefore these, too, may be considered the diagonal and the multiplying factor, respectively. The decision circuit is constructed as shown in Fig. 6.11.

6.6-2 Taking into account correlations between successive sampled data. When there exists a correlation between successive sampled data, Eq. (6.49) is directly used for determining the decision threshold, because

Eq. (6.50) does not hold. By substituting Eq. (6.49) into Eq. (6.45) we have

$$\lambda_i(\boldsymbol{\theta}) = \xi_i (2\pi)^{-n/2} \, |\mathbf{M}_s + \mathbf{M}_n|^{-\frac{1}{2}} \exp[-\tfrac{1}{2}\boldsymbol{\theta}'(\mathbf{M}_s + \mathbf{M}_n)^{-1}\boldsymbol{\theta}]$$

$$(6.59a)$$

Furthermore, it can easily be shown that

$$\lambda_0(\boldsymbol{\theta}) = (2\pi)^{-n/2} \, |\mathbf{M}_n|^{-\frac{1}{2}} \exp(-\tfrac{1}{2}\boldsymbol{\theta}'\mathbf{M}_n^{-1}\boldsymbol{\theta}) \qquad (6.59b)$$

Then we have

$$\frac{\lambda_i(\boldsymbol{\theta})}{\lambda_0(\boldsymbol{\theta})} = \xi_i \frac{|\mathbf{M}_s + \mathbf{M}_n|^{-\frac{1}{2}}}{|\mathbf{M}_n|^{-\frac{1}{2}}} \exp\{\tfrac{1}{2}\boldsymbol{\theta}'[\mathbf{M}_n^{-1} - (\mathbf{M}_s + \mathbf{M}_n)^{-1}]\boldsymbol{\theta}\} \quad (6.60)$$

Therefore, if the logarithmic forms of both sides of Eq. (6.60) are taken Eq. (6.55) becomes

$$\Lambda_i(\boldsymbol{\theta}) = \mathbf{C}_i + \tfrac{1}{2}\boldsymbol{\theta}'\mathbf{D}_i\boldsymbol{\theta} \qquad (6.61a)$$

where

$$\mathbf{C}_i = \log \xi_i - \tfrac{1}{2}\log|\mathbf{I} + \mathbf{M}_s\mathbf{M}_n^{-1}| \qquad (6.61b)$$

$$\mathbf{D}_i = \mathbf{M}_n^{-1} - (\mathbf{M}_s + \mathbf{M}_n)^{-1} - \frac{\mathbf{M}_s}{\mathbf{M}_n(\mathbf{M}_n + \mathbf{M}_s)} \qquad (6.61c)$$

For the purpose of realizing this decision device in the form of practical filters our attention is now directed to the second term of the right-hand member of Eq. (6.61a).

(a) *White noise background.*   Since the circuit may be derived from the second term of the right-hand side of Eq. (6.61a), it is sufficient to consider

$$\phi_n = \boldsymbol{\theta}'\mathbf{D}_i\boldsymbol{\theta}$$
$$= \psi_n^{-1}\boldsymbol{\theta}'\mathbf{D}_i\psi_n\boldsymbol{\theta} \qquad (6.62)$$

If we let

$$\mathbf{x} = \mathbf{D}_i\psi_n\boldsymbol{\theta} \qquad (6.63)$$

then Eq. (6.62) yields

$$\phi_n = \psi_n^{-1}\boldsymbol{\theta}'\mathbf{x}$$

Expressing the kth elements of $\boldsymbol{\theta}'$ and $\mathbf{x}$ by θ_k and x_k, respectively, we have

$$\phi_n = \psi_n^{-1} \sum_{k=1}^{n} x_k \theta_k$$

$$= \psi_n^{-1} \sum_{k=1}^{n} x(t_k)\, \theta(t_k) \tag{6.64}$$

On the other hand, from Eq. (6.61c), we have

$$\psi_n \mathbf{D}_i = \psi_n \mathbf{M}_n^{-1} - \psi_n (\mathbf{M}_s + \mathbf{M}_n)^{-1}$$

$$= \mathbf{k}_n^{-1} - (\mathbf{k}_n + \gamma_i^2 \mathbf{k}_s)^{-1} \tag{6.65}$$

where

$$k_n = \mathbf{M}_n / \psi_n \tag{6.66a}$$

$$k_s = \mathbf{M}_s / \psi_s \tag{6.66b}$$

Since $n(t)$ is a gaussian white noise, Eq. (6.65) becomes

$$\psi_n \mathbf{D}_i = \mathbf{I} - (\mathbf{I} + \gamma_i^2 \mathbf{k}_s)^{-1} \tag{6.67}$$

Letting

$$\psi_n \mathbf{D}_i = \| h_i(t_k, t_j)\, \Delta t \| \tag{6.68}$$

then from Eq. (6.63), we have

$$x_k = \sum_{j=1}^{n} h_i(t_k, t_j)\, \theta(t_j)\, \Delta t \tag{6.69}$$

Hence Eq. (6.64) becomes

$$\phi_n = \psi_n^{-1} \sum_{k=1}^{n} \theta(t_k) \sum_{j=1}^{n} h_i(t_k, t_j)\, \theta(t_j)\, \Delta t \tag{6.70}$$

When the additive random noise $n(t)$ can be considered the band-limited white gaussian noise whose spectral density is given by

$$S_n(f) = 2N_0, \qquad 0 \le f < f_0$$

$$= 0, \qquad (f > f_0) \tag{6.71}$$

then Eq. (6.70) is converted into a more realistic form with the help of the autocorrelation function $\psi_n(\tau)$ of the random noise $n(t)$. Through the well-known relation originated by Wiener and by Khintchine,[6] this function is related to the spectral density $S_n(f)$ by

$$\psi_n(\tau) = \int_0^\infty S_n(f) \cos(2\pi f\tau)\, df \qquad (6.72)$$

From Eqs. (6.71) and (6.72), we have

$$\psi_n(\tau) = \frac{2N_0 f_0 \sin 2\pi f_0 \tau}{2\pi f_0 \tau} \qquad (6.73)$$

It is apparent that the variance ψ_n of the random noise is given by $\psi_n(\tau)\big|_{\tau=0}$. From Eq. (6.73), it is determined as

$$\psi_n = \lim_{\tau \to 0} \psi_n(\tau) = 2N_0 f_0 \qquad (6.74)$$

From the sampling theorem established by Shannon[7] we know that, if the random noise is sampled at time interval Δt, then Δt should be chosen as $\Delta t = 1/2 f_0$. Equation (6.74) can, therefore, be expressed as

$$\psi_n = \frac{N_0}{\Delta t} \qquad (6.75)$$

By means of this expression Eq. (6.70) becomes

$$\phi_n = \frac{1}{N_0} \sum_{k=1}^n \theta(t_k) \sum_{j=1}^n h_i(t_k, t_j)\, \theta(t_j)(\Delta t)^2 \qquad (6.76)$$

In the case of continuous sampling, in which n becomes infinite in the fixed time interval of the observation (that is, $\Delta t \to 0$ and $n \to \infty$) this equation yields

$$\lim_{n \to \infty} \phi_n = \frac{1}{N_0} \int_0^T \theta(\tau_1)\, d\tau_1 \int_0^T h_i(\tau_1, \tau_2)\, \theta(\tau_2)\, d\tau_2 \qquad (6.77)$$

[6] N. Wiener, "Extrapolation, Interpolation and Smoothing of Stationary Time Series with Engineering Applications." Wiley, New York, 1954.
[7] C. E. Shannon, Communication in the presence of noise. *Proc. IRE.* **37**, 10 (1949).

Here the quantity $h_i(t, \tau)$ remains to be determined. By multiplying both sides of Eq. (6.61c) by $\psi_n(\mathbf{M}_n + \mathbf{M}_s)$ we have

$$\psi_n \mathbf{D}_i(\mathbf{M}_n + \mathbf{M}_s) = \psi_n[\mathbf{M}_n^{-1}(\mathbf{M}_n + \mathbf{M}_s) - \mathbf{I}] \qquad (6.78)$$

Since the background noise in the present case is considered white noise, then with the use of Eqs. (6.50b) and (6.66a), Eq. (6.78) can be expressed in an alternative form,

$$\sum_{k=1}^{n} \psi_n(\mathbf{D}_i)_{jk}[(\mathbf{M}_n)_{kl} + (\mathbf{M}_s)_{kl}] = \sum_{k=1}^{n}(\mathbf{k}_n^{-1})_{jk}(\mathbf{M}_s)_{kl} = \sum_{k=1}^{n}\delta_{jk}(\mathbf{M}_s)_{kl} = (\mathbf{M}_s)_{jl}$$

$$(6.79)$$

where $(\mathbf{D}_i)_{jk}$ and $(\mathbf{k}^{-1})_{jk}$ are the jth-column kth-row elements of the matrices $\mathbf{D}_i$ and $\mathbf{k}_n^{-1}$, respectively. Similarly, $(\mathbf{M}_n)_{kl}$ and $(\mathbf{M}_s)_{kl}$ are the kth-row lth-column elements of the matrices $\mathbf{M}_n$ and $\mathbf{M}_s$, respectively. Consequently, when Eq. (6.68) is used, Eq. (6.79) becomes

$$\sum_{k=1}^{n} h_i(t_j, t_k)[(\mathbf{M}_n)_{kl} + (\mathbf{M}_s)_{kl}]\Delta t = (\mathbf{M}_s)_{jl} \qquad (6.80)$$

In continuous sampling, where $n \to \infty$, we obtain

$$\int_0^T h_i(t, \sigma)[\mathbf{M}_n(\sigma, \tau) + \mathbf{M}_s(\sigma, \tau)]\,d\sigma = \mathbf{M}_s(t, \tau) \qquad (6.81)$$

where $\mathbf{M}_n(\sigma, \tau) = 2N_0\delta(\sigma - \tau)$. Thus, the term in Eq. (6.61a) which is the key part of decision systems given by Eq. (6.62), can be redesigned by means of Eqs. (6.77) and Eq. (6.81), provided that the values of $\mathbf{M}_n$ and $\mathbf{M}_s$ are given.

(b) *Strong signal in the presence of random noise.* Since $\gamma_i^2 \gg 1$ in Eq. (6.54), an approximate decision threshold can be obtained from Eq. (6.61c) for the design of a decision system with a strong signal. Equation (6.61c) is alternatively expressed as

$$\mathbf{D}_i = \mathbf{M}_n^{-1}(\mathbf{M}_n^{-1} + \mathbf{M}_s^{-1})^{-1}\mathbf{M}_n^{-1} \qquad (6.82)$$

This equation is our starting formula for determining an approximate decision threshold in the case of $\gamma_i^2 \gg 1$. Before giving the final formula we shall show that Eq. (6.82) can be derived by another method.

We have assumed that the output $\boldsymbol{\theta}_i^*$ of the ith model and the additive noise $\mathbf{n}$ are mutually independent; therefore we have

$$\int_{C_i} p(\boldsymbol{\theta} \mid \boldsymbol{\theta}_i^*) \, s(\boldsymbol{\theta}_i^*) \, d\boldsymbol{\theta}_i^* = \int_{C_i} p(\boldsymbol{\theta} - \boldsymbol{\theta}_i^*) \, s(\boldsymbol{\theta}_i^*) \, d\boldsymbol{\theta}_i^* \qquad (6.83)$$

Substituting Eqs. (6.47) and (6.48) into Eq. (6.83) we find that

$$\int_{C_i} p(\boldsymbol{\theta} \mid \boldsymbol{\theta}_i^*) s(\boldsymbol{\theta}_i^*) \, d\boldsymbol{\theta}_i^*$$

$$= \int_{C_i} (2\pi)^{-n} \, |\mathbf{M}_n \mathbf{M}_s|^{-\frac{1}{2}}$$

$$\times \exp[-\tfrac{1}{2}(\boldsymbol{\theta} - \boldsymbol{\theta}_i^*)' \mathbf{M}_n^{-1}(\boldsymbol{\theta} - \boldsymbol{\theta}_i^*) - \tfrac{1}{2}\boldsymbol{\theta}_i^{*\prime} \mathbf{M}_s^{-1} \boldsymbol{\theta}_i^*] \, d\boldsymbol{\theta}_i^*$$

$$= (2\pi)^{-n} \, |\mathbf{M}_n \mathbf{M}_s|^{-\frac{1}{2}} \exp(-\tfrac{1}{2}\boldsymbol{\theta}' \mathbf{M}_n^{-1}\boldsymbol{\theta}) J \qquad (6.84)$$

where, with the new symbol $\mathbf{s} = \mathbf{M}_n^{-1}\boldsymbol{\theta}$,

$$J = \int_{C_i} \exp(\tfrac{1}{2}\boldsymbol{\theta}_i^{*\prime} \mathbf{M}_n^{-1}\boldsymbol{\theta} + \tfrac{1}{2}\boldsymbol{\theta}' \mathbf{M}_n^{-1}\boldsymbol{\theta}_i^* - \tfrac{1}{2}\boldsymbol{\theta}_i^{*\prime} \mathbf{M}_n^{-1}\boldsymbol{\theta}_i^* - \tfrac{1}{2}\boldsymbol{\theta}_i^{*\prime} \mathbf{M}_s^{-1}\boldsymbol{\theta}_i^*) \, d\boldsymbol{\theta}_i^*$$

$$= \int_{C_i} \exp[\tfrac{1}{2}\boldsymbol{\theta}_i^{*\prime}\mathbf{s} + \tfrac{1}{2}\mathbf{s}'\boldsymbol{\theta}_i^* - \tfrac{1}{2}\boldsymbol{\theta}_i^{*\prime}(\mathbf{M}_n^{-1} + \mathbf{M}_s^{-1})\boldsymbol{\theta}_i^*] \, d\boldsymbol{\theta}_i^*$$

$$= \int_{C_i} \exp[\mathbf{s}'\boldsymbol{\theta}_i^* - \tfrac{1}{2}\boldsymbol{\theta}_i^{*\prime}(\mathbf{M}_n^{-1} + \mathbf{M}_s^{-1})\boldsymbol{\theta}_i^*] \, d\boldsymbol{\theta}_i^* \qquad (6.85)$$

and $\mathbf{s}'$ is the transposed vector of $\mathbf{s}$. We invoke here the integral formula[8]

$$\int_{\Omega(\mathbf{x})} \exp(j\mathbf{t}'\mathbf{x} - \tfrac{1}{2}\mathbf{x}'\mathbf{A}\mathbf{x}) \, d\mathbf{x} = (2\pi)^{n/2} |\mathbf{A}|^{-\frac{1}{2}} \exp(-\tfrac{1}{2}\mathbf{t}'\mathbf{A}^{-1}\mathbf{t}) \qquad (6.86)$$

where $\Omega(\mathbf{x})$ means the integral over the entire space of the vector process $\mathbf{x}$. In this case, since we have the equalities $\mathbf{x} = \boldsymbol{\theta}_i^*$, $j\mathbf{t}' = \mathbf{s}'$, and $\mathbf{A} = \mathbf{M}_n^{-1} + \mathbf{M}_s^{-1}$, then Eq. (6.85) becomes

$$J = (2\pi)^{n/2} |\mathbf{M}_n^{-1} + \mathbf{M}_s^{-1}|^{-\frac{1}{2}} \exp[\tfrac{1}{2}\boldsymbol{\theta}' \mathbf{M}_n^{-1}(\mathbf{M}_n^{-1} + \mathbf{M}_s^{-1})^{-1}\mathbf{M}_n^{-1}\boldsymbol{\theta}] \qquad (6.87)$$

---

[8] H. Cramer, "Mathematical Methods of Statistics," p. 118. Princeton Univ. Press, Princeton, New Jersey, 1946.

Consequently, we have Eq. (6.61a) again,

$$\Lambda_i(\boldsymbol{\theta}) = C_i + \tfrac{1}{2}\boldsymbol{\theta}'\mathbf{D}_i\boldsymbol{\theta} \tag{6.88a}$$

where

$$\mathbf{D}_i = \mathbf{M}_n^{-1}(\mathbf{M}_n^{-1} + \mathbf{M}_s^{-1})^{-1}\mathbf{M}_n^{-1} = \frac{\mathbf{M}_s}{\mathbf{M}_n(\mathbf{M}_n + \mathbf{M}_s)} \tag{6.88b}$$

Equation (6.88b) agrees with the result given by Eq. (6.61c). In the case of a strong signal (that is, $\gamma_i^2 \gg 1$) it may be expressed by means of Eqs. (6.66) as follows:

$$
\begin{aligned}
\mathbf{D}_i &= \frac{1}{\psi_n^2}\,\mathbf{k}_n^{-1}\!\left(\frac{\mathbf{k}_n^{-1}}{\psi_n} + \frac{\mathbf{k}_s^{-1}}{\psi_s}\right)^{-1}\!\mathbf{k}_n^{-1} \\
&= \frac{1}{\psi_n^3}\,\mathbf{k}_n^{-1}\!\left(\mathbf{k}_n^{-1} + \frac{\psi_n}{\psi_s}\mathbf{k}_s^{-1}\right)^{-1}\!\mathbf{k}_n^{-1} \\
&= \frac{1}{\psi_n^3}\,\mathbf{k}_n^{-1}[\mathbf{k}_n^{-1}(\mathbf{I} + \gamma_i^{-2}\mathbf{k}_n\mathbf{k}_s^{-1})]^{-1}\mathbf{k}_n^{-1} \\
&= \mathbf{M}_n^{-1}\mathbf{M}_n(\mathbf{I} + \gamma_i^{-2}\mathbf{E}_i)^{-1}\mathbf{M}_n^{-1} \tag{6.89a}
\end{aligned}
$$

where

$$\mathbf{E}_i = \mathbf{k}_n\mathbf{k}_s^{-1} \tag{6.89b}$$

Since $\gamma_i^2 \gg 1$, Eq. (6.89a) may be approximately expressed as

$$
\begin{aligned}
\mathbf{D}_i &= \mathbf{M}_n^{-1}[\mathbf{M}_n(\mathbf{I} - \gamma_i^{-2}\mathbf{E}_i)]\mathbf{M}_n^{-1} \\
&= (\mathbf{I} - \gamma_i^{-2}\mathbf{E}_i)\mathbf{M}_n^{-1} \tag{6.90}
\end{aligned}
$$

The second term of the right-hand member of Eq. (6.88a) can, therefore, be described by

$$\Lambda_i(\boldsymbol{\theta}) = C_i + \tfrac{1}{2}\boldsymbol{\theta}'\mathbf{M}_n^{-1}\boldsymbol{\theta} - \tfrac{1}{2}\gamma_i^{-2}\boldsymbol{\theta}'\mathbf{E}_i\mathbf{M}_n^{-1}\boldsymbol{\theta} \tag{6.91}$$

(c) *Weak signal in the presence of random noise.* A weak signal in random noise is expressed as $\gamma_i^2 \ll 1$. From Eqs. (6.61c) and (6.66), we have

$$
\begin{aligned}
\mathbf{D}_i &= \mathbf{M}_n^{-1} - (\mathbf{M}_s + \mathbf{M}_n)^{-1} \\
&= \psi_n^{-1}\mathbf{k}_n^{-1} - (\psi_s\mathbf{k}_s + \psi_n\mathbf{k}_n)^{-1} \tag{6.92}
\end{aligned}
$$

Furthermore, on substitution of Eq. (6.54) into Eq. (6.92), we have

$$\mathbf{D}_i = \psi_n^{-1}\mathbf{k}_n^{-1} - \psi_n^{-1}\mathbf{k}_n^{-1}(\mathbf{I} + \gamma_i^2\mathbf{F}_i)^{-1} \tag{6.93a}$$

where

$$\mathbf{F}_i = \mathbf{k}_n^{-1}\mathbf{k}_s \tag{6.93b}$$

Since $\gamma_i^2 \ll 1$, Eq. (6.93a) can be expanded,

$$\mathbf{D}_i \cong \psi_n^{-1}\mathbf{k}_n^{-1} - \psi_n^{-1}\mathbf{k}_n^{-1}(\mathbf{I} - \gamma_i^2\mathbf{F}_i)$$
$$= \gamma_i^2\psi_n^{-1}\mathbf{k}_n^{-1}\mathbf{F}_i = \gamma_i^2\mathbf{M}_n^{-1}\mathbf{F}_i \tag{6.94}$$

where Eq. (6.66a) is used once again. Consequently, by applying Eq. (6.94) to Eq. (6.61a), we obtain the following:

$$\Lambda_i(\boldsymbol{\theta}) = \mathbf{C}_i + \frac{\gamma_i^2}{2}\,\boldsymbol{\theta}'\mathbf{M}_n^{-1}\mathbf{F}_i\boldsymbol{\theta} \tag{6.95}$$

The technique described above is equivalent to the one developed in communications theory. Some excellent work on it has been done by Middleton.[9]

6.7 Numerical Examples of Application of Decision Concept to Averaging Devices

A common problem in the statistical study of control systems is measuring the average value θ^* of a random signal $\theta(t)$. In practice it is almost impossible to make a precise evaluation of this average value, because it fluctuates around the true value θ^*. Therefore, considering that the random signal $\theta(t)$ and its mean value θ^* correspond respectively to the observed data $\theta(t)$ and the message signal $\theta^*(t)$ in the previous description, we introduce here the decision concept for the purpose of inferring the true mean value θ^*. We consider our situation to be

$$\theta(t) = \theta^* + n(t) \tag{6.96}$$

[9] D. Middleton, "An Introduction to Statistical Communication Theory." McGraw-Hill, New York, 1960.

where $n(t)$ is the random portion of the observed signal $\theta(t)$ and can be considered additive noise. Figure 6.12 illustrates the situation. Since the averaging device produces $\theta^*(t)$ as the output, we assume that the true mean value $\theta^*(t)$ takes only one of N preassigned values, $\theta_1^*, \theta_2^*, \ldots,$ $\theta_{N-1}^*, \theta_N^*$. Then with the help of Eqs. (6.19) and (6.20) and by taking the

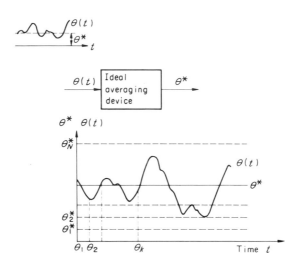

FIG. 6.12. Averaging procedure.

logarithmic form of Eq. (6.14) and considering $\xi_k \equiv \xi$ for all values of k we state the solution of the decision problem:

Decide $\theta^* = \theta_k^*,$ when $\log p(\boldsymbol{\theta} \mid \theta_k^*) = \max_j [\log p(\boldsymbol{\theta} \mid \theta_j^*)].$

Here θ_j^* does not change during the observing time interval. If the random noise $n(t)$ has independent normal distribution with mean of zero and a variance of σ_n^2, then

$$p(\boldsymbol{\theta} \mid \theta_i^*) = (2\pi\sigma_n^2)^{-n/2} \exp\left[-\frac{1}{2\sigma_n^2}\sum_{k=1}^{n}(\theta_k - \theta_i^*)^2\right], \qquad i = 1, \ldots, N$$

$$(6.97)$$

Hence, as shown in Fig. 6.13, the acceptance region R_{a1} of the hypothesis $[H_1 : \theta^* = \theta_1^*]$ is defined as a subset in the n-dimensional space R^n, where the following $N - 1$ inequalities are simultaneously satisfied:

$$\log p(\boldsymbol{\theta} \mid \theta_1^*) > \log p(\boldsymbol{\theta} \mid \theta_i^*), \qquad i = 2, 3, \ldots, N \qquad (6.98)$$

By substituting Eq. (6.97) into Eq. (6.98), the conditions shown by Eq. (6.98) are converted into

$$\bar{\theta} \lessgtr \kappa_i \qquad \text{for} \quad \theta_1^* \gtrless \theta_i^* \qquad (6.99)$$

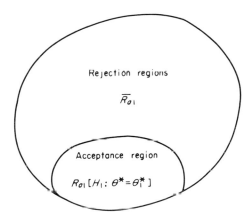

FIG. 6.13. Acceptance and rejection regions.

where

$$\bar{\theta} = \frac{1}{n} \sum_{k=1}^{n} \theta_k \qquad (6.100)$$

and

$$\kappa_i = \frac{\theta_1^* + \theta_i^*}{2} \qquad (6.101)$$

The error probability, as mentioned previously, is defined in the following way. The rejection region $\bar{R}_{a1}$ is defined as the complementary subset of R_{a1}, as shown in Fig. 6.13. By means of Eq. (6.97), the error probability of the first kind is given by

$$\epsilon_1 = \int_{\bar{R}_{a1}} p(\boldsymbol{\theta} \mid \theta_1^*) \, d\boldsymbol{\theta} \qquad (6.102)$$

as we can observe in Eq. (6.99); however, the decision-making is performed by the arithmetical mean $\bar{\theta}$, so by a consideration similar to that outlined in Sect. 5.3, this equation should be expressed as

$$
\begin{aligned}
\epsilon_1 &= \int_{\bar{r}_{a1}} \frac{n^{1/2}}{(2\pi)^{1/2}\sigma_n} \exp\left(-\frac{n}{2\sigma_n^2}(\bar{\theta}-\theta_1^*)^2\right) d\bar{\theta} \\
&= \frac{1}{(2\pi)^{1/2}} \int_{\bar{r}_{a1}(y)} \exp(-\tfrac{1}{2}y^2)\, dy
\end{aligned}
\tag{6.103}
$$

where $\bar{r}_{a1}$ is the rejection region in the vector space $\bar{\theta}$ corresponding to the rejection region $\bar{R}_{a1}$ and

$$
y = (\bar{\theta}-\theta_1^*)\Big/\frac{\sigma_n}{n^{1/2}}.
\tag{6.104}
$$

We shall now construct the decision device realizing the condition expressed by Eq. (6.98). This may be done by means of Eq. (6.28) or Fig. 6.7, where $\eta(t)$ has been given by Eq. (6.30) and $\hat{\mu}_i$ can be obtained as follows. From Eqs. (6.29) and (6.33a), we have

$$
\begin{aligned}
\bar{\mu}_i &= \log \xi_i - \tfrac{1}{2}\theta_i^{*2}\int_0^T w(t)\, dt \\
&= \log \xi_i - \tfrac{1}{2}\theta_i^{*2}\rho
\end{aligned}
\tag{6.105a}
$$

where

$$
\rho = \int_0^T w(t)\, dt.
\tag{6.105b}
$$

We now consider a simple example, that of two quantized levels $\theta^* = \theta_1^*$ and $\theta^* = \theta_2^*$, the case in which $N = 2$. By means of Fig. 6.7 the decision averaging device shown in Fig. 6.14 can be constructed. This figure and Eqs. (6.28) and (6.105a) show that the decision-making may be described as follows:

If

$$
\theta_1^*\int_0^T w(t)\,\theta(t)\, dt - \tfrac{1}{2}\theta_1^{*2}\rho > \theta_2^*\int_0^T w(t)\,\theta(t)\, dt - \tfrac{1}{2}\theta_2^{*2}\rho,
\tag{6.106a}
$$

then decide $\theta^* = \theta_1^*$.

If

$$\theta_1^* \int_0^T w(t)\,\theta(t)\,dt - \tfrac{1}{2}\theta_1^{*2}\rho < \theta_2^* \int_0^T w(t)\theta(t)\,dt - \tfrac{1}{2}\theta_2^{*2}\rho, \qquad (6.106b)$$

then decide $\theta^* = \theta_2^*$.

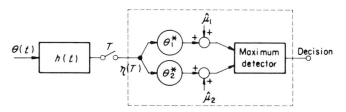

FIG. 6.14. Decision averaging device for $N = 2$.

Here $\xi_1 = \xi_2$, as before. When $\theta_1^* < \theta_2^*$, the condition given by Ineqs. (6.106) will depend on the relation

$$\int_0^T w(t)\,\theta(t)\,dt \lessgtr \tfrac{1}{2}(\theta_1^* + \theta_2^*)\rho \qquad (6.107)$$

From Eqs. (6.30) and (6.33c) we have

$$\eta(T) = \int_0^T w(t)\,\theta(t)\,dt \qquad (6.108a)$$

and from Eq. (6.101) we have

$$\kappa_2 = \frac{\theta_1^* + \theta_2^*}{2} = \bar{\theta}^* \qquad (6.108b)$$

Therefore the decision-making can be compactly stated:

$$
\begin{aligned}
&\text{Decide} \quad \theta^* = \theta_1^*, \quad \text{when} \quad \eta < \bar{\theta}^*\rho. \\
&\text{Decide} \quad \theta^* = \theta_2^*, \quad \text{when} \quad \eta > \bar{\theta}^*\rho.
\end{aligned}
\qquad (6.109)
$$

We must evaluate ρ here. Its value may be found by using Eq. (6.105b) and specifying the form of the autocorrelation function of the random noise. For example, let the noise $n(t)$ be a colored noise having the autocorrelation function

$$m(\tau) = \frac{\psi_n}{2} [\delta(\tau) + k \exp(-\gamma |\tau|)] \qquad (6.110)$$

This form of the autocorrelation function often arises in adaptive control systems in which white noise is used as a test signal for system identification. By substituting Eq. (6.110) into Eq. (6.33b) the following solution can be obtained:

$$w(t) = \frac{2\gamma^2}{\mu^2 \psi_n} [1 + C_1 \exp(-\mu t) + C_2 \exp(\mu t)] \qquad (6.111)$$

where

$$\mu^2 = \gamma^2 + 2\gamma k \qquad (6.112)$$

$$C_1 = \frac{2k}{(\gamma - \mu) \exp(-\mu T) + \gamma + \mu} = C_2 \exp(\mu T)$$

$$\qquad (6.113)$$

$$C_2 = \frac{2k}{(\gamma - \mu) + (\gamma + \mu) \exp(\mu T)} = C_1 \exp(-\mu T)$$

Substituting Eq. (6.111) into Eq. (6.105b) and using Eq. (6.113) gives

$$\rho = \int_0^T w(t) \, dt$$

$$= \frac{2}{\psi_n} \left(\frac{\gamma}{\mu}\right)^2 \left\{ T + \frac{2}{\mu} C_1 [1 - \exp(-\mu T)] \right\}$$

$$= \frac{2}{\psi_n} \left(\frac{\gamma}{\mu}\right)^2 \left\{ T + \frac{2}{\mu} C_2 [\exp(\mu T) - 1] \right\} \qquad (6.114)$$

From the result of the decision [Eq. (6.109)], the averaging device incorporating the decision approach can be constructed as shown in

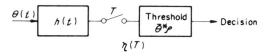

FIG. 6.15. Final scheme of decision averaging device derived from Fig. 6.14.

Fig. 6.15, where only two quantized levels, θ_1^* and θ_2^*, of the fluctuating mean value are considered. However, an extension of this approach to N quantized levels is very simple.

Although the decision rule for the averaging device has been established and this may be applied by designing the simple logic element, the error involved should be evaluated. We focus our attention on the value of T, because $\eta(T)$ is the value of the output of the linear filter with weighting function $h(t)$ at time $t = T$. Therefore, we consider that the value of $\eta(T)$ is a random process with respect to the value of T.

In the example given above one of two quantized levels θ_1^* and θ_2^* is decided, and therefore the error may be considered as it is in binary detection; see Fig. 6.16. Because the rejection region in Eq. (6.102) becomes the region $[\bar{\theta}^*\rho, \infty]$ in this case, the mathematical form of the error probability of the first kind given by that equation is converted into

$$\epsilon_1 = \int_{\theta^*\rho}^{\infty} p_1(\eta)\, d\eta \tag{6.115}$$

where $p_1(\eta)$ is the probability density function of η when $\theta^* = \theta_1^*$. Similarly, the error probability of the second kind is

$$\epsilon_2 = \int_{-\infty}^{\bar{\theta}^*\rho} p_2(\eta)\, d\eta \tag{6.116}$$

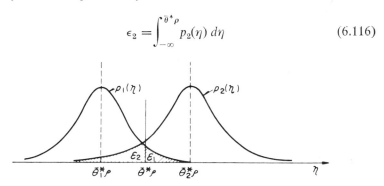

FIG. 6.16. The error probabilities ϵ_1 and ϵ_2.

where $p_2(\eta)$ is the probability density function when $\theta^* = \theta_2^*$. We compute the probability density functions $p_i(\eta)$ under the assumption that $\eta(T)$ is the gaussian random process, where $i = 1, 2$. First, the mean value m_η of $\eta(T)$ is readily obtained as

$$m = \langle \eta(T) \rangle_{\text{av}} = \int_0^T w(t) \langle \theta(t) \rangle_{\text{av}} \, dt = \theta_i^* \int_0^T h(t) \, dt = \rho \theta_i^* \qquad (6.117)$$

Second, the variance ψ_η of $\eta(T)$ can be calculated as

$$\psi_\eta = \langle \eta^2(T) \rangle_{\text{av}} - [\langle \eta(T) \rangle_{\text{av}}]^2 = \int_0^T d\tau_1 \int_0^T h(\tau_1) h(\tau_2) m(\tau_1 - \tau_2) \, d\tau_2$$

Invoking Eq. (6.33b) gives

$$\psi_\eta = \int_0^T h(\tau_1) \, d\tau_1$$

$$= \rho \qquad (6.118)$$

From Eqs. (6.117) and (6.118), we have

$$p_i(\eta) = \frac{1}{(2\pi\rho)^{1/2}} \exp\left(- \frac{(\eta - \theta_i^* \rho)^2}{2\rho}\right) \qquad (6.119)$$

By means of this equation we calculate Eqs. (6.115) and (6.116):

$$\varepsilon_1 = \frac{1}{(2\pi\rho)^{1/2}} \int_{\bar{\theta}^*\rho}^{\infty} \exp\left[- \frac{(\eta - \theta_1^* \rho)^2}{2\rho}\right] d\eta = \frac{1}{(2\pi)^{1/2}} \int_{\bar{\theta}_0^*}^{\infty} \exp\left(- \frac{t^2}{2}\right) dt$$

$$(6.120)$$

$$\varepsilon_2 = \frac{1}{(2\pi\rho)^{1/2}} \int_{-\infty}^{\bar{\theta}^*\rho} \exp\left[- \frac{(\eta - \theta_2^* \rho)^2}{2\rho}\right] d\eta$$

$$= \frac{1}{(2\pi)^{1/2}} \int_{-\infty}^{-\bar{\theta}_0^*} \exp\left[- \frac{t^2}{2}\right] dt = \varepsilon_1 \qquad (6.121)$$

where, with help of Eq. (6.108b), we find that

$$\bar{\theta}_0^* = \tfrac{1}{2}(\theta_2^* - \theta_1^*)\rho^{1/2} \qquad (6.122)$$

For an example a set of numerical values of the parameter of the auto-correlation function $m(\tau)$ in Eq. (6.110) is selected: $\psi_n = 0.1$, $\gamma = 0.1$, and $k = 1.0$. We assume, furthermore, that $\theta_1^* = 0.8$ and $\theta_2^* = 1.4$. With these values and Eq. (6.113), the two integral constants C_1 and C_2 are computed:

$$C_1 = \frac{2}{0.558 - 0.358 \exp(-0.458T)} \tag{6.123}$$

$$C_2 = C_1 \exp(-0.458T) \tag{6.124}$$

Furthermore, from Eq. (6.114), we have

$$\rho = \frac{20}{21}\left\{T + \frac{C_1}{0.229}[1 - \exp(-0.458T)]\right\} \tag{6.125}$$

Applying this to Eq. (6.122) with the values $\theta_1^* = 0.8$ and $\theta_2^* = 1.4$ gives

$$\bar{\theta}_0^* = \frac{3}{10}\left(\frac{20}{21}\left\{T + \frac{C_1}{0.229}[1 - \exp(-0.458T)]\right\}\right)^{1/4}$$

$$= \left(\frac{3}{35}\left\{T + \frac{C_1}{0.229}[1 - \exp(-0.458T)]\right\}\right)^{1/2} \tag{6.126}$$

If we consider the ideal case, in which the value of T tends to infinity, then from Eqs. (6.123), (6.124), and (6.126), we have

$$C_1 = \frac{2}{0.558} = 3.58$$

$$C_2 = 0 \tag{6.127}$$

$$\bar{\theta}_0^* = \infty$$

By applying these results to Eq. (6.121), and referring to Fig. 6.16 we see that $\epsilon_1 = \epsilon_2 = 0$; that is, error-free decision-making would be established.

On the other hand, the averaging operation is expressed as a time average in the form

$$\theta^* = \lim_{T \to \infty} \frac{1}{T} \int_0^T \theta(t)\, dt \tag{6.128}$$

It is a well-known fact, however, that this computation is impossible to realize. In practice it is computed as an approximation, a finite time average:

$$\theta_T^* = \frac{1}{T} \int_0^T \theta(t)\, dt \tag{6.129}$$

Of course, it is apparent that

$$\lim_{T \to \infty} \theta_T^* = \theta^* \tag{6.130}$$

Since the value of θ_T^* also depends on the value of T, the variance of θ_T^* yields

$$\sigma_T^2 = \langle (\theta_T^* - \theta^*)^2 \rangle_{\mathrm{av}} = \langle \theta_T^{*2} \rangle_{\mathrm{av}} - \theta^{*2}$$

$$= \frac{1}{T^2} \int_0^T dt_1 \int_0^T dt_2 \langle \theta(t_1)\, \theta(t_2) \rangle_{\mathrm{av}} - \theta^{*2}$$

$$= \frac{1}{T^2} \int_0^T dt_1 \int_0^T dt_2 \langle [\theta^* + n(t_1)][\theta^* + n(t_2)] \rangle_{\mathrm{av}} - \theta^{*2}$$

$$= \frac{1}{T^2} \int_0^T dt_1 \int_0^T dt_2\, m(t_1 - t_2) \tag{6.131a}$$

With the use of Eq. (6.110), this becomes

$$\sigma_T^2 = \frac{1}{T^2} \int_0^T dt_1 \int_0^T dt_2\, \frac{\psi_n}{2} \{ \delta(t_1 - t_2) + k \exp[-\gamma\, |t_1 - t_2|] \}$$

$$= \frac{\psi_n}{2} \frac{1}{T^2} \int_0^T dt_1 \left\{ 1 + \int_0^{t_1} k \exp[-\gamma(t_1 - t_2)]\, dt_2 \right.$$

$$\left. + \int_{t_1}^T k \exp[-\gamma(t_2 - t_1)]\, dt_2 \right\}$$

$$= \frac{\psi_n}{2T^2} \int_0^T \left(1 + \frac{k}{\gamma}[1 - \exp(-\gamma t)] + \frac{k}{\gamma}\{1 - \exp[-\gamma(T - t)]\} \right) dt$$

$$= \frac{\psi_n}{2T} + \frac{k\psi_n}{\gamma T} \left\{ 1 - \frac{1}{\gamma T}[1 - \exp(-\gamma T)] \right\} \tag{6.131b}$$

In this case, by a process similar to Eq. (6.120), the error probability ϵ_{1T} becomes

$$\epsilon_{1T} = \frac{1}{(2\pi)^{\frac{1}{2}}\sigma_T} \int_{\bar{\theta}^*}^{\infty} \exp\left[-\frac{(\theta_T^* - \theta_1)^2}{2\sigma_T^2}\right] d\theta_T^* = \frac{1}{(2\pi)^{\frac{1}{2}}} \int_{\bar{\theta}_{0T}}^{\infty} \exp(-\tfrac{1}{2}\zeta^2)\, d\zeta$$

(6.132)

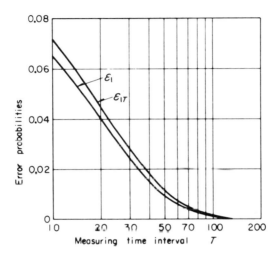

FIG. 6.17. Error probabilities ϵ_1 and ϵ_{1T}.

where, if the numerical values originally given are applied to Eq. (6.131b) and Eq. (6.108b) is used, it follows that

$$\bar{\theta}_{0T} = \frac{\theta_2^* - \theta_1^*}{2\sigma_T}$$

$$= (3/35)^{\frac{1}{2}} T/\{T - 9.8[1 - \exp(-0.1T)]\}^{\frac{1}{2}} \qquad (6.133)$$

The value of the error probability ϵ_1 computed by Eq. (6.120) is compared with that of the error probability ϵ_{1T} calculated by Eq. (6.132) with respect to the measuring time interval T, as shown in Fig. 6.17. From this figure it can easily be concluded that, when the decision concept is introduced into the averaging device, the error probability is smaller than in conventional time-averaging devices. The example given in this section shows the advantage thus guaranteed. In practical systems only two averaging devices usually are considered. One is the finite time integrator, given by Eq. (6.129), and the other is a low-pass filter. However, an integrator being more efficient than a low-pass filter,[10] the discussion here has covered all aspects of the situation.

6.8 Application of Decision Concept to Nondata Problems

So far we have dealt with the situation in which the observing time interval or the sample size of the observed data is fixed. Furthermore, we have assumed that the a priori probability density function of the true value to be inferred is known and time-invariant. This assumption implies that the true value may be considered a stationary random process. There is no need to say that such an assumption is not proper to a practical situation but to an ideal one, seeing that our observing time interval is of finite duration. Recognizing the fact that the change in the true value has nonstationary characteristics, in our approach to the true value we shall use a method of repeatedly correcting the a priori probability density function rather than the a priori stationary probability density function.

The variational range of the true value of a parameter is divided into N regions, $C_1, C_2, \ldots, C_{N-1}, C_N$, as shown in Fig. 6.1. We express the a priori probability that the true value $\theta^*(t)$ of the parameter occurs in the region C_i, that is, $\theta^*(t) \in C_i$, by the symbol $P_{k-1}(C_i)$, and this can be assumed to be given before the value $\theta_k = \theta(kT)$ at time $t = kT$ is observed. Hence, the a posteriori probability $P(C_i \mid \theta_k)$, that $\theta^* \in C_i$ when the value $\theta_k = \theta(kT)$ is given, can be described by the Bayes formula, Eq. (2.17), as

$$P_k(C_i) = P(C_i \mid \theta_k) = \frac{P_{k-1}(C_i)\, p(\theta_k \mid C_i)}{\sum_{i=1}^{N} P_{k-1}(C_i)\, p(\theta_k \mid C_i)} \tag{6.134}$$

This may be considered the a priori probability in the kth sampling

[10] O. L. R. Jacobs, The measurement of the mean square value of certain random signals. *Information and Control* **9**, 149 (1960).

interval $kT \leq t \leq (k + 1)T$. Then we have the following sequence:

$$P_{k-1}(C_i) = \frac{P_{k-2}(C_i)\, p(\theta_{k-1} \mid C_i)}{\sum_{i=1}^{N} P_{k-2}(C_i)\, p(\theta_{k-1} \mid C_i)}$$

$$P_{k-2}(C_i) = \frac{P_{k-3}(C_i)\, p(\theta_{k-2} \mid C_i)}{\sum_{i=1}^{N} P_{k-3}(C_i)\, p(\theta_{k-2} \mid C_i)}$$

$$\vdots$$

$$(6.135)$$

$$P_{k-m+1}(C_i) = \frac{P_{k-m}(C_i)\, p(\theta_{k-m+1} \mid C_i)}{\sum_{i=1}^{N} P_{k-m}(C_i)\, p(\theta_{k-m+1} \mid C_i)}$$

By using these equations we can rewrite Eq. (6.134):

$$P_k(C_i) = \frac{P_{k-m}(C_i)\, p(\theta_k \mid C_i)\, p(\theta_{k-1} \mid C_i) \cdots p(\theta_{k-m+1} \mid C_i)}{\sum_{i=1}^{N} P_{k-m}(C_i)\, p(\theta_k \mid C_i)\, p(\theta_{k-1} \mid C_i) \cdots p(\theta_{k-m+1} \mid C_i)} \qquad (6.136)$$

As the value of m tends to infinity, this probability converges to a constant value and serves as information on the stationary random process. However, we confine our attention to the acquisition of finite data, consisting of m data of which those acquired before $t = (k - m)T$ are disregarded. In other words, the a priori probability is corrected by the m latest sample data.

If the a priori probability $P_{k-m}(C_i)$ before the observed value $\theta_{k-m+1} = \theta[t = (k - m + 1)T]$ is obtained is uniform with respect to the value i for all values of k, that is,

$$P_{k-m}(C_i) = 1/N \qquad \text{for all } i \qquad (6.137)$$

then Eq. (6.136) becomes

$$P_k(C_i) = \frac{p(\theta_k \mid C_i)\, p(\theta_{k-1} \mid C_i) \cdots p(\theta_{k-m+1} \mid C_i)\, p(\theta_{k-m} \mid C_i)/p(\theta_{k-m} \mid C_i)}{\sum_{i=1}^{N} p(\theta_k \mid C_i)\, p(\theta_{k-1} \mid C_i) \cdots p(\theta_{k-m+1} \mid C_i)\, p(\theta_{k-m} \mid C_i)/p(\theta_{k-m} \mid C_i)}$$

$$= \frac{\dfrac{p(\theta_{k-1} \mid C_i) \cdots p(\theta_{k-m+1} \mid C_i)\, p(\theta_{k-m} \mid C_i)\, p(\theta_k \mid C_i)}{\sum_{i=1}^{N} p(\theta_{k-1} \mid C_i) \cdots p(\theta_{k-m+1} \mid C_i)\, p(\theta_{k-m} \mid C_i)\, p(\theta_{k-m} \mid C_i)}}{\dfrac{\sum_{i=1}^{N} p(\theta_{k-1} \mid C_i) \cdots p(\theta_{k-m+1} \mid C_i)\, p(\theta_{k-m} \mid C_i)/p(\theta_k \mid C_i)}{\sum_{i=1}^{N} p(\theta_{k-1} \mid C_i) \cdots p(\theta_{k-m+1} \mid C_i)\, p(\theta_{k-m} \mid C_i)\, p(\theta_{k-m} \mid C_i)}}$$

$$= \frac{P_{k-1}(C_i)\, p(\theta_k \mid C_i)/p(\theta_{k-m} \mid C_i)}{\sum_{i=1}^{N} P_{k-1}(C_i)\, p(\theta_k \mid C_i)/p(\theta_{k-m} \mid C_i)} \qquad (6.138)$$

In constructing the region C_i we express the upper and lower values of $\theta^*(t)$ by θ^*_{i-1} and θ^*_i, respectively, and the conditional probability density function $p(\theta_{k-m} \mid C_i)$ in Eq. (6.138) is then given by

$$p(\theta_{k-m} \mid C_i) = \frac{\displaystyle\int_{\theta_{i-1}}^{\theta^*_i} p(\theta^*)\, p(\theta_{k-m} \mid \theta^*)\, d\theta^*}{\displaystyle\int_{\theta^*_{i-1}}^{\theta^*_i} p(\theta^*)\, d\theta^*} \qquad (6.139)$$

Considering the statistical independence of $\theta^*(t)$ and $n(t)$, we have, for the conditional probability density function,

$$p(\theta_{k-m} \mid \theta^*) = p(\theta_{k-m} - \theta^*) = p(n) \qquad (6.140)$$

We assume here that the probability density function $p(\theta^*)$ of the true value is constant within a quantized region C_i,

$$p(\theta^*) = p_i \qquad \text{for} \quad \theta^*_{i-1} \le \theta^* < \theta^*_i; \qquad \text{i.e.,} \quad \theta^* \in C_i \quad (6.141)$$

or the probability may be expressed as

$$P(C_i) = \int_{\theta^*_{i-1}}^{\theta_i^*} p(\theta^*)\, d\theta^* = (\theta^*_i - \theta^*_{i-1}) p_i \qquad (6.142)$$

and that the additive random noise is gaussian, that is, that the probability density function $p(n)$ is given by

$$p(n) = \frac{1}{(2\pi)^{1/2} \sigma_n} \exp\left(-\frac{n^2}{2\sigma_n^2}\right) \qquad (6.143)$$

Then by applying Eq. (6.140) to Eq. (6.143), we approximate Eq. (6.139) as

$$p(\theta_{k-m} \mid \theta^*) = \frac{p_i}{(2\pi)^{1/2} \sigma_n (\theta^*_i - \theta^*_{i-1}) p_i} \int_{\theta^*_{i-1}}^{\theta_i^*} \exp\left(-\frac{(\theta_{k-m} - \theta^*)^2}{2\sigma_n^2}\right) d\theta^*$$

$$= \frac{1}{(2\pi)^{1/2} \sigma_n (\theta^*_i - \theta^*_{i-1})} \int_{\theta_{k-m}-\theta^*_{i-1}}^{\theta_{k-m}-\theta_i^*} \exp\left(-\frac{\xi^2}{2\sigma_n^2}\right) d\xi$$

$$(6.144)$$

where $\xi = \theta_{k-m} - \theta^*$. By using the datum θ_{k-m} acquired at each stage the calculation of the conditional probability density function $p(\theta_{k-m} \mid C_i)$ is performed with Eq. (6.144). By substituting this result for $p(\theta_{k-m} \mid C_i)$ in Eq. (6.138), the a priori probability $P_k(C_i)$ can be calculated. It is clear that the a priori probability chosen at the beginning of the process of computation may be far from accurate. However, we can repeatedly correct it by increasing the sample size of the data and using Bayes' formula.

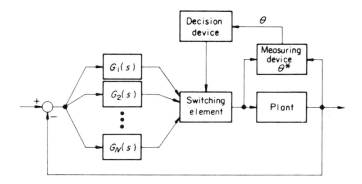

FIG. 6.18. Block diagram of decision adaptive control system.

An application to a control system is shown in Fig. 6.18, with the same situation as that in Chapter 5. Here the Bayes solution is given as follows. Let us denote the loss function associated with the choice of compensator $G_j(s)$, when actually $\theta^* \in C_i$, by $L(C_i, G_j) = L_{ij}$. The average risk may be expressed as

$$R(P_k, G_j) = \sum_{i=1}^{T} P_k(C_i) L(C_i, G_j) \qquad (6.145)$$

The Bayes solution is therefore given by the condition

$$\min_{j} [R(P_k, G_j)] \qquad (6.146)$$

In the approach described here, although we have no data at each stage, we can obtain the Bayes solution with the help of successive corrections of the a priori probability of the true value arbitrarily assumed in the beginning. This approach is, therefore, an application of the nondata problem[11] to decision adaptive control. A numerical example has been given by Takeda *et al.*[12]

[11] H. Chernoff and L. Moses, "Elementary Decision Theory." Wiley, New York, 1959.
[12] H. Takeda, K. Ono, and N. Honda, Application of decision theory to adaptive control system. *J. Soc. Instrument and Control Eng.* **3** (No. 8), 596 (1964); in Japanese.

CHAPTER 7

Sequential Decision Approaches in Adaptive Control Systems

7.1 Introductory Remarks

The adaptive control systems described in the previous chapter contain a decision device designed for nonsequential decision-making. The key notion of nonsequential decision is to fix the observation of data in a definite preassigned time interval. However, frequently the required observation time or sample size depends on an unknown parameter distribution and cannot, therefore, be fixed in advance. In such case at each stage the observer will base his decision, whether to continue the observations or not, on the situation presented by the data up to that point. If the sample size (number of observed data or observation time) is not, then, fixed in advance but permitted to depend on the processing, we have the possibility of more practical decision adaptive control systems with better performance. In this chapter, therefore, we establish the sequential decision rule in adaptive control systems. Although this will still involve testing the hypothesis $[H_i : \theta^*(t) \in C_i]$ against multiple alternatives, the decision-making will be carried out according to a sequential decision procedure.

7.2 An Average Risk of Sequential Decision Procedure

A sequential decision procedure may be described in terms of testing hypotheses as follows. On the basis of the observed vector $\boldsymbol{\theta}$ it must be decided whether a hypothesis $[H_i : \theta^*(t) \in C_i]$ may be accepted or not. If it may be accepted, the observation is terminated; if not, the observation is continued until some one hypothesis may be.

We shall consider here a case in which the decision-making is based on n sampled values $\theta_1, \theta_2, \ldots, \theta_{n-1}, \theta_n$. Now we use the symbol δ_j^t to express the terminal decision-making, which means the acceptance of the hypothesis $[H_j : \theta^*(t) \in C_j]$, and the symbol δ^e, which means the continuance of the observation. The vector function $p_d(\boldsymbol{\delta}^t \mid \boldsymbol{\theta}_n) = [p_d(\delta_1^t \mid \boldsymbol{\theta}_n),$ $p_d(\delta_2^t \mid \boldsymbol{\theta}_n), \ldots, p_d(\delta_{N-1}^t \mid \boldsymbol{\theta}_n), p_d(\delta_N^t \mid \boldsymbol{\theta}_n)]$ expresses the terminal decision rule, and $p_d(\delta_j^t \mid \boldsymbol{\theta}_n)\, d\boldsymbol{\theta}_n$ is the probability that the terminal decision δ_j^t will be made for the given observed vector $\boldsymbol{\theta}_n$. Furthermore, we introduce the loss function $L_{ij} = L(C_i, \delta_j^t)$ as the loss due to making a terminal decision δ_j^t when in reality $\theta^* \in C_i$. It is reasonable also to take into account the cost associated with the data acquisition. This cost may depend on the actual observation and on the observation time. Let us assume that the cost of observation depends only on the number of observed data and is proportional to it, with a proportionality constant c. We may, then, express the total loss as the sum of the loss function and the observation cost. This may be written

$$r(C_i, \delta_j^t) = L[C_i, \delta_j^t(\boldsymbol{\theta}_n)] + cn \tag{7.1}$$

where, as in Chapter 6, the symbol $\boldsymbol{\theta}_n$ is a vector expressing the observation process: $\boldsymbol{\theta}_n = (\theta_1, \theta_2, \ldots, \theta_n)$.

Let $p(\boldsymbol{\theta}_n \mid C_i)$ be the conditional probability density function of the observed vector $\boldsymbol{\theta}_n$ when $\theta^* \in C_i$ is the true state. The a priori probability density that the state $\theta^* \in C_i$ occurs is denoted by $p_i(\theta^*) = \xi_i s_i(\theta^*)$, and the average risk is denoted by

$$R(\mathbf{p}, p_d) = \sum_{i=1}^{N} \sum_{j=1}^{N} \sum_{k=1}^{\infty} \int_{\mathscr{D}_a^{k}} \int_{Ci} r[C_i, \delta_j^t(\boldsymbol{\theta}_k)] p_i(\theta^*)$$

$$\times\ p_d(\delta_j^t \mid \boldsymbol{\theta}_k) p(\boldsymbol{\theta}_k \mid C_i)\, d\boldsymbol{\theta}_k\, d\theta^* \tag{7.2}$$

where $\mathbf{p}$ is $[p_1(\theta^*), p_2(\theta^*), \ldots, p_i(\theta^*), \ldots, p_{N-1}(\theta^*), p_N(\theta^*)]$ and $\mathscr{D}_a^k$ signifies the integral over the k-dimensional observed signal space. As we have already considered in Chapter 6, if we let $p_i(\theta^*) = \xi_i \delta(\theta^* - \theta_i^*)$, then Eq. (7.2) becomes

$$R(\xi, p_d) = \sum_{i=1}^{N} \sum_{j=1}^{N} \sum_{k=1}^{\infty} \int_{\mathscr{D}_a^{k}} \xi_i r[C_i, \delta_j^t(\boldsymbol{\theta}_k)] p_d(\delta_j^t \mid \boldsymbol{\theta}_k) p(\boldsymbol{\theta}_k \mid C_i)\, d\boldsymbol{\theta}_k \tag{7.3}$$

The problem is then to select the decision rule so that the average risk $R(\xi, p_d)$ given by Eq. (7.3) is minimized.

7.3   Derivation of Bayes Solution

The a priori probability $\xi = (\xi_1, \xi_2, \ldots, \xi_N)$ may conveniently be represented by a point with coordinates $\xi_1, \xi_2, \ldots, \xi_{N-1}, \xi_N$ in N-dimensional space, in which each point satisfies the relation

$$\xi_i \geq 0$$

$$\sum_{i=1}^{N} \xi_i = 1 \tag{7.4}$$

We express the closed surface defined by Eq. (7.4) by the symbol $\mathscr{E}$.

Since the function $L(C_i, \delta_j^t)$ expresses the loss suffered from the terminal decision δ_j^t, then we shall state that this decision is a correct one if this function is equal to zero and an incorrect one if it is not. We can, therefore, express the loss as

$$L(C_i, \delta_j^t) = 0, \qquad i = j$$

$$> 0, \qquad i \neq j \tag{7.5}$$

For an arbitrary a priori probability ξ_i we consider the function

$$\eta_j(\xi) = \min_i [\eta_i(\xi)] \tag{7.6a}$$

where, by using the symbol $L_{mi} = L(C_m, \delta_i^t)$, we have

$$\eta_i(\xi) = \sum_{m=1}^{N} \xi_m L_{mi} \tag{7.6b}$$

As shown in Fig. 7.1, v_j are subsets of the set $\mathscr{E}$ and satisfy the following relations, where $j = 1, 2, \ldots, N - 1, N$:

For any p_d, $\quad \eta_j(\xi) \leq R(\xi, p_d)$.

Subsets v_j are closed and convex.

Subsets v_j are nonoverlapping.

Furthermore, by expressing

$$v = \sum_{j=1}^{N} v_j$$

$$v^c = \mathscr{E} - v$$

The Bayes solution relative to the a priori probability ξ can immediately be given as follows.

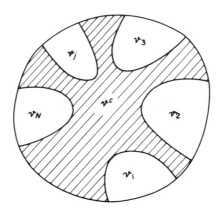

FIG. 7.1. The sets v_j and v^c.

THEOREM. Decision Rule 1: If $\xi \in v_j$, then do not make any more observations and make decision δ_j^t. Decision Rule 2: If $\xi \in v^c$, then make one more observation θ_{n+1} and compute the a posteriori probability ζ_{n+1} by using ξ and θ_{n+1}, where $n = 1, 2, \ldots, n, \ldots$, from Bayes' formula [Eq. (2.17)]. If $\zeta_{n+1} \in v_j$, then we terminate the observation and make a terminal decision δ_j^t but, if $\zeta_{n+1} \in v^c$, then we continue the observation.

We shall describe the case of $N = 2$.[1] In this case, as shown in Fig. 7.2, the situation may be represented by an (ξ_1, ξ_2) plane like the 2-dimensional plane of Fig. 7.1. It follows from Eq. (7.6a) that

$$\begin{aligned} \eta_1 < \eta_2 \quad &\text{for} \quad \xi \in v_1 \\ \eta_1 > \eta_2 \quad &\text{for} \quad \xi \in v_2 \end{aligned} \tag{7.7}$$

[1] A. Wald, "Statistical Decision Function," Chap. 4. Wiley, New York, 1950.

From Eq. (7.6b), this is expressed as

$$\xi_2 L_{21} < \xi_1 L_{12} \qquad \text{for} \quad \boldsymbol{\xi} \in v_1$$
$$\xi_2 L_{21} > \xi_1 L_{12} \qquad \text{for} \quad \boldsymbol{\xi} \in v_2 \tag{7.8}$$

If we express by the symbol (ξ_1', ξ_2') the a priori probability that will guarantee a condition of equality,

$$\xi_2' L_{21} = \xi_1' L_{12}$$

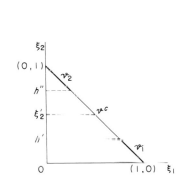

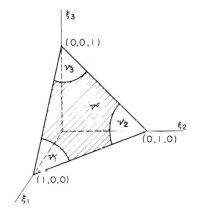

FIG. 7.2. The 2-dimensional sets v_1 and v_2.

FIG. 7.3. The 3-dimensional sets v_1, v_2, and v_3.

then Ineqs. (7.8) may be written

$$\xi_2 < \xi_2' \qquad \text{for} \quad \boldsymbol{\xi} \in v_1$$
$$\xi_2 > \xi_2' \qquad \text{for} \quad \boldsymbol{\xi} \in v_2 \tag{7.9}$$

Since both v_1 and v_2 are closed and convex, there exist two positive numbers such that

$$0 < h' < \xi_2' < h'' < 1 \tag{7.10}$$

Then the Bayes Decision Rule 2 is rewritten as follows:

$$\text{Make} \quad \delta_1^t, \quad \text{if} \quad \zeta_{n+1} < h'. \tag{7.11a}$$

$$\text{Make} \quad \delta_2^t, \quad \text{if} \quad \zeta_{n+1} > h''. \tag{7.11b}$$

$$\text{Make} \quad \delta^e, \quad \text{if} \quad h' < \zeta_{n+1} < h''. \tag{7.11c}$$

Where ζ_{n+1} represents the a posteriori probability after n observations have been made ($n = 1, 2, \ldots, \infty$). From Eq. (2.17), this is given by

$$\zeta_{n+1} = \frac{\xi_2 p(\boldsymbol{\theta}_n \mid C_2)}{(1 - \xi_2)\, p(\boldsymbol{\theta}_n \mid C_1) + \xi_2 p(\boldsymbol{\theta}_n \mid C_2)} \tag{7.12}$$

where the case of $n = 0$ corresponds to Decision Rule 1. By using this equation in the first of the decision rules (7.11a) and the relation $\xi_1 + \xi_2 = 1$ we get

$$\xi_2 p(\boldsymbol{\theta}_n \mid C_2) < h' \xi_1 p(\boldsymbol{\theta}_n \mid C_1) + h' \xi_2 p(\boldsymbol{\theta}_n \mid C_2) \tag{7.13}$$

If the following symbols are used,

$$\lambda_n(\boldsymbol{\theta}_n) = \frac{p(\boldsymbol{\theta}_n \mid C_2)}{p(\boldsymbol{\theta}_n \mid C_1)} \tag{7.14}$$

$$B = \frac{h'}{1 - h'} \cdot \frac{\xi_1}{\xi_2} \tag{7.15}$$

then the Bayes solution, Eq. (7.11a), is as follows:

$$\text{Make} \quad \delta_1^t, \quad \text{if} \quad \lambda_n(\boldsymbol{\theta}_n) < B. \tag{7.16}$$

Similar procedures give the following:

$$\text{Make} \quad \delta_2^t, \quad \text{if} \quad \lambda_n(\boldsymbol{\theta}_n) > A. \tag{7.17}$$

$$\text{Make} \quad \delta^e, \quad \text{if} \quad A > \lambda_n(\boldsymbol{\theta}_n) > B. \tag{7.18}$$

$$A = \frac{h''}{1 - h''} \cdot \frac{\xi_1}{\xi_2} \tag{7.19}$$

These results reveal that the Bayes solution is identical with the sequential probability ratio test in the case in which $N = 2$. When $N = 3$, the situation is that illustrated by Fig. 7.3.

7.4   Application of Sequential Decision-Making to Adaptive Control Systems

Since directly applying the decision rules described above to an adaptive control system is impracticable except in the case of $N = 2$, we shall now introduce the modified concept of testing binary hypotheses.

As in Chapter 6, the variational range of a parameter is divided into N regions, which are labeled C_i $(i = 1, 2, \ldots, N)$. Furthermore, we denote the boundaries of the regions by θ_i^* $(i = 1, 2, \ldots, N - 1)$, as shown in Fig. 7.4, and we state:

$$\theta^*(t) \in C_j, \qquad \text{if} \quad \theta^*(t) > \theta_{j-1}^* \quad \text{and} \quad \theta^*(t) < \theta_j^*$$

$$\theta^*(t) \subset C_1, \qquad \text{if} \quad \theta^*(t) < \theta_1^* \tag{7.20}$$

$$\theta^*(t) \in C_N, \qquad \text{if} \quad \theta^*(t) > \theta_{N-1}^*$$

Here j, of course, is a position among $2, \ldots, N - 1$. We consider the jth boundary expressed by θ_j^*. The present problem is to test the hypothesis $[II_j : \theta^*(t) < \theta_j^*]$ against the alternative hypothesis $[\bar{H}_j : \theta^*(t) > \theta_j^*]$. To carry out the sequential test procedure, we define the desired acceptance region R_a and the rejection region R_r in the true signal space $\mathcal{D}_s$. Therefore, the region $\mathcal{D}_s - R_a - R_r$ is called the indifference zone*; see Fig. 7.5.

FIG. 7.4. Regions C_i and their boundaries θ_i^*.

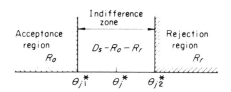

FIG. 7.5. Indifference zone.

* Often this is also called the test interval, because the test goes on as long as $\Lambda_j(\boldsymbol{\theta}_n)$, shown by Eq. (7.21), lies in this interval.

According to the sequential probability ratio test described in Sect. 7.3, the decision rule at each stage corresponding to $n = 1, 2, \ldots$ can be given by the following logarithmic forms in the rules (7.16), (7.17), and (7.18):

$$\text{Reject the hypothesis } H_j, \quad \text{if} \quad \Lambda_j(\boldsymbol{\theta}_n) > \log A_j.$$

$$\text{Accept the hypothesis } H_j, \quad \text{if} \quad \Lambda_j(\boldsymbol{\theta}_n) < \log B_j. \qquad (7.21)$$

$$\text{Repeat the test,} \quad \text{if} \quad \log A_j > \Lambda_j(\boldsymbol{\theta}_n) > \log B_j.$$

From Fig. 7.5, recognizing that C_1 and C_2 of the previous section correspond respectively to θ_{j1}^* and θ_{j2}^*, we have

$$\Lambda_j(\boldsymbol{\theta}_n) = \log \lambda_j(\boldsymbol{\theta}_n) = \log \frac{p(\boldsymbol{\theta}_n \mid \theta_{j2}^*)}{p(\boldsymbol{\theta}_n \mid \theta_{j1}^*)} \qquad (7.22)$$

In these decision rules both B_j and A_j can be obtained in slightly modified forms of Eqs. (7.15) and (7.19), and they will be given in explicit forms in Sect. 7.5.

If the probability density function of the additive noise $n(t)$ is assumed gaussian, the conditional probability density functions $p(\boldsymbol{\theta}_n \mid \theta_{j1}^*)$ and $p(\boldsymbol{\theta}_n \mid \theta_{j2}^*)$ may be expressed as

$$p(\boldsymbol{\theta}_n \mid \theta_{jk}^*) = (2\pi)^{-n/2} |\mathbf{M}|^{-\frac{1}{2}} \exp[-\tfrac{1}{2}(\boldsymbol{\theta}_n - \theta_{jk}^*)'\mathbf{M}^{-1}(\boldsymbol{\theta}_n - \theta_{jk}^*)] \qquad (7.23)$$

where k is 1 or 2. Considering an analytical situation in which the additive noise may be assumed to be band-limited white noise, we shall obtain a concrete form of the decision rules given by Eq. (7.21). In Chapter 6 the autocorrelation function of band-limited white noise, Eq. (6.71), was expressed by Eq. (6.73). If the data are sampled at a time interval $\Delta t = 1/2 f_0$, the covariance matrix becomes, by means of the sampling theorem, the matrix given by Eq. (6.50b). Usings Eqs. (7.23) and (6.50b), by a similar procedure to the derivation of Eq. (6.57) the Rule (7.21) may be rewritten:

$$\text{Reject the hypothesis } H_j, \quad \text{if} \quad \sum_{i=1}^{n} \theta_i > a_j(n).$$

$$\text{Accept the hypothesis } H_j, \quad \text{if} \quad \sum_{i=1}^{n} \theta_i < b_j(n). \qquad (7.24)$$

$$\text{Repeat the test,} \quad \text{if} \quad a_j(n) > \sum_{i=1}^{n} \theta_i > b_j(n).$$

Here

$$a_j(n) = \frac{\psi_n}{\theta_{j2}^* - \theta_{j1}^*} \log A_j + \frac{\theta_{j1}^* + \theta_{j2}^*}{2} n \qquad (7.25)$$

$$b_j(n) = \frac{\psi_n}{\theta_{j2}^* - \theta_{j1}^*} \log B_j + \frac{\theta_{j1}^* + \theta_{j2}^*}{2} n \qquad (7.26)$$

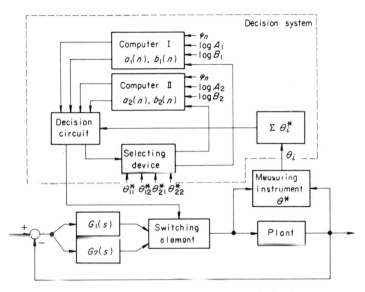

FIG. 7.6. Construction of decision computer for sequential adaptive control system.

Consequently, for the hypothesis $[H_j : \theta^* \in C_j]$, where $j = 1, 2, \ldots, N$, the corresponding decision at each stage can be summarized as

$$\text{Make decision } \delta_j^t, \quad \text{if} \quad b_j(n) > \sum_{i=1}^{n} \theta_i > a_{j-1}(n). \qquad (7.27)$$

Make decision δ^e otherwise.

in which we define that $a_0 = -\infty$ and $b_N = \infty$, using the boundaries described by Eq. (7.20). A detailed scheme of the decision computer for a sequential adaptive control system is given by Hsu and Meserve[2]; see Fig. 7.6.[2]

[2] J. C. Hsu and W. E. Meserve, Decision-making in adaptive control systems. *IRE Trans. PGAC* **7** (No. 1), 24 (1962).

Applying the relation $\psi_n = 2N_0 f_0 = N_0/\Delta t$ given by Eq. (6.75) to ψ_n in Eqs. (7.25) and (7.26), and taking the limit as $\Delta t \to 0$, the decision rule (7.27) may be rewritten:

$$\text{Make } \delta_j^t, \quad \text{if} \quad b_j(t) > \int_0^t \theta(t)\, dt > a_{j-1}(t).$$

$$\text{Make } \delta^e \quad \text{otherwise.} \tag{7.28}$$

Here

$$a_j(t) = k_j t + k_{Aj} \tag{7.29}$$

$$b_j(t) = k_j t + k_{Bj} \tag{7.30}$$

and*

$$k_j = \frac{\theta_{j1}^* + \theta_{j2}^*}{2} \tag{7.31}$$

$$k_{Aj} = \frac{N_0}{\theta_{j2}^* - \theta_{j1}^*} \log A_j \tag{7.32}$$

$$k_{Bj} = \frac{N_0}{\theta_{j2}^* - \theta_{j1}^*} \log B_j \tag{7.33}$$

Consequently, the decision system consists of an integrator and a logic circuit, as shown in Fig. 7.7; it is schematically illustrated in Fig. 7.8 for the case of $N = 3$. As soon as the integrated value $\int_0^t \theta(t)\, dt$ enters

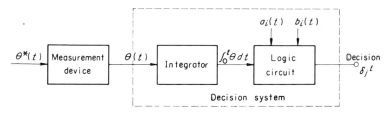

FIG. 7.7. Sequential decision system for continuous sampling.

* The symbol k_j represents the mean value of θ_{j1}^* and θ_{j2}^*, so that $k_j = \bar{\theta}_j^*$. In particular, it must be noted that we have $k_j = \bar{\theta}_j^*$ for the symmetrix indifference zone.

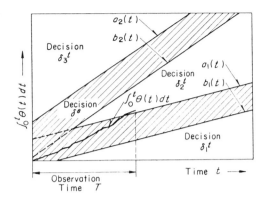

Fig. 7.8. Rule (7.28).

the unshaded area, the observation is terminated and the appropriate decision made, the integrating time T not being specified in advance. Thus, the observation time T (or sample size n) becomes a random variable that depends on the true value of θ^*. This fact will be discussed in the next section.

7.5 Operating Characteristic Function (OC Function) and Average Sample Number Function (ASN Function)

In this section we describe some statistical preliminaries required for discussing the sequential decision scheme. As previously shown in this chapter, an observation is continued until a terminating decision is made, which decision is equivalent to testing the hypothesis $[H_1 : \theta^* \in C_1]$ against the alternative hypothesis $[H_2 : \theta^* \in C_2]$, and the number of observed data required for the decision is a random variable.

These two primary characteristics are applicable to the case of independently observed data. Bearing them in mind will help to simplify the discussion that follows.

7.5-1 Determination of the constants A and B. Our first step now is to determine the constants A and B of the previous section. To do so we introduce a new quantity. Since the observation time is a random variable, we may consider a probability that a decision will be made. In other words, in the binary test the conditional probability of accepting the hypothesis H_1 when θ_1^* is the true value can be introduced. We express this conditional probability by $L(\theta_1^*)$. It is called an operating characteristic function (OC function). In the case in which the true signal $\theta^*(t)$ takes two values, θ_1^* when $\theta^*(t) \in C_1$ and θ_2^* when $\theta^*(t) \in C_2$, the operating characteristic function is defined by

$$L(\theta_i^*) = \sum_{n=1}^{\infty} \int_{u_n} p(\boldsymbol{\theta}_n \mid \theta_i^*) \, d\boldsymbol{\theta}_n \qquad (7.34)$$

where i is equal to 1 or 2 and u_n means that the integral is taken over the space occupied by the set of vectors $\boldsymbol{\theta}_n$. Referring to the Bayes solution, from Eqs. (7.16) and (7.18), we consider a case in which u_n satisfies the inequalities

$$B < \frac{p(\boldsymbol{\theta}_k \mid \theta_2^*)}{p(\boldsymbol{\theta}_k \mid \theta_1^*)} < A, \qquad \text{if} \quad k = 1, 2, \ldots, n-1 \qquad (7.35)$$

$$\frac{p(\boldsymbol{\theta}_k \mid \theta_2^*)}{p(\boldsymbol{\theta}_k \mid \theta_1^*)} \leq B, \qquad \text{if} \quad k = n \qquad (7.36)$$

Since the OC function expresses the conditional probability depending on the respective values θ_1^* and θ_2^* of the true signal $\theta^*(t)$, then, by introducing the error probabilities of the first and second types, ϵ_1 and ϵ_2, and combining them with the OC function we determine the constant B in Ineq. (7.36) such that

$$\begin{aligned} L(\theta_1^*) &= 1 - \epsilon_1 \\ L(\theta_2^*) &= \epsilon_2 \end{aligned} \qquad (7.37)$$

For this purpose Ineq. (7.36) is rewritten

$$p(\boldsymbol{\theta}_n \mid \theta_2^*) \leq B \, p(\boldsymbol{\theta}_n \mid \theta_1^*) \qquad (7.38)$$

By integrating both sides of this inequality over u_n and summing the result from $n = 1$ to $n = \infty$ we have, with the help of Eq. (7.34),

$$L(\theta_2^*) \leq B \, L(\theta_1^*) \qquad (7.39)$$

Then substituting Eqs. (7.37) into this relation gives us

$$B \geq \frac{\epsilon_2}{1 - \epsilon_1} \qquad (7.40a)$$

The constant A, similarly determined, is

$$A \leq \frac{1 - \epsilon_2}{\epsilon_1} \qquad (7.40b)$$

Thus the constants A and B are given by the inequalities that depend on the values of the error probabilities ϵ_1 and ϵ_2. The values of probabilities ϵ_1 and ϵ_2 for which equality holds in Eqs. (7.40) are denoted by ϵ_1' and ϵ_2' :

$$\frac{\epsilon_2'}{1 - \epsilon_1'} < \frac{\epsilon_2}{1 - \epsilon_1} \qquad (7.41a)$$

$$\frac{1 - \epsilon_2'}{\epsilon_1'} > \frac{1 - \epsilon_2}{\epsilon_1} \qquad (7.41b)$$

From these inequalities it follows, since $0 < \epsilon_1' < 1$ and $0 < \epsilon_2' < 1$, that

$$\epsilon_2' < \frac{\epsilon_2'}{1 - \epsilon_1'} < \frac{\epsilon_2}{1 - \epsilon_1} \qquad (7.42a)$$

$$\epsilon_1' < \frac{\epsilon_1'}{1 - \epsilon_2'} < \frac{\epsilon_1}{1 - \epsilon_2} \qquad (7.42b)$$

These relations give the upper bounds of the values ϵ_1' and ϵ_2'. Since in practice the values of ϵ_1 and ϵ_2 will be rather small positive numbers, often 0.05 or less, the following approximations are made:

$$\frac{\epsilon_1}{1 - \epsilon_2} \simeq \epsilon_1 \qquad (7.43a)$$

$$\frac{\epsilon_2}{1 - \epsilon_1} \simeq \epsilon_2 \qquad (7.43b)$$

On the other hand, since the following relations are easily obtained from inequalities (7.41)

$$\epsilon_2(1 - \epsilon_1') > \epsilon_2'(1 - \epsilon_1) \tag{7.44a}$$

$$\epsilon_1(1 - \epsilon_2') > \epsilon_1'(1 - \epsilon_2) \tag{7.44b}$$

it is easily verified that

$$\epsilon_1' + \epsilon_2' < \epsilon_1 + \epsilon_2 \tag{7.45}$$

This guarantees that the sum $\epsilon_1' + \epsilon_2'$ will never exceed the sum $\epsilon_1 + \epsilon_2$. The relation also may be derived from Eqs. (7.43) and (7.42). The result reveals that it is justifiable in practical applications to adopt the following as the respective values of A and B:

$$A = \frac{1 - \epsilon_2}{\epsilon_1} \tag{7.46}$$

$$B = \frac{\epsilon_2}{1 - \epsilon_1} \tag{7.47}$$

It should be noted that these two equations are precise in the case of continuous sampling, because the computation of $p(\boldsymbol{\theta}_k \mid \theta_2^*)/p(\boldsymbol{\theta}_k \mid \theta_1^*)$ can be carried out in a continuous form, and the equality conditions hold, rather than Ineqs. (7.35) and (7.36). It is not very difficult to show that the test always terminates with probability 1 for some definite number n.[3] This fact may also be true when the correlation between successively acquired data must be taken into account.

7.5-2   Operational characteristic function.

In the last section we determined the two constants A and B by considering the probability of accepting hypothesis H_1 when θ_1^* is true and preassigning this new quantity as given in Eqs. (7.37). Thus the OC function plays an important role in the determination of the two constants A and B, which are the decision thresholds. However, the OC function as given by Eqs. (7.37) is defined with respect to only two values, θ_1^* and θ_2^*, of the true signal $\theta^*(t)$; in other words, it is not given as a function of $\theta^*(t)$. In practice we are

---

[3] A. Wald, "Statistical Decision Function." Wiley, New York, 1950. It is not difficult to prove this theorem. See also Chapter 6, Sect. 4.

seldom presented with such a simple problem as that of testing $[H_1 : \theta^* \in C_1]$ against one alternative, $[H_2 : \theta^* \in C_2]$; usually $[H_1 : \theta^* \in C_1]$ must be tested against multiple alternatives, $[H_2 : \theta^* \in C_2]$, $[H_3 : \theta^* \in C_3]$, etc. Consequently, many forms of the OC functions of Eqs. (7.37) are required, and it must be known in its general form, $L(\theta^*)$ with respect to θ^*, rather than in its particular forms $L(\theta_1^*)$, $L(\theta_2^*)$, etc. We shall establish the OC function $L(\theta^*)$ by testing $[H_1 : \theta^* \in C_1]$ against the alternative, $[H_2 : \theta^* \in C_2]$. To this end we pose a new question: What is the probability of accepting hypothesis H_1 when $\theta^*(t)$ is the true signal? Now, the OC function $L(\theta^*)$ gives the conditional probability of accepting H_1 when $\theta^*(t)$ is the true signal. To answer our question we introduce the function

$$\bar{p}(\theta \mid \theta^*) = \left(\frac{p(\theta \mid \theta_2^*)}{p(\theta \mid \theta_1^*)}\right)^{h(\theta^*)} p(\theta \mid \theta^*) \qquad (7.48)$$

where $p(\theta \mid \theta^*)$ is the probability density function of the observed value θ when the true value of the signal $\theta^*(t)$ is θ^*. The function $h(\theta^*)$ in Eq. (7.48) is determined by the normalizing condition

$$\int_{-\infty}^{\infty} \left(\frac{p(\theta \mid \theta_2^*)}{p(\theta \mid \theta_1^*)}\right)^{h(\theta^*)} p(\theta \mid \theta^*) \, d\theta = 1 \qquad (7.49)$$

Furthermore, in general it can be shown that there is just one nonzero solution $h(\theta^*)$ satisfying it. Two possibilities, of course, exist: $h(\theta^*) > 0$ or $h(\theta^*) < 0$. Let us consider $h(\theta^*) > 0$. We consider a sequential test of hypothesis $[H : p(\theta \mid \theta^*)]$, which is that the conditional probability density function $p(\theta \mid \theta^*)$ is true, against the hypothesis $[\bar{H} : \bar{p}(\theta \mid \theta^*)]$, which is that the conditional probability density function $\bar{p}(\theta \mid \theta^*)$ is true. Since this serves the situation of a binary test, then, if we express the two constants as A^h and B^h, Rules (7.16), (7.17), and (7.18) may be written:

If $\qquad \dfrac{\bar{p}(\boldsymbol{\theta}_n \mid \theta^*)}{p(\boldsymbol{\theta}_n \mid \theta^*)} < B^h, \qquad$ accept H.

If $\qquad \dfrac{\bar{p}(\boldsymbol{\theta}_n \mid \theta^*)}{p(\boldsymbol{\theta}_n \mid \theta^*)} > A^h, \qquad$ reject H (accept $\bar{H}$). $\qquad (7.50)$

If $\quad A^h > \dfrac{\bar{p}(\boldsymbol{\theta}_n \mid \theta^*)}{p(\boldsymbol{\theta}_n \mid \theta^*)} > B^h, \qquad$ continue the observation.

Since from Eq. (7.48) we have

$$\frac{\bar{p}(\boldsymbol{\theta}_n \mid \theta^*)}{p(\boldsymbol{\theta}_n \mid \theta^*)} = \left(\frac{p(\boldsymbol{\theta}_n \mid \theta_2^*)}{p(\boldsymbol{\theta}_n \mid \theta_1^*)}\right)^{h(\theta^*)} \tag{7.51}$$

then it is easily seen that these rules are directly equivalent to Rules (7.16), (7.17), and (7.18). Let us denote the probability of rejecting H when H is true by $\bar{\epsilon}_1$ and the probability of accepting H when $\bar{H}$ is true by $\bar{\epsilon}_2$. Recalling the Ineq. (7.40) it follows from the decision rule that

$$B^h \geq \frac{\bar{\epsilon}_2}{1 - \bar{\epsilon}_1} \tag{7.52}$$

$$A^h \leq \frac{1 - \bar{\epsilon}_2}{\bar{\epsilon}_1} \tag{7.53}$$

By a process similar to the derivation of Eqs. (7.46) and (7.47) the equality signs in these equations approximately hold; that is,

$$B^h = \frac{\bar{\epsilon}_2}{1 - \bar{\epsilon}_1} \tag{7.54}$$

$$A^h = \frac{1 - \bar{\epsilon}_2}{\bar{\epsilon}_1} \tag{7.55}$$

Solving these equations simultaneously, we obtain

$$\bar{\epsilon}_1 = \frac{1 - B^h}{A^h - B^h} \tag{7.56}$$

Since from Eq. (7.37) we have

$$\bar{\epsilon}_1 = 1 - L(\theta^*) \tag{7.57}$$

the OC function can be obtained in the form

$$L(\theta^*) = \frac{A^h - 1}{A^h - B^h} \tag{7.58}$$

where both A and B are as given in Eqs. (7.46) and (7.47). At the point

θ_0^* satisfying the relation $h(\theta^*)\big|_{\text{at }\theta^*=\theta_0^*} = 0$ the OC function as now given is indeterminate and must be rewritten as

$$L(\theta_0^*) = \lim_{\theta^* \to \theta_0^*} \frac{A^h - 1}{A^h - B^h}$$

$$= \lim_{\theta^* \to \theta_0^*} \frac{A^h \log A}{A^h \log A - B^h \log B}$$

$$= \frac{\log A}{\log A - \log B} \tag{7.59}$$

The function $L(\theta^*)$ gives the confidence with which hypothesis H may be accepted as a function of the parameter θ^*. The case where $h(\theta^*) < 0$ can be treated similarly, and the same result [Eq. (7.58)] is obtained. The practical procedure for deriving the OC function is as follows: if the conditional probability density function is given, for example, as the gaussian probability density function, then $h(\theta^*)$ can be obtained by solving Eq. (7.49). On substitution of this into Eq. (7.58), the OC function is determined.

7.5-3   Average sample number function.
The sample size is not fixed before starting an observation; hence, as we have already pointed out, the sample number required before a terminal decision is made becomes a random variable. We are particularly interested in the average value of this random variable. When θ^* is the true value, the average number of samples required for the termination of a sequential test may be expressed by the Average Sample Number function (ASN function). The principal object of a sequential test is to make the ASN function small. Now we shall derive an approximate expression of this function. By considering a constant integer N which is sufficiently large so that the decision always terminates within $N > n$ sample size, where n is the number of data required by the sequential test, we can write

$$\sum_{i=1}^{N} z_i = \sum_{i=1}^{n} z_i + \sum_{i=n+1}^{N} z_i \tag{7.60}$$

where

$$z_i = \log \frac{p(\theta_i \mid \theta_2^*)}{p(\theta_i \mid \theta_1^*)} \tag{7.61}$$

Let us denote by $E_{\theta^*}[z]$ the conditional expectation that θ^* is the true value. Taking the average values of Eq. (7.60), we obtain

$$N E_{\theta^*}[z] = E_{\theta^*}\left[\sum_{i=1}^{n} z_i\right] + E_{\theta^*}\left[\sum_{i=n+1}^{N} z_i\right] \tag{7.62}$$

where

$$z = \log \frac{p(\theta \mid \theta_2^*)}{p(\theta \mid \theta_1^*)} \tag{7.63}$$

Since the values z_i for $i > n$ are distributed independently of n, Eq. (7.62) can be written

$$N E_{\theta^*}[z] = E_{\theta^*}\left[\sum_{i=1}^{n} z_i\right] + E_{\theta^*}[(N - n)E_{\theta^*}[z]]$$

$$= E_{\theta^*}\left[\sum_{i=1}^{n} z_i\right] + N E_{\theta^*}[z] - E_{\theta^*}[n]\, E_{\theta^*}[z] \tag{7.64}$$

Therefore, we have

$$E_{\theta^*}[n] = \frac{E_{\theta^*}\left[\sum_{i=1}^{n} z_i\right]}{E_{\theta^*}[z]} \tag{7.65}$$

provided that the denominator in Eq. (7.65) is not equal to zero. According to Rule (7.21) and with A and B as given by Eqs. (7.46) and (7.47), if we assume that the probability ratio $p(\mathbf{\theta}_n \mid \theta_2^*)/p(\mathbf{\theta}_n \mid \theta_1^*)$ is always equal to the values A and B of the thresholds at the test termination, it can be stated that the random variable $\sum_{i=1}^{n} z_i$ takes only the values of $\log A$ and $\log B$ with probabilities $1 - L(\theta^*)$ and $L(\theta^*)$, respectively. The numerator of Eq. (7.65) can, therefore, be approximately taken as

$$E_{\theta^*}\left[\sum_{i=1}^{n} z_i\right] = L(\theta^*) \log B + [1 - L(\theta^*)] \log A \tag{7.66a}$$

and the mathematical expression of the ASN function is given, to a good approximation, in the form

$$E_{\theta^*}[n] = \frac{L(\theta^*) \log B + [1 - L(\theta^*)] \log A}{E_{\theta^*}[z]} \tag{7.66b}$$

From this equation and Eq. (7.37) we obtain the relations

$$E_{\theta^*}[n] = \frac{(1 - \epsilon_1) \log B + \epsilon_1 \log A}{E_{\theta^*}[z]}, \qquad \text{at} \quad \theta^* = \theta_1^* \qquad (7.67a)$$

$$= \frac{\epsilon_2 \log B + (1 - \epsilon_2) \log A}{E_{\theta^*}[z]}, \qquad \text{at} \quad \theta^* = \theta_2^* \qquad (7.67b)$$

As shown in Eq. (7.67b) the ASN function can be obtained only if the value of $E_{\theta^*}[z]$ is given. This value is derived by means of the conditional probability density function $p(\theta \mid \theta_i^*)$, where i is 1 or 2. For example, if we consider the additive gaussian random noise and since, in general, we have

$$p(\theta \mid \theta_i^*) = \frac{1}{(2\pi\psi_n)^{1/2}} \exp\left[-\frac{(\theta - \theta_i^*)^2}{2\psi_n}\right] \qquad (7.68a)$$

then it follows from Eq. (7.63) that

$$z = \frac{1}{2\psi_n} [2(\theta_2^* - \theta_1^*)\theta + \theta_1^{*2} - \theta_2^{*2}] \qquad (7.68b)$$

Therefore, we have

$$E_{\theta^*}[z] = \frac{1}{2\psi_n} [2(\theta_2^* - \theta_1^*)\theta^* + \theta_1^{*2} - \theta_2^{*2}] \qquad (7.68c)$$

To derive the ASN function at the indeterminate point θ_0^* we shall now consider the value θ^* in the neighborhood of θ_0^*. Since $h(\theta^*)$ is very small in the neighborhood of θ_0^*, then, by referring to Eq. (7.63) and the relation

$$e^{zh} = \left(\frac{p(\theta \mid \theta_2^*)}{p(\theta \mid \theta_1^*)}\right)^h$$

we shall use the following expansion:

$$E_{\theta^*}[e^{zh}] = 1 + h\, E_{\theta^*}[z] + \tfrac{1}{2}h^2 E_{\theta^*}[z^2] + \cdots \qquad (7.69)$$

Applying Eq. (7.49) gives

$$E_{\theta^*}[z] = -\tfrac{1}{2}h\, E_{\theta^*}[z^2] \qquad (7.70)$$

Substituting this into Eq. (7.65), we have

$$E_{\theta^*}[n] = -\frac{2E_{\theta^*}[\sum_{i=1}^{n} z_i]}{h \, E_{\theta^*}[z^2]} \tag{7.71}$$

To derive $E_{\theta^*}[\sum_{i=1}^{n} z_i]$ in the neighborhood of θ_0^* we consider the identity

$$E\left[\exp\left\{t \sum_{i=1}^{n} z_i + t\left(\sum_{i=1}^{N} z_i - \sum_{i=1}^{n} z_i\right)\right\}\right] = E\left[\exp\left(t \sum_{i=1}^{N} z_i\right)\right]$$

$$= \phi^N(t) \tag{7.72}$$

The expression $\sum_{i=1}^{N} z_i - \sum_{i=1}^{n} z_i$ is independent of $\sum_{i=1}^{n} z_i$; therefore,

$$E\left[\exp\left\{t \sum_{i=1}^{n} z_i + t\left(\sum_{i=1}^{N} z_i - \sum_{i=1}^{n} z_i\right)\right\}\right] = E\left[\exp\left(t \sum_{i=1}^{n} z_i\right)\phi^{N-n}(t)\right] \tag{7.73}$$

Substituting this into Eq. (7.72), we have

$$E\left[\exp\left(t \sum_{i=1}^{n} z_i\right)\phi^{N-n}(t)\right] = \phi^N(t) \tag{7.74}$$

Divided by $\phi^N(t)$, this becomes

$$E\left[\exp\left(t \sum_{i=1}^{n} z_i\right)\phi^{-n}(t)\right] = 1 \tag{7.75}$$

Now, noting the definition $\phi(t) = E[\exp(tz)]$ given by Eq. (7.72) and substituting $h(\theta^*)$ for t in Eq. (7.75), we obtain the following identity with the help of Eq. (7.49):

$$E_{\theta^*}\left[\exp\left\{h(\theta^*) \sum_{i=1}^{n} z_i\right\}\right] = 1 \tag{7.76}$$

We can expand the left side of this equation into a Taylor series:

$$E_{\theta^*}\left[\exp\left\{h(\theta^*) \sum_{i=1}^{n} z_i\right\}\right] = 1 + h \, E_{\theta^*}\left[\sum_{i=1}^{n} z_i\right] + \tfrac{1}{2}h^2 E_{\theta^*}\left[\left(\sum_{i=1}^{n} z_i\right)^2\right] + \cdots \tag{7.77}$$

From this, with the use of Eq. (7.76), we obtain

$$E_{\theta^*}\left[\sum_{i=1}^{n} z_i\right] = -\tfrac{1}{2}h \, E_{\theta^*}\left[\left(\sum_{i=1}^{n} z_i\right)^2\right] \tag{7.78}$$

Substituting this into Eq. (7.71) gives the ASN function expressed as

$$E_{\theta_0^*}[n] = \frac{E_{\theta_0^*}[(\sum_{i=1}^{n} z_i)^2]}{E_{\theta_0^*}[z^2]} \tag{7.79}$$

By a derivation similar to that of Eq. (7.66a) the following relation may be obtained from Eq. (7.79):

$$E_{\theta_0^*}[n] = \frac{L(\theta_0^*)(\log B)^2 + [1 - L(\theta_0^*)](\log A)^2}{E_{\theta_0^*}[z^2]} \tag{7.80}$$

Substituting Eq. (7.59) into this gives an approximate expression of the ASN function at $\theta^* = \theta_0^*$:

$$E_{\theta_0^*}[n] = -\frac{\log A \log B}{E_{\theta_0^*}[z^2]} \tag{7.81}$$

It should be noted that this equation takes the maximal value of the ASN function. The ASN function will play a very important role in the discussion of the sequential decision rule.

7.6 Average Amount of Observation Time

We return to Rule (7.24) or (7.28) and consider the case of discrete sampling. From Eq. (7.66b) the average number of samples required for a sequential procedure is given by the ASN function, which is expressed as

$$E_{\theta^*}[n]_j = \frac{L(\theta^*) \log B_j + [1 - L(\theta^*)] \log A_j}{\int_{-\infty}^{\infty} \log \frac{p(\theta \mid \theta_{j2}^*)}{p(\theta \mid \theta_{j1}^*)} p(\theta \mid \theta^*) \, d\theta} \tag{7.82}$$

where the relation derived by Eq. (7.61)

$$E_{\theta^*}[z] = \int_{-\infty}^{\infty} \log \frac{p(\theta \mid \theta_{j2}^*)}{p(\theta \mid \theta_{j1}^*)} p(\theta \mid \theta^*) \, d\theta$$

has been used. For the gaussian disturbance, Eq. (7.68c), this becomes

$$E_{\theta*}[n]_j = \frac{2\psi_n\{L(\theta^*)\log B_j + [1 - L(\theta^*)]\log A_j\}}{2\theta^*(\theta^*_{j2} - \theta^*_{j1}) + \theta^{*2}_{j1} - \theta^{*2}_{j2}} \qquad (7.83)$$

By means of the relation $\psi_n = N_0/\Delta t$ given in Eq. (6.75) the average amount of observation time required before terminating the sequential test is given by

$$\bar{T}_j(\theta^*) = E_{\theta*}[n]_j\,\Delta t$$
$$= \frac{2\{[1 - L(\theta^*)]\log A_j + L(\theta^*)\log B_j\}}{(\theta^*_{j2} - \theta^*_{j1})[2\theta^* - (\theta^*_{j1} + \theta^*_{j2})]}\,N_0 \qquad (7.84a)$$

Referring to Eqs. (7.46) and (7.47), we define the two constant A_j and B_j in Rule (7.21) as

$$A_j = \frac{1 - \epsilon_{2j}}{\epsilon_{1j}} \qquad (7.84b)$$

$$B_j = \frac{\epsilon_{2j}}{1 - \epsilon_{1j}} \qquad (7.84c)$$

For the case of $\epsilon_{1j} = \epsilon_{2j}$ Eq. (7.84a) may be expressed as

$$\frac{\bar{T}_j(\theta^*)}{2N_0} = \frac{[1 - 2L(\theta^*)]\log A_j}{(\theta^*_{j2} - \theta^*_{j1})(2\theta^* - \theta^*_{j1} - \theta^*_{j2})} \qquad (7.85)$$

7.7 Numerical Example

In Fig. 7.9 the true signal $\theta^*(t)$ to be estimated is divided into the three regions

$$C_1 = (0, 0.5), \qquad C_2 = (0.5, 1.0), \qquad \text{and} \quad C_3 = (1.0, \infty)$$

For a numerical example let

$$\epsilon = \epsilon_{1j} = \epsilon_{2j} = 0.05, \qquad j = 1, 2$$
$$N_0 = 0.25$$
$$\theta^*_{11} = 0.45, \qquad \theta^*_{21} = 0.95$$
$$\theta^*_{12} = 0.55, \qquad \theta^*_{22} = 1.05$$

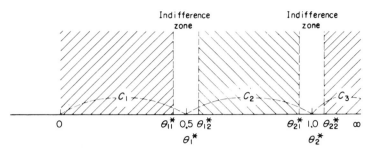

FIG. 7.9. Numerical example of application of sequential decision rule. Divided regions of the true signal $\theta^*(t)$ to be estimated.

Then by means of Eqs. (7.84b) and (7.84c) we express Eqs. (7.29) and (7.30), respectively, as

$$a_1(t) = 0.5t + 7.36, \qquad b_1(t) = 0.5t - 7.36 \qquad (7.86)$$

$$a_2(t) = t + 7.36, \qquad b_2(t) = t - 7.36 \qquad (7.87)$$

The condition for the decision-making is schematically illustrated in Fig. 7.10. When the output of an integrator approaches the appropriate

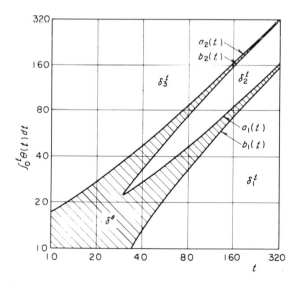

FIG. 7.10. The region of decision-making and the thresholds.

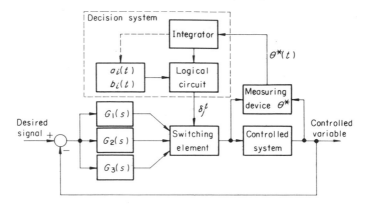

FIG. 7.11. Configuration of an adaptive control system containing the sequential decision device.

region, the corresponding decision δ_j^t will be made. The whole construction of the system containing a decision device in the adaptive loop is shown in Fig. 7.11.

7.8   Comparison of Sequential and Nonsequential Decision Procedures

A satisfactory comparison of the sequential test (undetermined sample size) with the nonsequential test (fixed sample size) requires that we know at least the average amount of observation time.* To compare numerically the two decision procedures we shall consider a practical situation, in which the true signal $\theta^*(t)$ to be specified is divided into the regions

$$C_1 = (0, 0.4) \quad \text{and} \quad C_2 = (0.4, 0.8)$$

For convenience, the value of the true signal $\theta^*(t)$ is taken as either $\theta_1^* = 0.2$ or $\theta_2^* = 0.6$, which are the representative values of the true signal in the regions C_1 and C_2, respectively.

---

* Moreover, the variance of a random observation time should be calculated. However, this calculation is extremely difficult and is therefore usually omitted.

Rule (7.28) now becomes

If $\displaystyle\int_0^t \theta(t)\,dt > a_1(t),$ make δ_2^t (i.e., $\theta^* = \theta_2^*$).

If $\displaystyle\int_0^t \theta(t)\,dt < b_1(t),$ make δ_1^t (i.e., $\theta^* = \theta_1^*$).

If $a_1(t) > \displaystyle\int_0^t \theta(t)\,dt > b_1(t),$ make δ^e (i.e., repeat test).

By Eqs. (7.29) and (7.30),

$$a_1(t) = 0.4t + 2.5N_0 \log A_1$$
$$b_1(t) = 0.4t - 2.5N_0 \log B_1 \tag{7.88}$$

It follows that, in the case of $\epsilon_{11} = \epsilon_{21} = \epsilon,$

$$a_1(t) = 0.4t + 2.5N_0\,\gamma$$
$$b_1(t) = 0.4t - 2.5N_0\,\gamma \tag{7.89}$$

where

$$\gamma = \log \frac{1 - \epsilon}{\epsilon} \tag{7.90}$$

Consequently, in the sequential procedure the average amount of observation time for $\theta^* = \theta_1^*$ is

$$\bar{T}_1(\theta_1^*) = 2N_0 \frac{[2L(\theta_1^*) - 1]\gamma}{(\theta_2^* - \theta_1^*)^2}$$

and for $\theta^* = \theta_2^*$ it is

$$\bar{T}_2(\theta_2^*) = 2N_0 \frac{[1 - 2L(\theta_2^*)]\gamma}{(\theta_2^* - \theta_1^*)^2} \tag{7.91a}$$

where $L(\theta_1^*) = 1 - \epsilon$ and $L(\theta_2^*) = \epsilon.$

Applying the values $\theta^* = 0.2$ and $\theta^* = 0.6$ to Eq. (7.91a) gives the average amount of observation time:

$$\bar{T} = \bar{T}_1(\theta_1^*) = \bar{T}_2(\theta_2^*) = 12.5N_0(1 - 2\epsilon)\gamma \tag{7.91b}$$

We shall now consider the same situation in a nonsequential procedure. As described in Sect. 6.3, the Bayes solution of this situation is

$$
\begin{aligned}
&\text{If} \quad \log \lambda(\boldsymbol{\theta}_n) < 0, \qquad \text{make } \delta_1 \qquad \text{that is,} \quad \theta^* = \theta_1^* . \\
&\text{If} \quad \log \lambda(\boldsymbol{\theta}_n) > 0, \qquad \text{make } \delta_2 \qquad \text{that is,} \quad \theta^* = \theta_2^* .
\end{aligned}
\tag{7.92}
$$

In this statement

$$
\log \lambda(\boldsymbol{\theta}_n) = \log \frac{\xi_2 p(\boldsymbol{\theta}_n \mid \theta_2^*)}{\xi_1 p(\boldsymbol{\theta}_n \mid \theta_1^*)} = \log \frac{\xi_2}{\xi_1} + \log \frac{p(\boldsymbol{\theta}_n \mid \theta_2^*)}{p(\boldsymbol{\theta}_n \mid \theta_1^*)}
\tag{7.93}
$$

If the probability density function of the additive noise $n(t)$ is assumed to be of gaussian white noise, then the conditional probability density functions $p(\boldsymbol{\theta}_n \mid \theta_2^*)$ and $p(\boldsymbol{\theta}_n \mid \theta_1^*)$ are respectively given by

$$
p(\boldsymbol{\theta}_n \mid \theta_2^*) = (2\pi)^{-n/2} |\mathbf{M}|^{-\frac{1}{2}} \exp[-\tfrac{1}{2}(\boldsymbol{\theta}_n - \theta_1^*)' \mathbf{M}^{-1}(\boldsymbol{\theta}_n - \theta_1^*)]
\tag{7.94}
$$

$$
p(\boldsymbol{\theta}_n \mid \theta_1^*) = (2\pi)^{-n/2} |\mathbf{M}|^{-\frac{1}{2}} \exp[-\tfrac{1}{2}(\boldsymbol{\theta}_n - \theta_2^*)' \mathbf{M}^{-1}(\boldsymbol{\theta}_n - \theta_2^*)]
\tag{7.95}
$$

Since

$$
\log \frac{p(\boldsymbol{\theta}_n \mid \theta_2^*)}{p(\boldsymbol{\theta}_n \mid \theta_1^*)} = -\frac{1}{2} \sum_{i=1}^{n} \left(\frac{\theta_i - \theta_2^*}{(\psi_n)^{\frac{1}{2}}} \right)^2 + \frac{1}{2} \sum_{i=1}^{n} \left(\frac{\theta_i - \theta_1^*}{(\psi_n)^{\frac{1}{2}}} \right)^2
\tag{7.96}
$$

then a calculation similar to that of Eq. (7.25) leads us to

$$
\sum_{i=1}^{n} \theta_i \lesssim n \frac{\theta_1^* + \theta_2^*}{2} + \frac{\psi_n}{\theta_2^* - \theta_1^*} \log \frac{\xi_1}{\xi_2}
\tag{7.97}
$$

By means of Eq. (6.75), this inequality may be expressed as

$$
\sum_{i=1}^{n} \theta_i \Delta t \lesssim \frac{\theta_1^* + \theta_2^*}{2} n \Delta t + \frac{N_0}{\theta_2^* - \theta_1^*} \log \frac{\xi_1}{\xi_2}
\tag{7.98}
$$

By taking the limit $\Delta t \to 0$, this is expressed in continuous form as

$$
\theta_T \equiv \frac{1}{T} \int_0^T \theta(t)\, dt \lesssim \frac{\theta_1^* + \theta_2^*}{2} + \frac{N_0}{T(\theta_2^* - \theta_1^*)} \log \frac{\xi_1}{\xi_2}
\tag{7.99}
$$

By a computation similar to that of Eq. (6.120), the error probability of the first kind may now be given:

$$\alpha_T = \frac{1}{(2\pi N_0/T)^{1/2}} \int_\kappa^\infty \exp\left[-\frac{(\theta - \theta_1^*)^2}{2N_0/T}\right] d\theta \tag{7.100}$$

where

$$\kappa = \frac{\theta_1^* + \theta_2^*}{2} + \frac{N_0}{T(\theta_2^* - \theta_1^*)} \log\frac{\xi_1}{\xi_2} \tag{7.101}$$

Changing the variable from θ to ξ by the relation

$$(\theta - \theta_1^*)\left(\frac{T}{N_0}\right)^{1/2} \equiv \xi$$

express Eq. (7.100) in the more convenient form

$$\alpha_T = \frac{1}{(2\pi)^{1/2}} \int_{(\kappa-\theta_1^*)(T/N_0)^{1/2}}^\infty \exp\left(-\frac{\xi^2}{2}\right) d\xi$$

$$= \operatorname{erfc}\left[(\kappa - \theta_1^*)\left(\frac{T}{N_0}\right)^{1/2}\right] \tag{7.102}$$

where $\operatorname{erfc}(\xi)$ expresses the complementary error function with respect to ξ. Similarly, the error probability of the second kind is

$$\beta_T = \frac{1}{(2\pi N_0/T)^{1/2}} \int_{-\infty}^\kappa \exp\left[-\frac{(\theta - \theta_2^*)^2}{2N_0/T}\right] d\theta$$

$$= \frac{1}{2}\left\{1 + \operatorname{erfc}\left[\left(\frac{T}{N_0}\right)^{1/2}(\kappa - \theta_2^*)\right]\right\} \tag{7.103}$$

If we assume $\xi_1 = \xi_2$, then from Eq. (7.101), we have

$$\kappa = \frac{\theta_1^* + \theta_2^*}{2} \tag{7.104}$$

and Eqs. (7.102) and (7.103) may respectively be expressed as

$$\alpha_T = \frac{1}{(2\pi)^{1/2}} \int_{[(\theta_2{}^*-\theta_1{}^*)/2](T/N_0)^{1/2}}^{\infty} \exp\left(-\frac{\xi^2}{2}\right) d\xi \qquad (7.105)$$

$$\beta_T = \frac{1}{(2\pi)^{1/2}} \int_{-\infty}^{[-(\theta_1{}^*-\theta_2{}^*)/2](T/N_0)^{1/2}} \exp\left(-\frac{\eta^2}{2}\right) d\eta = \alpha_T \qquad (7.106)$$

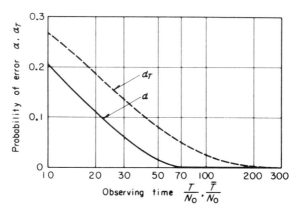

FIG. 7.12. Numerical illustration of the difference between sequential and non-sequential procedures.

where $\eta = (\theta - \theta_2^*)(T/N_0)^{1/4}$. Since $\theta_1^* = 0.2$, and $\theta_2^* = 0.6$, then from Eqs. (7.105) and (7.106), we have

$$\alpha_T = \mathrm{erfc}[0.2(T/N_0)^{1/2}] = \beta_T \qquad (7.107)$$

The numerical plots of both Eqs. (7.91b) and (7.107) are shown in Fig. 7.12. It can easily be observed from this figure that the error probability α of the sequential procedure is less than that of the nonsequential procedure for a fixed observation time and that the sequential procedure is helpful in reducing the observation time for a fixed value of the error probability. It can, therefore, be concluded that the sequential procedure is an acceptable approach in the design of adaptive control systems, because it limits the amount of observation time.

CHAPTER 8

Adaptive Adjustment of Parameters of Nonlinear Control Systems

8.1 Introductory Remarks

It was emphasized in the introduction that actual control systems are nonlinear and subject to drastic random changes of environment. There is no need to mention that, in practical situations, we must take into account their nonlinear transfer characteristics. During the past decade there has been a growing interest in the effect of nonlinear characteristics on the performance of control systems.

The results of many studies[1-4] have shown that, since the signal in a nonlinear control system is not gaussian, even when the input signal is assumed to be gaussian, the application of statistical decision theory is extremely difficult, because a nongaussian random process requires multidimensional joint statistics, and from these must be extracted a decision rule. To circumvent this difficulty a new decision procedure will be explained in this chapter with the help of the theory of Bernoulli trials. This is the binomial decision procedure. The construction of the decision logic of an on-off relay control system with a second-order controlled element subjected to a gaussian random input is described in detail. The considerations presented in this chapter can, of course, be applied to any problem in both system and input adaptations.

[1] J. F. Barrett, Automatic and remote control. *Proc. First IFAC Congress, Moscow, 1960* Vol. II. Butterworths, London, 1961.
[2] T. K. Caughey, Derivation and application of the Fokker-Planck equation to discrete non-linear dynamic systems subjected to white random excitation. *J. Acoust. Soc. Am.* **35** (No. 11), 1683 (1963).
[3] K. Chuang and L. F. Kazda, A study of non-linear systems with random input. *Trans. AIEE, Appl. and Ind.* No. 42, p. 100 (1959).
[4] Y. Sawaragi, N. Sugai, and Y. Sunahara, "Statistical Studies on Non-Linear Control Systems. Nippon Printing, Osaka, Japan, 1962.

The configuration of the control system considered here is shown in Fig. 8.1. A parameter of the controlled element slowly and unpredictably varies with environmental conditions, and the adaptive device is used for preventing this variation, which is a major cause of excessive deterioration in control performance. It is, of course, possible to adjust the parameters of the controller in accordance with the measured value of the unknown parameter of the controlled element. The new type of adaptive control system proposed in this chapter contains an adaptive

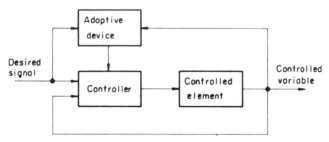

FIG. 8.1. Block diagram of decision adaptive control system.

device whose logical design is based on statistical decision theory, in particular the sequential decision scheme illustrated in Chapter 7.

8.2   Application of Sequential Decision Rule

We express the unknown parameter of the controlled element by $\theta^*(t)$. The variational range of its value is divided into two regions, $\theta^*(t) < \theta_0^*$ and $\theta^*(t) > \theta_0^*$, where θ_0^* is a specific preassigned value. We assume that the structure of the controller has been intelligently selected on the basis of a class of control performance criteria. It is convenient for our development of the principal idea to consider the case in which the adjustable parameters of the controller are fixed at two prescribed values α_1 and α_2. The adjustment must correspond to the variation of parameter $\theta^*(t)$ such that for optimal performance parameter α_1 is chosen for the controlled element whose parameter lies in $\theta^* < \theta_0^*$, and α_2 for the element whose parameter lies in $\theta^* > \theta_0^*$.

To initiate the statistical sequential decision procedure we define the indifference zone preassigned by the boundary values θ_1^* and θ_2^* shown in Fig. 8.2, where θ_1^* is the upper limit in the region of acceptance and θ_2^* is the lower limit in the region of rejection. Then the present problem may be interpreted as one of testing hypothesis $[H_1 : \theta^*(t) < \theta_0^*]$ against the alternative hypothesis $[H_2 : \theta^*(t) > \theta_0^*]$ by observing a signal in some part of the closed loop. It is best that the signal observed be the error response, because with this is a method of evaluating a certain type of control performance.

The situation mentioned above requires the sequential probability ratio test described in the preceding chapter. We denote here the sequence of sampled values $e_1 = e(t_1)$, $e_2 = e(t_2)$, ..., $e_{n-1} = e(t_{n-1})$, and $e_n = e(t_n)$ of the error response $e(t)$ by a vector e_n. We further express the n-dimensional probability density function of the vector process e_n, when $\alpha = \alpha_i$ and when $\theta^*(t) = \theta_j^*$, by $p(e_n : \alpha_i, \theta_j^*)$, where θ_j^* is the jth

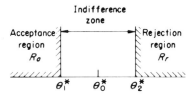

FIG. 8.2. Indifference zone.

quantized value of $\theta^*(t)$. With these notations the quantity $\Lambda_i(n)$ for the probability ratio test, given by Eq. (7.22), is expressed as

$$\Lambda_i(n) = \log \frac{p(e_n : \alpha_i, \theta_2^*)}{p(e_n : \alpha_i, \theta_1^*)} \tag{8.1}$$

where i equals 1 or 2. Hence, from Eqs. (7.46) and (7.47) we choose two positive numbers of the decision thresholds:

$$A_i = \frac{1 - \epsilon_{2i}}{\epsilon_{1i}} \tag{8.2a}$$

$$B_i = \frac{\epsilon_{2i}}{1 - \epsilon_{1i}} \tag{8.2b}$$

The observation is continued as long as the probability ratio satisfies the following inequality:

$$\log A_i > \Lambda_i(n) > \log B_i \tag{8.3}$$

Hypothesis H_1 is accepted or rejected at the first violation of either of the following:

$$\Lambda_i(n) < \log B_i \tag{8.4}$$

$$\Lambda_i(n) > \log A_i \tag{8.5}$$

If the probability density function $p(\mathbf{e}_n\colon \alpha_i, \theta_j^*)$ could be analytically evaluated, we can obtain the sequential decision rule by applying it to these three inequalities.* If it were assumed to be gaussian, then applying it directly would lead us to a pertinent decision rule. Unfortunately, however, the error probability density function in nonlinear control systems is nongaussian, and hence the decision rule is impractical. To avoid the difficulty and facilitate the practical realization of an adaptive decision loop, we transform the random process with nongaussian probability distribution into one with a binomial distribution.

8.2-1   Generation of binomial distribution.   In order to generate a new random process with binomial distribution we shall use an element with nonlinear characteristics of the form

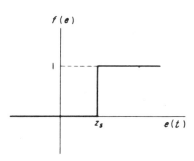

$f(e)$

z_s $e(t)$

FIG. 8.3. Transfer characteristic of the slicing function.

$$f(e_m) = 1 \qquad \text{for} \quad e_m > z_s$$
$$\qquad\quad = 0 \qquad \text{for} \quad e_m < z_s \qquad (8.6)$$

where e_m $(m = 1, 2, \ldots, n)$, an input sequence to the element, is the sampled values of the error response and consists of n observed data $e_1, e_2, \ldots,$ e_{n-1}, e_n, and where z_s is an arbitrary value, hereafter called the slicing level.

The nonlinear transfer characteristic defined by Eq. (8.6) is illustrated in Fig. 8.3. Applying e_m to the element as input, we have a new sequence as output, which takes only the value 0 or 1, and we can simultaneously observe k numbers of the value 1 and $n - k$ numbers of the value 0. The probability that the value 1 will occur k times and that the value 0 will occur $n - k$ times is given by the well-known binomial distribution[5]

$$B(k\colon n, F_{ij}) = \frac{n!}{k!\,(n-k)!}\, F_{ij}^k (1 - F_{ij})^{n-k} \qquad (8.7)$$

---

* If this probability density function of the error has a bell-shaped distribution (even if a nongaussian one), it may be used for a general formulation of the test.

[5] H. Blasbaly, The relationship of sequential filter theory to information theory and its application to the decision of signals in noise by Bernoulli trials. *IRE Trans. PGIT* **IT-3**, 122 (1957).

where F_{ij} represents the probability that the value 1 will occur, and this is equivalent to the probability $\Pr(e_m > z_s)$ that the values e_m exceed the slicing level z_s. Since the error response $e(t)$ depends on both the system parameters α_i and θ_j^*, and the probability $\Pr(e_m > z_s)$ depends not only on these but also on a value of the slicing level z_s, the probability F_{ij} is expressed as

$$F_{ij} = F(z_s : \alpha_i, \theta_j^*) = \int_{z_s}^{\infty} p(e : \alpha_i, \theta_j^*)\, de \qquad (8.8)$$

Therefore, a binomial test corresponding to a test of hypothesis $[H_1 : \theta^*(t) < \theta_1^*]$ against $[H_2 : \theta^*(t) > \theta_2^*]$ may be considered. We test the hypothesis

$$F(z_s : \alpha_i, \theta_2^*) < F(z_s : \alpha_i, \theta_1^*)$$

against the alternative hypothesis $F(z_s : \alpha_i, \theta_1^*) < F(z_s : \alpha_i, \theta_2^*)$.

8.2-2 Derivation of binomial sequential decision rule. In Eq. (8.1) by using $B(k : n, F_{i2})$ and $B(k : n, F_{i1})$, given by Eq. (8.7), instead of $p(e_m : \alpha_i, \theta_2^*)$ and $p(e_m : \alpha_i, \theta_1^*)$, respectively, the probability ratio in the binomial test may be written

$$\Lambda_i(n) = \log \frac{B(k; n, F_{i2})}{B(k; n, F_{i1})} \qquad (8.9)$$

Substituting Eq. (8.7) into this equation gives

$$\Lambda_i(n) = k \log \frac{F_{i2}(1 - F_{i1})}{F_{i1}(1 - F_{i2})} + n \log \frac{1 - F_{i2}}{1 - F_{i1}} \qquad (8.10)$$

With the help of Eq. (8.9) we find that Ineq. (8.5) yields

$$k \log \frac{F_{i2}(1 - F_{i1})}{F_{i1}(1 - F_{i2})} + n \log \frac{1 - F_{i2}}{1 - F_{i1}} > \log A_i \qquad (8.11)$$

In this we express by $\kappa_i^+(n)$ the value of k satisfying the equality condition

$$\kappa_i^+(n) = \left[\log \frac{F_{i2}(1 - F_{i1})}{F_{i1}(1 - F_{i2})} \right]^{-1} \left(\log A_i + n \log \frac{1 - F_{i1}}{1 - F_{i2}} \right) \qquad (8.12)$$

From this we take the rule:

$$\text{If} \quad k > \kappa_i^+(n), \qquad \text{accept } H_2. \tag{8.13a}$$

Similarly, from Ineqs. (8.3) and (8.4) and Eq. (8.9), we take:

$$\text{If} \quad k < \kappa_i^-(n), \qquad \text{accept } H_1. \tag{8.13b}$$

$$\text{If} \quad \kappa_i^+(n) > k > \kappa_i^-(n), \qquad \text{continue the observation.} \tag{8.13c}$$

Here $\kappa_n^-(n)$ is the value of k satisfying an equality condition that replaces Ineq. (8.4) and is given by

$$\kappa_i^-(n) = \left[\log \frac{F_{i2}(1 - F_{i1})}{F_{i1}(1 - F_{i2})} \right]^{-1} \left(\log B_i + n \log \frac{1 - F_{i1}}{1 - F_{i2}} \right) \tag{8.14}$$

8.2-3   Determination of the slicing level.   So far we have proposed, for the purpose of establishing a decision rule for a nongaussian random process, a method of converting the nongaussian probability density function to a binomial probability density function. However, it is apparent that the binomial decision rule depends on the value of the slicing level, so we must determine this value on the basis of a new concept taken from the viewpoint of practical applications. The key notion is to determine the value in such a way that the average sample number becomes minimal. It is thus natural for us to introduce the ASN function given in Chapter 7, because it is the average number of samples which depends on the unknown value of $\theta^*(t)$. It may, therefore, be desirable to choose the value of z_s such that

$$\min_{z_s} \max_{\theta^*} E_{\theta^*}[n; z_s] \tag{8.15}$$

where $E_{\theta^*}[n; z_s]$ represents the ASN function and shows that it depends also on the value of the slicing level z_s. The symbol $\min_{z_s} \max_{\theta^*}$ means in the Minimax sense that the minimization is to be performed on the maximal value of the ASN function. Our attention is, then, first directed to obtaining this value, $\max_{\theta^*} E_{\theta^*}[n; z_s]$.

It is recognized that

$$z = \log \frac{F_{i2}}{F_{i1}} \tag{8.16a}$$

$$E_{\theta^*}[n; z_s] = \frac{k}{n} \log \frac{F_{i2}}{F_{i1}} + \left(1 - \frac{k}{n}\right) \log \frac{1 - F_{i2}}{1 - F_{i1}} \tag{8.16b}$$

Therefore, the ASN function in this case may be derived by invoking the definition given by Eq. (7.66b) as

$$E_{\theta^*}[n; z_s] = \frac{L(\theta^*) \log B_j + [1 - L(\theta^*)] \log A_j}{\frac{k}{n} \log \frac{F_{i2}}{F_{i1}} + \left(1 - \frac{k}{n}\right) \log \frac{1 - F_{i2}}{1 - F_{i1}}} \tag{8.17}$$

At the indeterminate point the following relation holds:

$$\frac{k}{n} \log \frac{F_{i2}}{F_{i1}} + \left(1 - \frac{k}{n}\right) \log \frac{1 - F_{i2}}{1 - F_{i1}} = 0 \tag{8.18a}$$

$$k = \frac{\log \dfrac{1 - F_{i1}}{1 - F_{i2}}}{\log \dfrac{F_{i2}}{F_{i1}} + \log \dfrac{1 - F_{i1}}{1 - F_{i2}}} \tag{8.18b}$$

The ASN function at the indeterminate point is given by Eq. (7.80); in the present case we have

$$E_{\theta_0^*}[z^2] = \frac{k}{n} \left(\log \frac{F_{i2}}{F_{i1}}\right)^2 + \left(1 - \frac{k}{n}\right) \left(\log \frac{1 - F_{i2}}{1 - F_{i1}}\right)^2 \tag{8.19}$$

With the use of Eq. (8.18b) this becomes

$$E_{\theta_0^*}[z^2] = \log \frac{F_{i2}}{F_{i1}} \log \frac{1 - F_{i1}}{1 - F_{i2}} \tag{8.20}$$

By means of this result and Eq. (7.81) the ASN function at the indeterminate point is finally obtained as

$$E_{\theta_0*}[n; z_s] = -\frac{\log A_i \log B_i}{\log \dfrac{F_{i2}}{F_{i1}} \log \dfrac{1 - F_{i1}}{1 - F_{i2}}} \qquad (8.21)$$

which gives its maximal value. Therefore, we have

$$\max_{\theta*} E_{\theta*}[n; z_s] = E_{\theta_0*}[n; z_s] = -\frac{\log A_i \log B_i}{\log \dfrac{F_{i2}}{F_{i1}} \log \dfrac{1 - F_{i1}}{1 - F_{i2}}} \qquad (8.22)$$

Our next step is to find the minimal value of $\max_{\theta*} E_{\theta*}[n; z_s]$. Since this procedure is equivalent to a maximization of the denominator in Eq. (8.22), our attention is directed to handling the following quantity:

$$D_i(z_s) = \log \frac{F_{i2}}{F_{i1}} \log \frac{1 - F_{i1}}{1 - F_{i2}} \qquad (8.23)$$

The quantity $F_{i2} - F_{i1}$ is small, so we can expand the right-hand member here into the following Taylor series:

$$\log \frac{F_{i2}}{F_{i1}} = \log\left(1 + \frac{F_{i2} - F_{i1}}{F_{i1}}\right) = \frac{F_{i2} - F_{i1}}{F_{i1}} - \frac{1}{2}\left(\frac{F_{i2} - F_{i1}}{F_{i1}}\right)^2 + \cdots$$

$$(8.24a)$$

$$\log \frac{1 - F_{i1}}{1 - F_{i2}} = \frac{F_{i2} - F_{i1}}{1 - F_{i2}} - \frac{1}{2}\left(\frac{F_{i2} - F_{i1}}{1 - F_{i2}}\right)^2 + \cdots \qquad (8.24b)$$

If we neglect the terms of higher order than $(F_{i2} - F_{i1})^3$, then by applying these equations to Eq. (8.23) we have

$$D_i(z_s) \simeq \frac{(F_{i2} - F_{i1})^2}{F_{i1}(1 - F_{i2})} \qquad (8.25)$$

As shown by Eq. (8.8), the probabilities F_{ij} may be obtained as a function of the value of the slicing level z_s ; consequently, the value of $D_i(z_s)$ is computed by means of the values of F_{ij} as a function of z_s. For this purpose it is convenient to use the numerical plot of Eq. (8.25). As a practical procedure in determining the value of the slicing level we choose a value of z_s from among the values of $D_i(z_s)$ that become maximal.

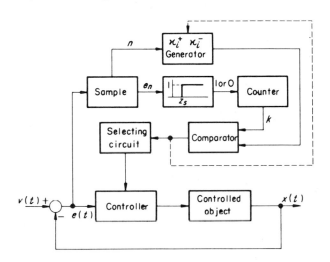

FIG. 8.4. Configuration of adaptive control system containing a binomial sequential decision device.

Two methods are as follows:

1. Determine the slicing level z_s from the condition

$$\max_{z_s} \min_i D_i(z_s)$$

2. First evaluate the values of z_{s1} and z_{s2} such that $D_i(z_s)$ become maximal for each i equal to 1 or 2; then select the slicing level z_{si} for i for which

$$\min_i [D_i(z_{s1}) - D_i(z_{s2})]$$

The binomial sequential decision rule may, thus, be adequately applied to the problem at hand. The configuration of a system containing a binomial sequential decision device is illustrated in Fig. 8.4.

8.3 On-Off Relay Decision Control Systems

An application of the binomial decision approach to nonlinear control systems is exemplified by an on-off relay control system subjected to a gaussian random input. The problem in designing on-off relay control systems is to construct the optimal switching function. If the controlled element is linear and time-invariant, the optimal switching function may also become time-invariant. Its configuration may be realized approxi-

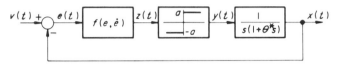

Fig. 8.5. Block diagram of on-off relay control system.

mately by a technique established by the authors.[6] If the dynamic characteristics are time-variant, then it may be necessary to incorporate a time-varying parameter in the switching function so as to maintain a minimal mean square error.

Let us consider an on-off relay control system whose original configuration is that of Fig. 8.5. The time constant $\theta^*(t)$ of the controlled element varies with the environmental conditions; the minimal value of the mean square error response may, then, vary with the time constant. Our major objective is to establish the configuration of an adaptive loop which generates parameter changes in the controller according to the information obtained by a statistical treatment of the error response signal. More specifically, since the key part of the controller in this system is a switching function generator, our present problem is to construct a switching function that adjusts its own parameter to the time-variant characteristics of the controlled element. It is, however, apparent that the error response becomes a nongaussian random process; so, before we clarify further the application of the decision concept to our present problem, we shall explore the statistical behavior of the error

[6] Y. Sawaragi, Y. Sunahara, and T. Nakamizo, A study of the control performance of relay control systems subjected to a random input. *Memoirs Faculty Eng., Kyoto Univ.* **25** (Pt. 3), 323 (1963).

response, directing our attention to evaluating the error probability density function.

8.3-1   Evaluation of error probability density function.

There are two ways of calculating the error probability density function: by means of the Fokker-Planck equation[7-9] and by successive calculations of higher-order cumulants.[10]

In the present discussion the former is the more suitable, the latter requiring much tedious calculation. The principal purpose of this section is, therefore, to extend the method of solving the Fokker-Planck equation by means of the theory of Markov random processes and then to discuss the operation of the controller generating the switching function.

For our theoretical development it will be appropriate, in choosing a type of random process, to consider mathematical convenience and the physical situation. A Markov process is a good choice, because many physical processes are Markovian and, furthermore, a Markov process is specified by its transition probability alone, which contains sufficient information for analysis.

It was shown in Eqs. (2.86)–(2.88) and Figs. 2.7 to 2.9 that the set of 1-, 2-, . . . , $(n - 1)$-, n-dimensional joint probability density functions completely defines a random process. In other words, the n-dimensional probability density function $p_n(y_1, t_1; y_2, t_2; \ldots; y_n, t_n)$ is used for the classification of a random process. For example, a purely random process is the simplest one, in which the value of $y(t_1)$ at an arbitrary time t_1 does not depend upon the value of $y(t_2)$ at any other time t_2. A more complicated one is the so-called Markov process, which is completely described by the 2-dimensional probability density function p_2. For the

[7] K. Chuang and L. F. Kazda, *op. cit.*

[8] Y. Sawaragi and Y. Sunahara, Modification of the equivalent gains of non-linear element considering the probability density function of the response of non-linear control systems subjected to a gaussian random input. *Tech. Repts. Eng. Res. Inst., Kyoto Univ.* **10** (No. 4), Rept. No. 68 (1960).

[9] Y. Sawaragi, Y. Sunahara, and T. Soeda, The discrepancy from the normal distribution of the probability of the response of non-linear control systems subjected to a gaussian random input. *Tech. Repts. Eng. Res. Inst., Kyoto Univ.* **21** (2) Rept. No. 79 (1961).

[10] Y. Sawaragi, Y. Sunahara, and T. Nakamizo, Statistical behavior of the response of non-linear control systems subjected to random inputs. *Tech. Repts. Eng. Res. Inst., Kyoto Univ.* **21** (No. 1), Rept. No. 78 (1961).

purpose of explaining a Markov process we recall the notion of the conditional probability density function described in Sect. 2.8. As we saw there, we can define the conditional probability $p(y_2 \mid y_1 ; t) \, dy_2$ as the probability that a given value of $y(t) = y_1$ at $t = 0$ will be found within the interval y_2 to $y_2 + dy_2$ at a later time t. The conditional probability density function is obtained as

$$p(y_2 \mid y_1 ; t_2 - t_1) = \frac{p_2(y_1, t_1, y_2, t_2)}{p_1(y_1, t_1)} \qquad (8.26)$$

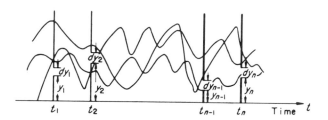

FIG. 8.6. The Markov process.

and this must, of course, satisfy the following three conditions:

$$p(y_2 \mid y_1 ; t_2 - t_1) \geq 0 \qquad (8.27a)$$

$$\int_{-\infty}^{\infty} p(y_2 \mid y_1 ; t_2 - t_1) \, dy_2 = 1 \qquad (8.27b)$$

$$p_1(y_2, t_2) = \int_{-\infty}^{\infty} p_2(y_1, t_1) \, p_2(y_2 \mid y_1 ; t_2 - t_1) \, dy_1 \qquad (8.27c)$$

From Eq. (8.26) the Markov process may now be defined. It is a random process whose conditional probability, that $y(t)$ lies between y_1 and $y_1 + dy_1$ at t_1, between y_2 and $y_2 + dy_2$ at $t_2, \ldots,$ between y_{n-1} and $y_{n-1} + dy_{n-1}$ at t_{n-1}, and between y_n and $y_n + dy_n$ at t_n, depends only upon the values of y at t_n and t_{n-1}; see Fig. 8.6. Consequently, for a Markov process we have

$$p(y_n, t_n \mid y_1, t_1 ; y_2, t_2 ; \ldots ; y_{n-1}, t_{n-1}) = p(y_n, t_n \mid y_{n-1}, t_{n-1}) \quad (8.28)$$

This definition implies that for a Markov process it is sufficient to consider the conditional probability density function $p(y_n, t_n \mid y_{n-1}, t_{n-1})$. From this point of view we shall focus our attention on such a time interval as $[t_{n-1}, t_n]$. To make the reading easier we shall change the symbol to $[t_1, t_2]$. Then, as shown in Fig. 8.7, the conditional probability density function $p(y_2, t_2 \mid y_1, t_1)$ will be an important center of our discussion. Next we consider an arbitrary time instant t in the interval $[t_1, t_2]$. Considering that at t the function $y(t)$ lies within the interval

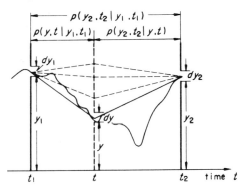

Fɪɢ. 8.7. The Kolmogorov-Chapman equation.

$y + dy$ to y, we obtain by a method similar to that yielding Eq. (8.26) the 3-dimensional probability density function $p_3(y_1, t_1, y, t, y_2, t_2)$.

$$p_3(y_1, t_1 ; y, t; y_2, t_2) = p_2(y_1, t_1 ; y, t)p(y_2, t_2 \mid y_1, t_1; y, t) \quad (8.29)$$

where $t_1 < t < t_2$. Integrating both sides of this equation with respect to y gives

$$p_2(y_1, t_1 ; y_2, t_2) = \int_{-\infty}^{\infty} p_2(y_1, t_1 ; y, t) \, p(y_2, t_2 \mid y_1, t_1 ; y, t) \, dy \quad (8.30)$$

The Markov property mentioned above is now invoked, and the equation becomes either of the following:

$$p_2(y_1, t_1 ; y_2, t_2) = \int_{-\infty}^{\infty} p_2(y_1, t_1 ; y, t) \, p(y_2, t_2 \mid y, t) \, dy \quad (8.31a)$$

$$p(y_2, t_2 \mid y_1, t_1) = \int_{-\infty}^{\infty} p(y, t \mid y_1, t_1) \, p(y_2, t_2 \mid y, t) \, dy \quad (8.31b)$$

This has been called the Kolmogorov-Chapman equation. It implies that the conditional probability density function $p(y_2, t_2 \mid y_1, t_1)$ may be represented by the integration of the probability over any path selected.

Sometimes a random process $y(t)$ is not Markovian. In such a case we can usually find another stochastic variable $z(t) = \dot{y} = dy/dt$, which is combined with the original process $y(t)$ or another coordinate. By this means we can make a Markov vector process with $y(t)$ and $z(t)$ as its components in the 2-dimensional probability space.

When a random process $\mathbf{y}(t)$ can be represented by the position vector of a point in N-dimensional probability space and its components are $y_1(t), y_2(t), \ldots, y_{N-1}(t), y_N(t)$, then Eq. (8.31b) may be generalized to the N-dimensional case,

$$p(\xi_1, \xi_2, \ldots, \xi_N ; t_2 \mid \eta_1, \eta_2, \ldots, \eta_N ; t_1)$$

$$= \int_{-\infty N\text{-fold}}^{\infty} \cdots \int_{-\infty}^{\infty} p(\xi_1, \xi_2, \ldots, \xi_N ; t_2 \mid \zeta_1, \zeta_2, \ldots, \zeta_N ; t)$$

$$\times \; p(\zeta_1, \zeta_2, \ldots, \zeta_N ; t \mid \eta_1, \eta_2, \ldots, \eta_N ; t_1) \, d\zeta_1 \, d\zeta_2 \cdots d\zeta_N \quad (8.32)$$

where $t_1 < t < t_2$ and

$$y_1(t_1) = \eta_1, \quad y_2(t_1) = \eta_2, \quad \ldots, \quad y_N(t_1) = \eta_N$$

$$y_1(t) = \zeta_1, \quad y_2(t) = \zeta_2, \quad \ldots, \quad y_N(t) = \zeta_N \quad (8.33)$$

$$y_1(t_2) = \xi_1, \quad y_2(t_2) = \xi_2, \quad \ldots, \quad y_N(t_2) = \xi_N$$

In Eq. (8.32) the left member is the conditional probability density function indicating that at time t_2 the random variables $y_1(t_2), y_2(t_2), \ldots,$ $y_{N-1}(t_2), y_N(t_2)$ are at $\xi_1, \xi_2, \ldots, \xi_{N-1}, \xi_N$, assuming that at time t_1 they were at $\eta_1, \eta_2, \ldots, \eta_{N-1}, \eta_N$. Similarly, $p(\xi_1, \xi_2, \ldots, \xi_N ; t_2 \mid \zeta_1, \zeta_2, \ldots,$ $\zeta_N ; t)$ is the conditional probability density function indicating that at time t_2 the random variables $y_1(t_2), y_2(t_2), \ldots, y_{N-1}(t_2), y_N(t_2)$ are at $\xi_1, \xi_2, \ldots, \xi_{N-1}, \xi_N$, assuming that at time t they were at $\zeta_1, \zeta_2, \ldots,$ ζ_{N-1}, ζ_N, and $p(\zeta_1, \zeta_2, \ldots, \zeta_N ; t \mid \eta_1, \eta_2, \ldots, \eta_N ; t_1)$ is the conditional probability density function indicating that at time t they are at $\zeta_1, \zeta_2, \ldots,$ ζ_{N-1}, ζ_N, assuming that at time t_1 they were at $\eta_1, \eta_2, \ldots, \eta_{N-1}, \eta_N$.

Although the Fokker-Planck equation is derived with the Kolmogorov-Chapman equation as the starting point of an argument, a detailed description of this derivation is not pertinent to the main purpose of this chapter and may be found in other books.[11-13] The following parabolic partial differential equation is known as the Fokker-Planck equation:

$$\frac{\partial p}{\partial t} = -\sum_{i=1}^{N} \frac{\partial}{\partial y_i}(m_i p) + \frac{1}{2}\sum_{i=1}^{N}\sum_{j=1}^{N}\frac{\partial^2}{\partial y_i\,\partial y_j}(m_{ij}p) \qquad (8.34)$$

where the symbol p is the conditional probability density function $p[\mathbf{y}(t), t \mid \mathbf{y}(0), 0] = p[\mathbf{y}(t) \mid \mathbf{y}(0); t]$ expressing that for a given $\mathbf{y}(0)$ at $t = 0$ the value of $\mathbf{y}(t)$ is found at time t later, and where

$$m_i = \lim_{\Delta t \to 0} \frac{A_i(\mathbf{y}, t)}{\Delta t} \qquad (8.35a)$$

$$m_{ij} = \lim_{\Delta t \to 0} \frac{B_{ij}(\mathbf{y}, t)}{\Delta t} \qquad (8.35b)$$

A_i and B_{ij} being respectively given by

$$A_i(\mathbf{y}, t) = \int_{-\infty}^{\infty}{}_{N\text{-fold}} \cdots \int_{-\infty}^{\infty} (\Delta y_i)\, p(\mathbf{y} + \Delta\mathbf{y} \mid \mathbf{y}, \Delta t)$$
$$\times\, d(\Delta y_1)\, d(\Delta y_2) \cdots d(\Delta y_N) \quad (8.36a)$$

$$B_{ij}(\mathbf{y}, t) = \int_{-\infty}^{\infty}{}_{N\text{-fold}} \cdots \int_{-\infty}^{\infty} (\Delta y_i)(\Delta y_j)\, p(\mathbf{y} + \Delta\mathbf{y} \mid \mathbf{y}, \Delta t)$$
$$\times\, d(\Delta y_1)\, d(\Delta y_2) \cdots d(\Delta y_N) \quad (8.36b)$$

The last two equations are respectively interpreted as the first and the second incremental statistical moments of the displacement of the random process in an infinitesimally short time. The assumption is made that as $\Delta t \to 0$ the limiting forms of Eqs. (8.35) exist and that the higher-order moments are negligibly small.

In many problems it happens that the conditional probability density function $p(\mathbf{y}(t) \mid \mathbf{y}(0); t)$ obtained by Eq. (8.34) becomes the stationary

[11] A. N. Kolmogorov, On analytical methods in probability theory. *Math. Ann.* **104**, 495 (1931).
[12] M. C. Wang and G. E. Uhlenbeck, On the theory of the Brownian motion. Pt. II. *Rev. Mod. Phys.* **17**, 323 (1945).
[13] N. Wax *et al.*, "Selected Papers on Noise and Stochastic Processes." Dover Publishing, New York, 1954.

probability density function $p(\mathbf{y})$ when a sufficiently long time interval is considered. This means that the probability density function is no longer a function of time and initial condition $\mathbf{y}(0)$. In such a case, by letting $\partial p / \partial t = 0$ in Eq. (8.34) we have the following form of the Fokker-Planck equation:

$$-\sum_{i=1}^{N} \frac{\partial}{\partial y_i}(m_i p) + \frac{1}{2}\sum_{i=1}^{N}\sum_{j=1}^{N} \frac{\partial^2}{\partial y_i \, \partial y_j}(m_{ij} p) = 0 \qquad (8.37)$$

We shall now return to our main subject and obtain the Fokker-Planck equation associated with the control equation of the system shown in Fig. 8.5. It is easy to show that the error response $e(t)$ is related to the desired stationary gaussian random signal $v(t)$ by the differential equation*

$$\theta * \frac{d^2 e}{dt^2} + \frac{de}{dt} + f(z) = \theta * \frac{d^2 v}{dt^2} + \frac{dv}{dt} \qquad (8.38)$$

where $f(z)$ is a nonlinear function expressing the on-off relay characteristic. In this equation, by letting

$$\dot{e} = de/dt \qquad (8.39a)$$

$$V(t) = \theta * \frac{d^2 v}{dt^2} + \frac{dv}{dt} \qquad (8.39b)$$

we have

$$\frac{d\dot{e}}{dt} + \frac{1}{\theta *}\dot{e} + \frac{1}{\theta *}f(z) = \frac{1}{\theta *}V(t) \qquad (8.40)$$

As shown by Eq. (8.39b) the spectral density $S_V(\omega)$ of $V(t)$ is related to the spectral density $S_v(\omega)$ of $v(t)$ as follows:

$$S_V(\omega) = |\theta *(j\omega)^2 + j\omega|^2 S_v(\omega) \qquad (8.41)$$

To explore the spectral density $S_V(\omega)$ we shall consider a case in which the desired signal $v(t)$ to the control system is a stationary gaussian random

---

* The meanings of y and z used in this description of the general concept of Markov processes and the Fokker-Planck equation will now be changed without consideration to careful correspondence. For example, $z(t)$ is hereafter not $z = dy/dt$, but the input signal to the nonlinear element.

process with a mean of zero and an autocorrelation function of the form

$$\psi_v(\tau) = \frac{N_0}{c_2^2 - c_1^2} \left[\frac{1}{c_1} \exp(-c_1|\tau|) - \frac{1}{c_2} \exp(-c_2|\tau|) \right] \quad (8.42a)$$

where both c_1 and c_2 are arbitrary constants and ψ_v is the variance of $v(t)$. The spectral density is, therefore, given by

$$S_v(\omega) = \frac{2N_0}{(\omega^2 + c_1^2)(\omega^2 + c_2^2)} \quad (8.42b)$$

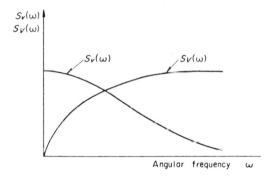

FIG. 8.8. Mutual relation between $S_V(\omega)$ and $S_v(\omega)$.

We assume here that $\omega^2 \gg c_1^2$. Thus Eq. (8.42b) becomes

$$S_v(\omega) = \frac{2N_0}{\omega^2(\omega^2 + c_2^2)} \quad (8.43)$$

Then, by means of Eq. (8.41), the spectral density $S_V(\omega)$ is given as

$$S_V(\omega) = \frac{2N_0(\theta^{*2}\omega^2 + 1)}{\omega^2 + c_2^2} \quad (8.44)$$

Consequently, in the frequency range in which the relations $\omega^2 \gg c_1^2$ and $c_2 \simeq 1/\theta^*$ hold, this can be approximately expressed as

$$S_V(\omega) = 2N_0\theta^{*2} \quad (8.45)$$

On the foregoing assumptions, the spectral density $S_V(\omega)$ may be conceived of as flat over any range of interest; see Fig. 8.8. Consequently, the random process $V(t)$ becomes a stationary gaussian white-noise random process with autocorrelation function $\psi_V(\tau)$:

$$\psi_V(\tau) = \langle V(t)V(t+\tau)\rangle_{av}$$

$$= 2N_0\theta^{*2}\delta(\tau) \qquad (8.46)$$

In this case, since the random process $\mathbf{e}(t)$, whose components are the two random variables $e(t)$ and $\dot{e}(t)$, may be considered Markovian,[14,15] the Fokker-Planck equation is established. The form of the 2-dimensional Fokker-Planck equation is easily written from Eq. (8.37) as

$$-\frac{\partial}{\partial e}[m_1 p_2(e,\dot{e})] - \frac{\partial}{\partial \dot{e}}[m_2 p_2(e,\dot{e})]$$

$$+ \frac{1}{2}\left\{\frac{\partial^2}{\partial e^2}[m_{11}p_2(e,\dot{e})] + \frac{\partial^2}{\partial \dot{e}^2}[m_{22}p_2(e,\dot{e})]\right.$$

$$\left.+ \frac{\partial^2}{\partial e\,\partial \dot{e}}[m_{12}p_2(e,\dot{e})] + \frac{\partial^2}{\partial \dot{e}\,\partial e}[m_{21}p_2(e,\dot{e})]\right\} = 0 \quad (8.47)$$

where from Eqs. (8.35) and (8.36)

$$m_1 = \lim_{\Delta t\to 0}\frac{1}{\Delta t}\int_{-\infty}^{\infty}\int_{-\infty}^{\infty}\Delta e\,p(e+\Delta e, \dot{e}+\Delta\dot{e};$$
$$t+\Delta t \mid e,\dot{e}; t)\,d(\Delta e)\,d(\Delta\dot{e}) \quad (8.48a)$$

$$m_2 = \lim_{\Delta t\to 0}\frac{1}{\Delta t}\int_{-\infty}^{\infty}\int_{-\infty}^{\infty}\Delta\dot{e}\,p(e+\Delta e, \dot{e}+\Delta\dot{e};$$
$$t+\Delta t \mid e,\dot{e}; t)\,d(\Delta e)\,d(\Delta\dot{e}) \quad (8.48b)$$

$$m_{11} = \lim_{\Delta t\to 0}\frac{1}{\Delta t}\int_{-\infty}^{\infty}\int_{-\infty}^{\infty}(\Delta e)^2 p(e+\Delta e, \dot{e}+\Delta\dot{e};$$
$$t+\Delta t \mid e,\dot{e}; t)\,d(\Delta e)\,d(\Delta\dot{e}) \quad (8.48c)$$

$$m_{22} = \lim_{\Delta t\to 0}\frac{1}{\Delta t}\int_{-\infty}^{\infty}\int_{-\infty}^{\infty}(\Delta\dot{e})^2 p(e+\Delta e, \dot{e}+\Delta\dot{e};$$
$$t+\Delta t \mid e,\dot{e}; t)\,d(\Delta e)\,d(\Delta\dot{e}) \quad (8.48d)$$

[14] Y. Sawaragi, N. Sugai, and Y. Sunahara, op. cit., p. 126.
[15] M. C. Wang and G. E. Uhlenbeck, op. cit.

$$m_{12} = \lim_{\Delta t \to 0} \frac{1}{\Delta t} \int_{-\infty}^{\infty} \int_{-\infty}^{\infty} (\Delta e)(\Delta \dot{e}) \, p(e + \Delta e, \dot{e} + \Delta \dot{e};$$

$$t + \Delta t \mid e, \dot{e}; t) \, d(\Delta e) \, d(\Delta \dot{e}) \quad (8.48e)$$

$$m_{21} = \lim_{\Delta t \to 0} \frac{1}{\Delta t} \int_{-\infty}^{\infty} \int_{-\infty}^{\infty} (\Delta \dot{e})(\Delta e) \, p(e + \Delta e, \dot{e} + \Delta \dot{e};$$

$$t + \Delta t \mid e, \dot{e}; t) \, d(\Delta e) \, d(\Delta \dot{e}) \quad (8.48f)$$

Our first line of attack is to calculate the values of the increments Δe and $\Delta \dot{e}$ of the random variables $e(t)$ and $\dot{e}(t)$, respectively, for the purpose of obtaining these six coefficients m_1, etc. Integrating both sides of Eq. (8.40) over the definite time interval $(t, t + \Delta t)$, we have

$$\int_t^{t+\Delta t} \frac{d\dot{e}}{dt} \, dt + \frac{1}{\theta*} \int_t^{t+\Delta t} \dot{e} \, dt + \frac{1}{\theta*} \int_t^{t+\Delta t} f(z) \, dt = \frac{1}{\theta*} \int_t^{t+\Delta t} V(t) \, dt \quad (8.49)$$

Invoking system dynamics and recalling that the time function $V(t)$ is a stationary gaussian white-noise random process, it can be concluded that both the random variables $e(t)$ and $\dot{e}(t)$ change with time more slowly than the random time function $V(t)$. This implies that

$$e(t + \Delta t) \simeq e(t), \qquad \dot{e}(t + \Delta t) \simeq \dot{e}(t), \qquad \text{and} \quad z(t + \Delta t) \simeq z(t) \quad (8.50)$$

Under the assumption permitted by these equations, Eq. (8.49) may be expressed in the forms

$$\Delta \dot{e} + \frac{1}{\theta*} \dot{e} \, \Delta t + \frac{1}{\theta*} f(z) \, \Delta t = \frac{1}{\theta*} \int_t^{t+\Delta t} V(t) \, dt \quad (8.51a)$$

$$\Delta \dot{e} = \frac{1}{\theta*} \int_t^{t+\Delta t} V(t) \, dt - \left[\frac{1}{\theta*} \dot{e} \, \Delta t + \frac{1}{\theta*} f(z) \, \Delta t \right] \quad (8.51b)$$

The coefficient m_1 defined by Eq. (8.48a) is easily obtained as

$$m_1 = \int_{-\infty}^{\infty} \int_{-\infty}^{\infty} \lim_{\Delta t \to 0} \frac{\Delta e}{\Delta t} \, p(e + \Delta e, \dot{e} + \Delta \dot{e}; t + \Delta t \mid e, \dot{e}; t) \, d(\Delta e) \, d(\Delta \dot{e})$$

$$= \dot{e} \int_{-\infty}^{\infty} \int_{-\infty}^{\infty} \lim_{\Delta t \to 0} p(e + \Delta e, \dot{e} + \Delta \dot{e}; t + \Delta t \mid e, \dot{e}; t) \, d(\Delta e) \, d(\Delta \dot{e})$$

$$= \dot{e} \quad (8.52)$$

The coefficient m_2, computed from Eq. (8.51b), is

$$m_2 = \lim_{\Delta t \to 0} \frac{1}{\Delta t} \int_{-\infty}^{\infty} \int_{-\infty}^{\infty} \left\{ \frac{1}{\theta*} \int_t^{t+\Delta t} V(t)\, dt - \left[\frac{1}{\theta*} \dot{e}\, \Delta t + \frac{1}{\theta*} f(z)\, \Delta t \right] \right\}$$

$$\times\, p(e + \Delta e,\, \dot{e} + \Delta \dot{e};\, t + \Delta t \mid e, \dot{e};\, t)\, d(\Delta e)\, d(\Delta \dot{e})$$

$$= \lim_{\Delta t \to 0} \frac{1}{\Delta t} \cdot \frac{1}{\theta*} \int_t^{t+\Delta t} V(t)\, dt - \left[\frac{1}{\theta*} \dot{e} + \frac{1}{\theta*} f(z) \right] \tag{8.53a}$$

As Eq. (8.39b) shows, since $v(t)$ is a random signal with a mean of zero, then $V(t)$ also has a mean of zero. Consequently, Eq. (8.53a) becomes

$$m_2 = -\left[\frac{1}{\theta*} \dot{e} + \frac{1}{\theta*} f(z) \right] \tag{8.53b}$$

The coefficient m_{11} is given by

$$m_{11} = \int_{-\infty}^{\infty} \int_{-\infty}^{\infty} \lim_{\Delta t \to 0} \Delta t \left(\frac{\Delta e}{\Delta t} \right)^2$$

$$\times\, p(e + \Delta e,\, \dot{e} + \Delta \dot{e};\, t + \Delta t \mid e, \dot{e};\, t)\, d(\Delta e)\, d(\Delta \dot{e})$$

$$= \dot{e}^2 \int_{-\infty}^{\infty} \int_{-\infty}^{\infty} \lim_{\Delta t \to 0} \Delta t$$

$$\times\, p(e + \Delta e,\, \dot{e} + \Delta \dot{e};\, t + \Delta t \mid e, \dot{e};\, t)\, d(\Delta e)\, d(\Delta \dot{e})$$

$$= 0 \tag{8.54}$$

The coefficient m_{22} is computed as

$$m_{22} = \lim_{\Delta t \to 0} \frac{1}{\Delta t} \int_{-\infty}^{\infty} \int_{-\infty}^{\infty} \left\{ \frac{1}{\theta*} \int_t^{t+\Delta t} V(t)\, dt - \left[\frac{1}{\theta*} \dot{e}\Delta t + \frac{1}{\theta*} f(z)\, \Delta t \right] \right\}^2$$

$$\times\, p(e + \Delta e,\, \dot{e} + \Delta \dot{e};\, t + \Delta t \mid e, \dot{e};\, t)\, d(\Delta e)\, d(\Delta \dot{e})$$

$$= \lim_{\Delta t \to 0} \frac{1}{\Delta t} \int_{-\infty}^{\infty} \int_{-\infty}^{\infty} \frac{1}{\theta*^2} \int_t^{t+\Delta t} dt \int_t^{t+\Delta t} dt'\, V(t)\, V(t')$$

$$\times\, p(e + \Delta e,\, \dot{e} + \Delta \dot{e};\, t + \Delta t \mid e, \dot{e};\, t)\, d(\Delta e)\, d(\Delta \dot{e})$$

$$-\, 2 \lim_{\Delta t \to 0} \frac{1}{\Delta t} \int_{-\infty}^{\infty} \int_{-\infty}^{\infty} \left[\frac{1}{\theta*} \dot{e}\Delta t + \frac{1}{\theta*} f(z)\, \Delta t \right] \frac{1}{\theta*} \int_t^{t+\Delta t} V(t)\, dt$$

$$\times\, p(e + \Delta e,\, \dot{e} + \Delta \dot{e};\, t + \Delta t \mid e, \dot{e};\, t)\, d(\Delta e)\, d(\Delta \dot{e})$$

$$+\, \lim_{\Delta t \to 0} \frac{1}{\Delta t} \int_{-\infty}^{\infty} \int_{-\infty}^{\infty} \left[\frac{1}{\theta*} \dot{e}\Delta t + \frac{1}{\theta*} f(z)\, \Delta t \right]^2$$

$$\times\, p(e + \Delta e,\, \dot{e} + \Delta \dot{e};\, t + \Delta t \mid e, \dot{e};\, t)\, d(\Delta e)\, d(\Delta \dot{e}) \tag{8.55a}$$

Since, as mentioned above, $v(t)$ has a mean of zero and therefore so does $V(t)$, the second term of the right-hand member of this equation becomes zero and the third term is also evidently zero in the limit as $\Delta t \to 0$. By invoking Eqs. (8.46) m_{22} is finally obtained from Eq. (8.55a) as

$$m_{22} = \lim_{\Delta t \to 0} \frac{1}{\Delta t} \frac{1}{\theta^{*2}} \int_t^{t+\Delta t} dt \int_t^{t+\Delta t} dt' N_0 \theta^{*2} \delta(t - t')$$

$$= N_0 \qquad\qquad (8.55b)$$

The coefficient m_{12} is

$$m_{12} = \lim_{\Delta t \to 0} \frac{1}{\Delta t} \int_{-\infty}^{\infty} \int_{-\infty}^{\infty} \Delta e \left\{ \frac{1}{\theta^*} \int_t^{t+\Delta t} V(t)\, dt - \left[\frac{1}{\theta^*} \dot{e} \Delta t + \frac{1}{\theta^*} f(z)\, \Delta t \right] \right\}$$

$$\times\ p(e + \Delta e, \dot{e} + \Delta \dot{e}; t + \Delta t \mid e, \dot{e}; t)\, d(\Delta e)\, d(\Delta \dot{e})$$

$$= \dot{e} \int_{-\infty}^{\infty} \int_{-\infty}^{\infty} \lim_{\Delta t \to 0} \frac{1}{\theta^*} \int_t^{t+\Delta t} V(t)\, dt$$

$$\times\ p(e + \Delta e, \dot{e} + \Delta \dot{e}; t + \Delta t \mid e, \dot{e}; t)\, d(\Delta e)\, d(\Delta \dot{e})$$

$$-\ \dot{e} \lim_{\Delta t \to 0} \int_{-\infty}^{\infty} \int_{-\infty}^{\infty} \left| \frac{1}{\theta^*} \dot{e} \Delta t + \frac{1}{\theta^*} f(z) \Delta t \right]$$

$$\times\ p(e + \Delta e, \dot{e} + \Delta \dot{e}; t + \Delta t \mid e, \dot{e}; t)\, d(\Delta e)\, d(\Delta \dot{e})$$

$$= 0 \qquad\qquad (8.56)$$

It similarly follows that

$$m_{21} = 0 \qquad\qquad (8.57)$$

When the results of Eqs. (8.52), (8.53b), (8.54), (8.55b), (8.56), and (8.57) are applied to Eq. (8.47), the Fokker-Planck equation associated with Eq. (8.40) is expressed as

$$-\frac{\partial}{\partial e}(\dot{e} p_2) + \frac{\partial}{\partial \dot{e}} \left\{ \left[\frac{1}{\theta^*} \dot{e} + \frac{1}{\theta^*} f(z) \right] p_2 \right\} + N_0 \frac{\partial^2 p_2}{\partial \dot{e}^2} = 0 \qquad (8.58)$$

The Fokker-Planck equation has been solved by many persons.[16-20] The following procedure is that of Caughey.[20]

By adding the terms $N_0\theta*\partial^2p/\partial e\partial\dot{e}$ and $-N_0\theta*\partial^2p/\partial e\partial\dot{e}$ to Eq. (8.58), it may be expressed as

$$\frac{\partial}{\partial\dot{e}}\left\{\frac{1}{\theta*}\,[f(z)p_2] + N_0\theta*\,\frac{\partial p_2}{\partial e}\right\} + \left(\frac{1}{\theta*}\cdot\frac{\partial}{\partial\dot{e}} - \frac{\partial}{\partial e}\right)\left(\dot{e}p_2 + N_0\theta*\,\frac{\partial p_2}{\partial\dot{e}}\right) = 0$$

$$(8.59)$$

The solution of this must satisfy the following two equations:

$$\frac{1}{\theta*}\,[f(z)p_2] + N_0\theta*\,\frac{\partial p_2}{\partial e} = 0 \qquad (8.60a)$$

$$\dot{e}p_2 + N_0\theta*\,\frac{\partial p_2}{\partial\dot{e}} = 0 \qquad (8.60b)$$

If a solution of the following form is assumed,

$$p_2(e, \dot{e}) = A\,\exp\left[C_1\dot{e}^2 + C_2\int f(z)\,de\right] \qquad (8.61)$$

where A is a normalizing constant, then the two constants C_1 and C_2 can respectively be determined as

$$C_1 = -\frac{1}{2N_0\theta*} \qquad (8.62a)$$

$$C_2 = -f(z)\bigg/N_0\theta*^2\,\frac{d}{de}\int f(z)\,de \qquad (8.62b)$$

[16] M. C. Wang and G. E. Uhlenbeck, *op. cit.*
[17] H. A. Kramers, Brownian motion of a field of force and the diffusion model of chemical reactions. *Physica* **7**, 248 (1940).
[18] F. G. Dressel, The fundamental solution of the parabolic equation. *Duke Math. J.* **7**, 186 (1940); **13**, 61 (1946).
[19] K. Chuang and L. F. Kazda, *op. cit.*
[20] T. K. Caughey, *op. cit.*

With the use of these two equations, then, the solution may be written

$$p_2(e, \dot{e}) = A \exp \left\{ -\frac{1}{2N_0\theta*} \dot{e}^2 - \frac{f(z)}{N_0\theta*^2 \frac{d}{de} \int f(z)\, de} \int f(z)\, de \right\} \quad (8.63)$$

Here the output of the relay element, as already mentioned, is characterized by

$$f(z) = a\, \text{sgn}[z(t)]$$

$$= a \qquad \text{for} \quad z(t) > 0$$

$$= -a, \qquad \text{for} \quad z(t) < 0 \qquad (8.64)$$

These equations show that the driving signal $z(t)$ to the relay element,
which will determine the on-off position of the manipulating signal $y(t)$,
depends upon the error signal $e(t) = v(t) - x(t)$ and its first derivative
$\dot{e}(t) = de(t)/dt$ in a certain nonlinear fashion. The driving signal with
respect to e and $\dot{e}$ is expressed as

$$z(t) = \varphi(e, \dot{e}) \qquad (8.65)$$

Combining Eqs. (8.64) and (8.65) and substituting the result for $f(z)$ in
Eq. (8.63) yields a solution of the Fokker-Planck equation as given by
Eq. (8.59):

$$p_2(e, \dot{e}) = A \exp \left\{ -\frac{1}{2N_0\theta*} \dot{e}^2 - \frac{ae}{N_0\theta*^2} \text{sgn}[\varphi(e, \dot{e})] \right\} \qquad (8.66)$$

where the normalizing factor A is determined by the condition

$$\int_{-\infty}^{\infty} \int_{-\infty}^{\infty} p_2(e, \dot{e})\, de\, d\dot{e} = 1 \qquad (8.67)$$

The probability density function $p(e)$ of the error signal $e(t)$ is easily found by using the relation

$$p(e) = \int_{-\infty}^{\infty} p_2(e, \dot{e}) \, d\dot{e} \qquad (8.68)$$

Substitution of Eq. (8.66) for $p_2(e, \dot{e})$ in this gives

$$p(e) = A \int_{-\infty}^{\infty} \exp\left(-\frac{\dot{e}^2}{2N_0\theta^*}\right) \exp\left\{-\frac{ae}{N_0\theta^{*2}} \, \mathrm{sgn}[\varphi(e, \dot{e})] \, d\dot{e}\right\} \qquad (8.69)$$

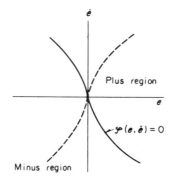

FIG. 8.9. Portrait of the function $\varphi(e, \dot{e}) = 0$

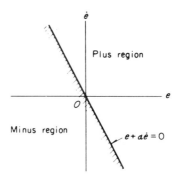

FIG. 8.10. Linear switching function.

Attention must be paid here to the function $\varphi(e, \dot{e})$ of Eq. (8.66). The following assumptions are made concerning the form of this function, shown in Fig. 8.9:[21]

1. The function exists only in the second and fourth quadrants of the $(e, \dot{e})$ phase plane.

2. The function is symmetric with respect to the origin of the $(e, \dot{e})$ phase plane.

3. The function is single-valued with respect to both variables, e and $\dot{e}$.

From a practical standpoint these assumptions may be applied to the present analysis without loss of generality. Equation (8.69) may be used to evaluate each of the half phase planes as follows. For the condition

[21] T. R. Benedict, Predictor relay servo with random inputs. *IRE Trans. Automatic Control* **AC-4**, 234 (1957).

that $\varphi(e, \dot{e}) > 0$ the equation becomes

$$
\begin{aligned}
p(e) &= A \int_{\varphi(e,\dot{e})=0}^{\infty} \exp\left(-\frac{\dot{e}^2}{2N_0\theta^*}\right) \exp\left\{-\frac{ae}{N_0\theta^{*2}} \operatorname{sgn}[\varphi(e, \dot{e})]\right\} d\dot{e} \\
&= A \exp\left(-\frac{ae}{N_0\theta^{*2}}\right) \int_{\varphi(e,\dot{e})=0}^{\infty} \exp\left(-\frac{\dot{e}^2}{2N_0\theta^*}\right) d\dot{e} \\
&= A \exp\left(-\frac{ae}{N_0\theta^{*2}}\right) \left[\int_{0}^{\infty} \exp\left(-\frac{\dot{e}^2}{2N_0\theta^*}\right) d\dot{e} \right. \\
&\qquad\qquad\qquad \left. - \int_{0}^{\varphi(e,\dot{e})=0} \exp\left(-\frac{\dot{e}^2}{2N_0\theta^*}\right) d\dot{e} \right] \\
&= A \exp\left(-\frac{ae}{N_0\theta^{*2}}\right) \left[\tfrac{1}{2}(2\pi N_0\theta^*)^{\frac{1}{2}} \right. \\
&\qquad\qquad\qquad \left. - \int_{0}^{\varphi(e,\dot{e})=0} \exp\left(-\frac{\dot{e}^2}{2N_0\theta^*}\right) d\dot{e} \right] \qquad (8.70)
\end{aligned}
$$

For the condition that $\varphi(e, \dot{e}) < 0$

$$
\begin{aligned}
p(e) &= A \int_{-\infty}^{\varphi(e,\dot{e})=0} \exp\left(-\frac{\dot{e}^2}{2N_0\theta^*}\right) \exp\left\{-\frac{ae}{N_0\theta^{*2}} \operatorname{sgn}[\varphi(e, \dot{e})]\right\} d\dot{e} \\
&= A \exp\left(\frac{ae}{N_0\theta^{*2}}\right) \int_{-\infty}^{\varphi(e,\dot{e})=0} \exp\left(-\frac{\dot{e}^2}{2N_0\theta^*}\right) d\dot{e} \\
&= A \exp\left(\frac{ae}{N_0\theta^{*2}}\right) \left[\int_{-\infty}^{0} \exp\left(-\frac{\dot{e}^2}{2N_0\theta^*}\right) d\dot{e} \right. \\
&\qquad\qquad\qquad \left. + \int_{0}^{\varphi(e,\dot{e})=0} \exp\left(-\frac{\dot{e}^2}{2N_0\theta^*}\right) d\dot{e} \right] \\
&= A \exp\left(\frac{ae}{N_0\theta^{*2}}\right) \left[\tfrac{1}{2}(2\pi N_0\theta^*)^{\frac{1}{2}} + \int_{0}^{\varphi(e,\dot{e})=0} \exp\left(-\frac{\dot{e}^2}{2N_0\theta^*}\right) d\dot{e} \right] \\
&\qquad\qquad\qquad\qquad\qquad\qquad\qquad\qquad\qquad\qquad\qquad (8.71)
\end{aligned}
$$

From Eqs. (8.70) and (8.71), the error probability density function is expressed as

$$p(e) = A(2\pi N_0\theta^*)^{\frac{1}{2}} \frac{1}{2}\left[\exp\left(-\frac{ae}{N_0\theta^{*2}}\right) + \exp\left(\frac{ae}{N_0\theta^{*2}}\right)\right]$$

$$+ A\left[\exp\left(\frac{ae}{N_0\theta^{*2}}\right) - \exp\left(-\frac{ae}{N_0\theta^{*2}}\right)\right]$$

$$\times \int_0^{\varphi(e,\dot{e})=0} \exp\left(-\frac{\dot{e}^2}{2N_0\theta^*}\right) d\dot{e}$$

$$= A(2\pi N_0\theta^*)^{\frac{1}{2}} \cosh\left(\frac{ae}{N_0\theta^{*2}}\right) + 2A \sinh\left(\frac{ae}{N_0\theta^{*2}}\right)$$

$$\times \int_0^{\varphi(e,\dot{e})=0} \exp\left(-\frac{\dot{e}^2}{2N_0\theta^*}\right) d\dot{e} \quad (8.72)$$

On the other hand, on the three assumptions listed above the switching function $\varphi(e, \dot{e}) = 0$ can be solved by putting $\dot{e}(t)$ in the form

$$\dot{e}(t) = -g(e) \quad (8.73)$$

Using Eq. (8.73), Eq. (8.72) becomes

$$p(e) = A(2\pi N_0\theta^*)^{\frac{1}{2}} \cosh\left(\frac{ae}{N_0\theta^{*2}}\right) + 2A \sinh\left(\frac{ae}{N_0\theta^{*2}}\right)$$

$$\times \int_0^{-g(e)} \exp\left(-\frac{\dot{e}^2}{2N_0\theta^*}\right) d\dot{e} \quad (8.74)$$

The condition determining the normalizing constant A, Eq. (8.67), may now be written in the following forms:

$$\int_{-\infty}^{\infty} p(e)\, de = 1 \quad (8.75a)$$

$$\int_0^{\infty} p(e)\, de = \tfrac{1}{2} \quad (8.75b)$$

Substituting Eq. (8.74) into Eq. (8.75b) and integrating by parts on the second term yields

$$
\int_0^\infty p(e)\,de = A(2\pi N_0\theta^*)^{1/2}\frac{N_0\theta^{*2}}{a}\sinh\left(\frac{ae}{N_0\theta^{*2}}\right)\Big]_0^\infty
$$

$$
+\frac{2AN_0\theta^{*2}}{a}\cosh\left(\frac{ae}{N_0\theta^{*2}}\right)\int_0^{-g(e)}\exp\left(-\frac{\dot{e}^2}{2N_0\theta^*}\right)d\dot{e}\Big]_0^\infty
$$

$$
+\int_0^\infty 2A\frac{N_0\theta^{*2}}{a}\cosh\left(\frac{ae}{N_0\theta^{*2}}\right)\frac{dg(e)}{de}\exp\left(-\frac{g^2(e)}{2N_0\theta^*}\right)de
$$

$$
(8.76)
$$

It is apparent that the first and second terms of the right-hand member of this equation each tend to zero. The normalizing constant A can, therefore, be determined by

$$
2A\frac{N_0\theta^{*2}}{a}\int_0^\infty\cosh\left(\frac{ae}{N_0\theta^{*2}}\right)\frac{dg(e)}{de}\exp\left(-\frac{g^2(e)}{2N_0\theta^*}\right)de = \tfrac{1}{2} \qquad (8.77)
$$

with the help of the specific form of the switching function $g(e)$.

A typical form of switching functions is the linear switching function illustrated in Fig. 8.10. This is mathematically expressed as

$$
\psi(e,\dot{e}) - e + \alpha\dot{e} = 0 \qquad (8.78)
$$

where α is an arbitrary positive constant. Since, as this shows, $\dot{e} = -e/\alpha$, Eq. (8.74) becomes

$$
p(e) = A(2\pi N_0\theta^*)^{1/2}\cosh\left(\frac{ae}{N_0\theta^{*2}}\right) + 2A\sinh\left(\frac{ae}{N_0\theta^{*2}}\right)
$$

$$
\times\int_0^{-e/\alpha}\exp\left(-\frac{\dot{e}^2}{2N_0\theta^*}\right)d\dot{e} \qquad (8.79)
$$

and the normalizing constant A may be determined by means of Eq. (8.77), that is,

$$
\frac{2AN_0\theta^{*2}}{a\alpha}\int_0^\infty\cosh\left(\frac{ae}{N_0\theta^{*2}}\right)\exp\left(-\frac{1}{2N_0\theta^*}\cdot\frac{e^2}{\alpha^2}\right)de = \tfrac{1}{2} \qquad (8.80a)
$$

$$
\int_0^\infty\cosh\left(\frac{ae}{N_0\theta^{*2}}\right)\exp\left(-\frac{1}{2N_0\theta^*}\cdot\frac{e^2}{\alpha^2}\right)de = \frac{a\alpha}{4AN_0\theta^{*2}} \qquad (8.80b)
$$

To calculate the left-hand member of Eq. (8.80b) we introduce the relation

$$\cosh\left(\frac{ae}{N_0\theta^{*2}}\right) = \frac{1}{2}\left[\exp\left(\frac{ae}{N_0\theta^{*2}}\right) + \exp\left(-\frac{ae}{N_0\theta^{*2}}\right)\right] \qquad (8.81)$$

Then Eq. (8.80b) may be rewritten:

$$\int_0^\infty \exp\left(-\frac{1}{2N_0\theta^*}\cdot\frac{e^2}{\alpha^2} + \frac{ae}{N_0\theta^{*2}}\right) de$$

$$+ \int_0^\infty \exp\left(-\frac{1}{2N_0\theta^{*2}}\cdot\frac{e^2}{\alpha^2} - \frac{ae}{N_0\theta^{*2}}\right) de = \frac{a\alpha}{2AN_0\theta^{*2}} \qquad (8.82)$$

The results of integrating the first and second terms on the left side of this equation are, respectively,

$$\int_0^\infty \exp\left(-\frac{1}{2N_0\theta^*}\cdot\frac{e^2}{\alpha^2} + \frac{ae}{N_0\theta^{*2}}\right) de$$

$$= \exp\left(\frac{a^2\alpha^2}{2N_0\theta^{*3}}\right)\left[\frac{\alpha}{2}(2\pi N_0\theta^*)^{\frac{1}{2}} + \int_0^{a\alpha^2/\theta^*}\exp\left(-\frac{u^2}{2N_0\theta^*\alpha^2}\right) du\right]$$

$$\qquad (8.83a)$$

$$\int_0^\infty \exp\left(-\frac{1}{2N_0\theta^*}\cdot\frac{e^2}{\alpha^2} - \frac{ae}{N_0\theta^{*2}}\right) de$$

$$= \exp\left(\frac{a^2\alpha^2}{2N_0\theta^{*3}}\right)\left[\frac{\alpha}{2}(2\pi N_0\theta^*)^{\frac{1}{2}} - \int_0^{a\alpha^2/\theta^*}\exp\left(-\frac{u^2}{2N_0\theta^*\alpha^2}\right) du\right]$$

$$\qquad (8.83b)$$

Using these in Eq. (8.80b) we finally obtain the normalizing constant:

$$A = \frac{1}{(2\pi N_0\theta^*)^{\frac{1}{2}}}\cdot\frac{a}{2N_0\theta^{*2}}\exp\left(-\frac{a^2\alpha^2}{2N_0\theta^{*3}}\right) \qquad (8.84)$$

8.3-2   Evaluation of variance of error response.   From Eqs. (8.79) and (8.84), the 1-dimensional probability density function $p(e)$ is completely obtained and the variance ψ_e of the error response $e(t)$ may be computed by the relation

$$\psi_e = \int_{-\infty}^\infty e^2 p(e)\, de \qquad (8.85)$$

Substitution of Eq. (8.79) for $p(e)$ in Eq. (8.85) gives us

$$\psi_e = A(2\pi N_0\theta^*)^{1/2} \int_{-\infty}^{\infty} e^2 \cosh\left(\frac{ae}{N_0\theta^{*2}}\right) de$$

$$+ 2A \int_{-\infty}^{\infty} e^2 \sinh\left(\frac{ae}{N_0\theta^{*2}}\right) \int_0^{-e/\alpha} \exp\left(-\frac{\dot{e}^2}{2N_0\theta^*}\right) d\dot{e}\, de \quad (8.86)$$

By letting

$$I_1 = \int_0^M e^2 \cosh\left(\frac{ae}{N_0\theta^{*2}}\right) de \quad (8.87a)$$

$$I_2 = \int_0^M e^2 \sinh\left(\frac{ae}{N_0\theta^{*2}}\right) \int_0^{-e/\alpha} \exp\left(-\frac{\dot{e}^2}{2N_0\theta^*}\right) d\dot{e}\, de \quad (8.87b)$$

$$\varphi_{eM} = 2A(2\pi N_0\theta^*)^{1/2} I_1 + 4AI_2 \quad (8.88)$$

we may rewrite Eq. (8.86):

$$\psi_e = \lim_{M\to\infty} \psi_{eM} = \lim_{M\to\infty} (2A(2\pi N_0\theta^*)^{1/2} I_1 + 4AI_2) \quad (8.89)$$

The integrals in Eqs. (8.87) are respectively computed as

$$I_1 = \frac{N_0\theta^{*2}}{a} M^2 \sinh\left(\frac{aM}{N_0\theta^{*2}}\right) - \frac{2N_0\theta^{*4}}{a^2} M \cosh\left(\frac{aM}{N_0\theta^{*2}}\right)$$

$$+ \frac{2N_0^3\theta^{*6}}{a^3} \sinh\left(\frac{aM}{N_0\theta^{*2}}\right) \quad (8.90a)$$

$$I_2 = \left[\frac{N_0\theta^{*2}}{a} M^2 \cosh\left(\frac{aM}{N_0\theta^{*2}}\right) - \frac{2N_0^2\theta^{*4}}{a^2} M \sinh\left(\frac{aM}{N_0\theta^{*2}}\right)\right.$$

$$\left. + \frac{2N_0^3\theta^{*6}}{a^3} \cosh\left(\frac{aM}{N_0\theta^{*2}}\right) - \frac{2N_0^3\theta^6}{a^3}\right] \int_0^{-M/\alpha} \exp\left(-\frac{\dot{e}^2}{2N_0\theta^*}\right) d\dot{e}$$

$$- \int_0^M \frac{1}{\alpha}\left[\frac{N_0\theta^{*2}}{a} e^2 \cosh\left(\frac{ae}{N_0\theta^{*2}}\right) - \frac{2N_0^2\theta^{*4}}{a^2} e \sinh\left(\frac{ae}{N_0\theta^{*2}}\right)\right.$$

$$\left. + \frac{2N_0^3\theta^{*6}}{a^3} \cosh\left(\frac{ae}{N_0\theta^{*2}}\right) - \frac{2N_0^3\theta^{*6}}{a^3}\right] \exp(-e^2/2N_0\theta^*\alpha^2) \quad (8.90b)$$

Then, by using Eqs. (8.88) and (8.90a) we get, for Eq. (8.89),

$$
\psi_e = \frac{4A}{\alpha} \int_0^\infty \left[\frac{N_0\theta^{*2}}{a} e^2 \cosh\left(\frac{ae}{N_0\theta^{*2}}\right) - \frac{2N_0^2\theta^{*4}}{a^2} e \sinh\left(\frac{ae}{N_0\theta^{*2}}\right) \right.
$$

$$
+ \frac{2N_0^3\theta^{*6}}{a^3} \cosh\left(\frac{ae}{N_0\theta^{*2}}\right) - \left. \frac{2N_0^3\theta^{*6}}{a^3} \right] \exp\left(-\frac{1}{2N_0\theta^{*2}} \cdot \frac{e^2}{\alpha^2} \right) de
$$

$$
+ \frac{8AN_0^3\theta^{*6}}{a^3} \int_0^\infty \exp\left(-\frac{\dot{e}^2}{2N_0\theta^*} \right) d\dot{e}
$$

$$
= \frac{4AN_0\theta^{*2}}{a\alpha} \int_0^\infty e^2 \cosh\left(\frac{ae}{N_0\theta^{*2}}\right) \exp\left(-\frac{1}{2N_0\theta^{*2}} \cdot \frac{e^2}{\alpha^2} \right) de
$$

$$
- \frac{8AN_0^2\theta^{*4}}{\alpha a^2} \int_0^\infty e \sinh\left(\frac{ae}{N_0\theta^{*2}}\right) \exp\left(-\frac{1}{2N_0\theta^{*2}} \cdot \frac{e^2}{\alpha^2} \right) de
$$

$$
+ \frac{8AN_0^3\theta^{*6}}{\alpha a^3} \int_0^\infty \cosh\left(\frac{ae}{N_0\theta^{*2}}\right) \exp\left(-\frac{1}{2N_0\theta^{*2}} \cdot \frac{e^2}{\alpha^2} \right) de
$$

$$
= \frac{2AN_0\theta^{*2}}{\alpha a} J_1 - \frac{4AN_0^2\theta^{*2}}{\alpha a^2} J_2 + \frac{4AN_0^3\theta^{*6}}{\alpha a^3} J_3 \tag{8.91}
$$

where

$$
J_1 = \int_{-\infty}^\infty e^2 \cosh\left(\frac{ae}{N_0\theta^{*2}}\right) \exp\left(-\frac{1}{2N_0\theta^{*2}} \cdot \frac{e^2}{\alpha^2} \right) de \tag{8.92a}
$$

$$
J_2 = \int_{-\infty}^\infty e \sinh\left(\frac{ae}{N_0\theta^{*2}}\right) \exp\left(-\frac{1}{2N_0\theta^{*2}} \cdot \frac{e^2}{\alpha^2} \right) de \tag{8.92b}
$$

$$
J_3 = \int_{-\infty}^\infty \cosh\left(\frac{ae}{N_0\theta^{*2}}\right) \exp\left(-\frac{1}{2N_0\theta^{*2}} \cdot \frac{e^2}{\alpha^2} \right) de \tag{8.92c}
$$

With the relation given in Eq. (8.81) the first of these may be written

$$
J_1 = \tfrac{1}{2} \exp\left(\frac{\alpha^2 a^2}{2N_0\theta^{*3}}\right) \left\{ \int_{-\infty}^\infty e^2 \exp\left[-\frac{1}{2N_0\theta^*\alpha^2}\left(e - \frac{\alpha^2 a}{\theta^*} \right)^2 \right] de \right.
$$

$$
+ \left. \int_{-\infty}^\infty e^2 \exp\left[-\frac{1}{2N_0\theta^*\alpha^2}\left(e + \frac{\alpha^2 a}{\theta^*} \right)^2 \right] de \right\} \tag{8.93}
$$

If we let

$$e \mp \frac{\alpha^2 a}{\theta*} = u \tag{8.94}$$

and invoke the relations

$$\int_0^\infty u^2 \exp\left(-\frac{u^2}{2\sigma^2}\right) du = \frac{(2\pi)^{\frac{1}{2}}}{2} \sigma^3 \tag{8.95a}$$

$$\int_0^\infty \exp\left(-\frac{u^2}{2\sigma^2}\right) du = \frac{(2\pi)^{\frac{1}{2}}}{2} \sigma \tag{8.95b}$$

then Eq. (8.93) yields

$$J_1 = (2\pi N_0 \theta*^3)^{\frac{1}{2}} \alpha^3 \left(N_0 \theta* + \frac{a^2 \alpha^3}{\theta*^2}\right) \exp\left(\frac{\alpha^2 a^2}{2 N_0 \theta*^3}\right) \tag{8.96}$$

Since Eq. (8.92b) is similarly rewritten,

$$J_2 = \tfrac{1}{2} \exp\left(\frac{\alpha^2 a^2}{2 N_0 \theta*^3}\right)\left\{\int_{-\infty}^\infty e \exp\left[-\frac{1}{2 N_0 \theta* \alpha^2}\left(e - \frac{\alpha^2 a}{\theta*}\right)^2\right] de \right.$$
$$\left. - \int_{-\infty}^\infty e \exp\left[-\frac{1}{2 N_0 \theta* \alpha^2}\left(e + \frac{\alpha^2 a}{\theta*}\right)^2\right] de\right\} \tag{8.97}$$

then, by applying Eq. (8.94) to Eq. (8.97) and using the relation

$$\int_{-\infty}^\infty u \exp\left(-\frac{u^2}{2\sigma^2}\right) du = 0 \tag{8.98}$$

it is easily obtained that

$$J_2 = \frac{\alpha^3 a}{\theta*} (2\pi N_0 \theta*)^{\frac{1}{2}} \exp\left(\frac{\alpha^2 a^2}{2 N_0 \theta*^3}\right) \tag{8.99}$$

From Eqs. (8.83) it is easily shown that the integral given by Eq. (8.92c) becomes

$$J_3 = \alpha (2\pi N_0 \theta*)^{\frac{1}{2}} \exp\left(\frac{\alpha^2 a^2}{2 N_0 \theta*^3}\right) \tag{8.100}$$

Finally, Eqs. (8.96), (8.99), and (8.100) are used to put Eq. (8.91) in the form

$$\psi_e = \frac{a^2}{\theta*^2}\alpha^4 - N_0\theta*\alpha^2 + \frac{2\theta*^4}{a^2}N_0^2 \qquad (8.101)$$

8.3-3 Numerical studies of error response. We shall consider a numerical example in which the values of the clipping level a and the constant N_0 related to the input spectral density $S_v(\omega)$ are respectively given by $a = 1.0$ and $N_0 = 0.5$. Then Eq. (8.101) becomes

$$\psi_e = \frac{\alpha^4}{\theta*^2} - 0.50*\alpha^2 + 0.50*^4 \qquad (8.102)$$

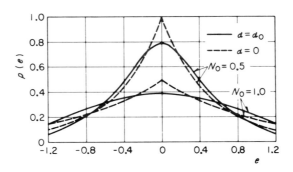

FIG. 8.11. Probability density function of the error signal.

The optimal inclination value α_0 of the switching line is so determined that this variance becomes minimal:

$$\alpha_0 = \tfrac{1}{2}\theta*^{3/2} \qquad (8.103)$$

Figure 8.11 shows the numerical plots of the error response probability density function $p(e)$ obtained by Eqs. (8.79) and (8.84). The solid curves show the error probability density functions when the inclination of the switching line is adjusted to the optimal value, and the dotted curves show them at the unadjusted condition of the switching function $e = 0$. The relation between the values of α_0 and $\theta*$ determined by Eq. (8.103) is illustrated in Fig. 8.12. In the system shown in Fig. 8.5 the time constant of the controlled element varies in a certain unpredictable fashion over the range between $\theta* = 1.0$, its maximum value, and

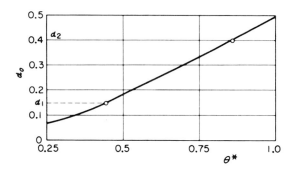

FIG. 8.12. Desired variation of α_0 with θ^*.

$\theta^* = 0.4$. Let us assume from Fig. 8.12 that the parameter α has been prescribed $\alpha_1 = 0.15$ and $\alpha_2 = 0.40$.

8.3-4   Choice of values θ_0^* , θ_1^* , and θ_2^* .   To find the values θ_0^* , θ_1^*, and θ_2^* from Eq. (8.102) we plot the variance ψ_e of the error response in relation to θ^* with the value of α_i as a parameter; see Fig. 8.13. We

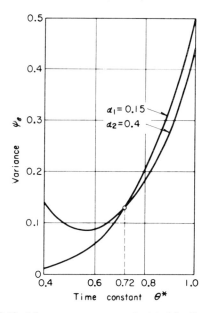

FIG. 8.13. Mean square error, calculated by Eq. (8.46).

assume the following rule:

$$\text{Set } \alpha_0 = \alpha_1, \quad \text{when} \quad \theta < \theta_0^*.$$
$$\text{Set } \alpha_0 = \alpha_2, \quad \text{when} \quad \theta > \theta_0^*. \tag{8.104}$$

Then it is obvious from the figure that $\theta_0^* = 0.72$. The requirement concerning the size of the indifference zone need not be stringent; thus, we may take $\theta_1^* = 0.70$ and $\theta_2^* = 0.75$, referring to Fig. 8.13.

8.3-5 Calculation of probability F_{ij}. To calculate the probability F_{ij} it is more convenient to calculate the following integral instead of Eq. (8.8):

$$P(z_s; \alpha_i, \theta_j^*) = \int_{-\infty}^{z_s} p(e; \alpha_i, \theta_j^*)\, de \tag{8.105}$$

The probability density function $p(e; \alpha_i, \theta_j^*)$ has already been given by Eqs. (8.79) and (8.84). The probability $P(z_s; \alpha_i, \theta_j^*)$ can, therefore, be computed as

$$P(z_s; \alpha_i, \theta_j^*) = \frac{1}{\theta^{*2}} \cdot \frac{1}{(\pi\theta^*)^{1/2}} \exp\left(-\frac{\alpha_i^2}{\theta_j^{*3}}\right) \int_{-\infty}^{z_s} \left[(\pi\theta_j^*)^{1/2} \cosh\left(\frac{2e}{\theta_j^{*2}}\right)\right.$$
$$\left. + 2\sinh\left(\frac{2e}{\theta_j^{*2}}\right) \int_0^{-e/\alpha_i} \exp\left(-\frac{\dot{e}^2}{\theta_j^*}\right) d\dot{e}\right] de \tag{8.106}$$

where the set of numerical values $N_0 = 0.5$ and $a = 1$ has been applied. A computation similar to that of Eq. (8.101) gives us

$$P(z_s; \alpha_i, \theta_j^*) = \int_{-\infty}^{z_s} p(e; \alpha_i, \theta_j^*)\, de$$
$$== \frac{1}{(\pi\theta_j^*)^{1/2}} \exp\left(-\frac{\alpha_i^2}{\theta_j^{*3}}\right) \left[\tfrac{1}{2}(\pi\theta_j^*)^{1/2} \sinh\left(\frac{2z_s}{\theta_j^{*2}}\right)\right.$$
$$- \cosh\left(\frac{2z_s}{\theta_j^{*2}}\right) \int_0^{z_s/\alpha_i} \exp\left(-\frac{\dot{e}^2}{\theta_j^*}\right) d\dot{e}$$
$$\left. + \frac{1}{\alpha_i} \int_{-\infty}^{z_s} \cosh\left(\frac{2e}{\theta_j^{*2}}\right) \exp\left(-\frac{e^2}{\theta_j^* \alpha_i^2}\right) de \right]$$
$$= \frac{1}{2}\left[1 + \exp\left(-\frac{\alpha_i^2}{\theta_j^{*3}}\right) \sinh\left(\frac{2z_s}{\theta_j^{*2}}\right)\right]$$
$$+ \phi\left[\frac{z_s}{\alpha_i}\left(\frac{2}{\theta_j^*}\right)^{1/2}\right]\left[1 - \exp\left(-\frac{\alpha_i^2}{\theta_j^{*3}}\right) \cosh\frac{2z_s}{\theta_j^{*2}}\right] \tag{8.107}$$

where

$$\phi(\xi) = \frac{1}{(2\pi)^{1/2}} \int_0^\xi \exp\left(-\frac{t^2}{2}\right) dt \tag{8.108}$$

Substituting $\alpha_1 = 0.15$, $\alpha_2 = 0.40$, $\theta_{1_i}^* = 0.70$, and $\theta_2^* = 0.75$ into Eq. (8.107), we obtain

$$P(z_s; \alpha_1, \theta_1^*) = \tfrac{1}{2}[1 + \exp(-0.06) \sinh 4.08 z_s]$$
$$+ \phi(11.27 z_s)[1 - \exp(-0.06) \cosh 4.08 z_s]$$

$$P(z_s; \alpha_1, \theta_2^*) = \tfrac{1}{2}[1 + \exp(-0.05) \sinh 3.56 z_s]$$
$$+ \phi(10.89 z_s)[1 - \exp(-0.05) \cosh 3.56 z_s]$$

$$P(z_s; \alpha_2, \theta_1^*) = \tfrac{1}{2}[1 + \exp(-0.47) \sinh 4.08 z_s]$$
$$+ \phi(4.23 z_s)[1 - \exp(-0.47) \cosh 4.08 z_s]$$

$$P(z_s; \alpha_2, \theta_2^*) = \tfrac{1}{2}[1 + \exp(-0.38) \sinh 3.56 z_s]$$
$$+ \phi(4.08 z_s)[1 - \exp(-0.38) \cosh 3.56 z_s]$$

(8.109)

Consequently, the probability F_{ij} can be calculated from

$$F_{ij} = 1 - P(z_0; \alpha_i, \theta_j^*), \qquad i, j = 1, 2 \tag{8.110}$$

The numerical results are illustrated in Fig. 8.14.

8.3-6 Determination of slicing level z_s. By means of the numerical results given above and Eq. (8.25) the value of $D_i(z_s)$ can be calculated and plotted as shown in Fig. 8.15. For $D_1(z_s)$ we have

$$z_s = 0.5 \tag{8.111}$$

and for $D_2(z_s)$ we have

$$z_s = 0.4 \tag{8.112}$$

Clearly, we may choose

$$z_s = 0.4 \tag{8.113}$$

as an adequate value of the slicing level.

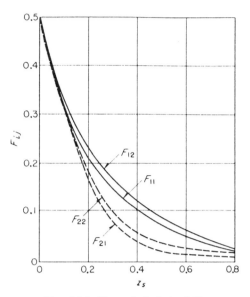

FIG. 8.14. Numerical plots of F_{ij}.

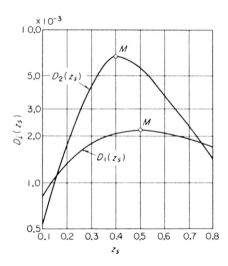

FIG. 8.15. Numerical plots of $D_i(z)$.

8.3-7   Resultant decision rule.   We begin by assigning to the first and second error probabilities ϵ_1 and ϵ_2 the value $\epsilon_1 = \epsilon_2 = 0.05$. Then the two constants A and B are, from Eqs. (8.2),

$$A = \frac{1 - \epsilon_2}{\epsilon_1} = 19 \qquad\qquad (8.114a)$$

$$B = \frac{\epsilon_2}{1 - \epsilon_1} = \frac{1}{19} \qquad\qquad (8.114b)$$

Since the value of the slicing level has been determined as $z_s = 0.4$ in the previous section, then, by using values of the probabilities F_{ij} obtained from Fig. 8.14, the decision thresholds for $i = 1$ are determined from Eqs. (8.12) and (8.14):

$$\kappa_1^+(n) = 0.12n + 22$$
$$\kappa_1^-(n) = 0.12\,n - 22 \qquad\qquad (8.115)$$

Similarly, the decision thresholds for $i = 2$ are

$$\kappa_2^+(n) = 0.05n + 9$$
$$\kappa_2^-(n) = 0.05n - 9 \qquad\qquad (8.116)$$

Rules (8.13a) and (8.13b) in conjunction with Eqs. (8.115) and (8.116) may now be written as follows:

1. When the control system is in an operating condition for the parameter $\alpha_0 = \alpha_1$ of the controller to be adjusted, if $k > \kappa_1^+(n)$, then $\theta^* > \theta_2^*$, and the parameter should be changed from α_1 to α_2, but if $k < \kappa_1^+(n)$, then $\theta^* < \theta_1^*$, and the parameter should not be changed.
2. When the control system is in an operating condition for the parameter $\alpha_0 = \alpha_2$ of the controller to be adjusted, if $k > \kappa_2^-(n)$, then $\theta^* > \theta_2^*$, and the parameter should not be changed, but if $k < \kappa_2^-(n)$, then the parameter should be changed from α_2 to α_1.

The region of decision for such a test is illustrated in Fig. 8.16. In accordance with this the complete configuration of the control system becomes as shown in Fig. 8.17.

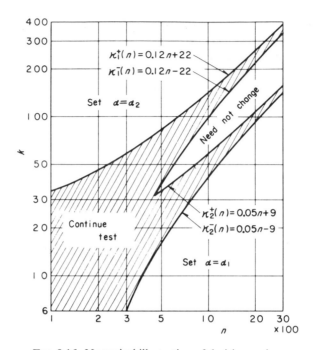

FIG. 8.16. Numerical illustration of decision regions.

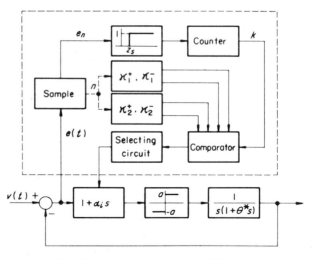

FIG. 8.17. Final construction of Fig. 8.3.

In the preceding sections we treated the case in which the range of parameter variation is divided into only two intervals. We did so in order to reduce the amount of calculation, although it would be more natural to assume that the range were divided into three or more intervals. The principle of the method may be extended to any finite number of intervals. When the intervals are three or more, we can construct the separable decision rule for various simple alternative tests, as stated in Chapter 7.

CHAPTER 9

Some Future Problems in Applications of Statistical Decision Theory to Control Processes

9.1 Introductory Remarks

We have seen how the methods of statistical decision theory may be applied to such control problems as system identification, adaptive control, and parameter adjustment of nonlinear control systems. The substance of our discussions has been introductory merely; no important problems have been touched upon, definite applications of the theory having only been indicated. However, in comprehending the theoretical feature of decision adaptive control described in the previous chapters we may observe that the present approach is quite general, not only because it uses all the practical information that may be acquired through observation of the random nature of environments, but also because it provides us with a reasonable means of determining the best strategy under the unavoidably uncertain conditions of human perception. We may note, furthermore, that statistical decision theory in automatic control offers us a much broader and more realistic technique for adaptive control system synthesis than do the classical methods based on correlation functions and spectral densities, both of which are related to lower-order joint statistics with respect to no more than second-order probability density functions. Nevertheless, we must not have the impression that statistical decision theory is applicable to problems of control processes without our making any assumptions or establishing any restrictions.

In this chapter we shall inquire into the future of decision adaptive control theory. We shall first consider some further applications of it by focusing our attention on a type of filtering problems. Then we shall state some future problems in applications of the statistical decision theory to control processes.

9.2 Filtering Problems with Statistical Decision Theory

When the input signal is represented by the sum of a signal component $s(t)$ and a random noise component $n(t)$, the method described in the previous chapters may be extended to problems of designing linear and nonlinear optimal control systems and to filtering theory in communications engineering. The theory of optimal linear filters for the prediction and smoothing of stationary time series was originally developed by Wiener[1] and was extended by other investigators[2-5] to the design of various types of complicated systems, notably in the field of automatic control. The statistical design of optimal nonlinear filters from the theoretical point of view has been treated by several others.[6-11] Our emphasis in this section is on showing the combination of statistical decision theory with Wiener filtering theory. We begin with the formulation of nonlinear filtering problems.

Let the input $v(t)$ be the sum of two independent random processes, namely, the message signal $s(t)$ and the random noise $n(t)$:

$$v(t) = s(t) + n(t) \qquad (9.1)$$

[1] N. Wiener, "The Extrapolation, Interpolation and Smoothing of Stationary Time Series " Wiley, New York, 1949.

[2] L. A. Zadeh and J. R. Ragazzini, An extension of Wiener theory of prediction. *J. Appl. Phys.* **21**, 645 (1950).

[3] G. C. Newton, L. A. Gould, and J. F. Kaiser, "Analytical Design of Linear Feedback Controls." Wiley, New York, 1957.

[4] C. W. Steeg, A time domain synthesis for optimum extrapolators. *IRE Trans. Automatic Control* **AC-4**, 32 (1957).

[5] C. E. Shannon, A simplified derivation of linear least square smoothing and prediction theory. *Proc. IRE* **38**, 417 (1950).

[6] N. Wiener, *In* "Non-Linear Prediction, Probability and Statistics" (J. Grenander, ed.). Wiley, New York, 1959.

[7] L. A. Zadeh, Optimum non-linear filters. *J. Appl. Phys.* **24**, 396 (1953).

[8] R. Drenick, A non-linear prediction theory. *IRE Trans. Information Theory* **IT-4**, 146 (1954).

[9] A. V. Balackrishnan and R. F. Drenick, On optimum non-linear extraction and coding filters. *IRE Trans. Information Theory* **IT-2**, 166 (1956).

[10] J. K. Lubbock, The optimization of a class of non-linear filters. *Proc. IRE*, Monograph No. 344E, p. 60 (1958).

[11] Y. Sawaragi, Y. Sunahara, and T. Nakamizo, A study on the statistical synthesis of optimum non-linear control systems subjected to non-gaussian random inputs. *Tech. Rept. Eng. Res. Inst., Kyoto Univ.* **11**, Rept. No. 90 (1961).

The two random vector processes are

$$\mathbf{v} = (v_1, v_2, \ldots, v_n)$$
$$\mathbf{s} = (s_1, s_2, \ldots, s_n)$$

The subscripts of the components v_i and s_i signify an ordering in time, so that $s_i = s(t_i)$ and $v_i = v(t_i)$, where $0 < t_1 < t_2 < \cdots < t_i < \cdots < t_n = t$ and the symbol t expresses the present time. Although we have used the following symbols frequently in the previous chapters, we shall summarize these once again, making a few minor changes in meaning:

$p_0(\mathbf{s})$ — The a priori probability density function of the vector random process $\mathbf{s}$.

$p(\mathbf{v} \mid \mathbf{s})$ — The conditional probability density function of the vector random process $\mathbf{v}$, when the vector random process $\mathbf{s}$ is given.

$p_d(\mathbf{s}^* \mid \mathbf{v})$ — The decision function based on the observed vector process $\mathbf{v}$.

$W(\mathbf{s}, \mathbf{s}^*)$ — The loss function.

$\mathscr{D}_s$ — The n-dimensional message-signal space.

$\mathscr{D}_a$ — The n-dimensional observed-data space.

$\mathscr{D}_d$ — The n-dimensional decision space.

The optimal estimate of $\mathbf{s}$ is expressed by the symbol $\mathbf{s}^*$. Referring to Eq. (4.6), we obtain the average risk:

$$R(p_0, p_d) = \int_{\mathscr{D}_s} p_0(\mathbf{s}) \, d\mathbf{s} \int_{\mathscr{D}_a} p(\mathbf{v} \mid \mathbf{s}) \, d\mathbf{v} \int_{\mathscr{D}_d} W(\mathbf{s}, \mathbf{s}^*) \, p_d(\mathbf{s}^* \mid \mathbf{v}) \, d\mathbf{s}^* \quad (9.2)$$

As shown in Fig. 9.1, the present problem is to decide on a functional form of the best operation $\mathbf{x} = x(\mathbf{v})$, on the incoming signal $\mathbf{v}$, that generates the best estimate s^* of the message signal s. For a case of practical interest it is sufficient to consider the nonrandomized decision rule.[12] If the loss function $W(\mathbf{s}, \mathbf{s}^*)$ is a convex function of $\mathbf{s}^*$ with respect to $\mathbf{s}$,

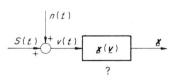

FIG. 9.1. Non-linear filtering problem, schematic.

[12] D. Blackwell and M. A. Girshick, "Theory of Games and Statistical Decisions." Wiley, New York, 1954.

then we may write[13]

$$p_d(\mathbf{s}^* \mid \mathbf{v}) = \delta(\mathbf{s}^* - \mathbf{x}) \qquad (9.3)$$

where the right-hand side represents Dirac's delta function. The best form of the functional operation should naturally be constructed in such a way that the average risk shown by Eq. (9.2) becomes minimal. However, by substituting Eq. (9.3) into Eq. (9.2), the average risk $R(p_0, p_d)$ may be expressed in an alternative form:

$$R(p_0, \mathbf{x}) = \int_{\mathcal{D}_s} p_0(\mathbf{s}) \, d\mathbf{s} \int_{\mathcal{D}_a} p(\mathbf{v} \mid \mathbf{s}) \, W(\mathbf{s}, \mathbf{x}) \, d\mathbf{v} \qquad (9.4)$$

When the loss function $W(\mathbf{s}, \mathbf{x})$ is differentiable with respect to $\mathbf{x}$, the following condition for a Bayesian decision rule may be derived:

$$\int_{\mathcal{D}_s} p_0(\mathbf{s}) \, p(\mathbf{v} \mid \mathbf{s}) \frac{\partial W(\mathbf{s}, \mathbf{x})}{\partial \mathbf{x}} \, d\mathbf{s} = 0 \qquad (9.5)$$

The error measure is now chosen to be the quadratic loss function, which is equivalent to the Wiener criterion:

$$W(\mathbf{s}, \mathbf{x}) = C_0(\mathbf{s} - \mathbf{x})'(\mathbf{s} - \mathbf{x}) = C_0 \sum_{i=1}^{n} (s_i - x_i)^2 \qquad (9.6)$$

where C_0 is an arbitrary constant. This type of loss function has convenient properties in mathematical treatments and is frequently used in the literature. By applying it to Eq. (9.5), we have

$$\int_{\mathcal{D}_s} (\mathbf{x} - \mathbf{s}) \, p(\mathbf{v} \mid \mathbf{s}) \, p_0(\mathbf{s}) \, d\mathbf{s} = 0 \qquad (9.7)$$

With the help of the relations

$$p(\mathbf{v} \mid \mathbf{s}) \, p_0(\mathbf{s}) = p(\mathbf{v}, \mathbf{s}) \qquad (9.8a)$$

$$\int_{\mathcal{D}_s} p(\mathbf{v} \mid \mathbf{s}) p_0(\mathbf{s}) \, d\mathbf{s} = \int_{\mathcal{D}_s} p(\mathbf{v}, \mathbf{s}) \, d\mathbf{s} = p(\mathbf{v}) \qquad (9.8b)$$

[13] J. L. Hodges and E. L. Lehmann, Some problems in minimax point estimation. *Ann. Math. Statistics* **21** (1950).

Eq. (9.7) becomes

$$\mathbf{x}(\mathbf{v}) = \frac{\int_{\mathcal{D}_s} \mathbf{s} p(\mathbf{v} \mid \mathbf{s}) \, p_0(\mathbf{s}) \, d\mathbf{s}}{\int_{\mathcal{D}_s} p(\mathbf{v} \mid \mathbf{s}) \, p_0(\mathbf{s}) \, d\mathbf{s}} = \int_{\mathcal{D}_s} \mathbf{s} \, p(\mathbf{s} \mid \mathbf{v}) \, d\mathbf{s} \qquad (9.9)$$

This equation reveals that the optimal operation $\mathbf{x}(\mathbf{v})$ is determined by evaluating the conditional expectation of the vector random process $\mathbf{s}$, provided that the vector random process $\mathbf{v}$ is given within the time interval $[0, t]$. This is often called the conditional mean estimate. Clearly, other estimates can be derived, depending upon other loss functions. It is easy to show how Eq. (9.7) agrees with the result derived by the Wiener theory under the assumption of a gaussian distribution of both message signal and random noise.[14] It must, however, be noted that in the Wiener theory the characteristics of the optimal filter derived by solving the Wiener-Hopf integral equation are constrained to be linear, even if nongaussian statistics of inputs are considered.

For the purpose of describing the derivation of the Wiener-Hopf integral equation from the viewpoint of statistical decision theory we must consider a method of further calculating Eq. (9.7). However, its solution has little general use, because calculations of conditional expectation usually involve a more detailed knowledge of the input than is usually available. In view of this fact we may also state that the Wiener theory gives us explicit and practical solutions but restricted classes of problems. However, since Eq. (9.7) is particularly important in the solution of nonlinear filtering problems, we shall discuss these in connection with it.

In order to calculate Eq. (9.7), we assume that the difference $\mathbf{x} - \mathbf{s}$ is relatively small. On this assumption the conditional probability density function $p(\mathbf{v} \mid \mathbf{s})$ can be expanded into the following Taylor series:

$$p(\mathbf{v} \mid \mathbf{s}) = p(\mathbf{v} \mid \mathbf{x}) + \boldsymbol{\beta}'(\mathbf{s} - \mathbf{x}) - \tfrac{1}{2}(\mathbf{s} - \mathbf{x})'\boldsymbol{\alpha}(\mathbf{s} - \mathbf{x}) + \cdots$$

$$(9.10)$$

---

[14] D. Middleton, "An Introduction to Statistical Communication Theory," Chap. 21. McGraw-Hill, New York, 1960.

where

$$\beta = \left(\frac{\partial p(\mathbf{v} \mid \mathbf{x})}{\partial s_1}, \frac{\partial p(\mathbf{v} \mid \mathbf{x})}{\partial s_2}, \ldots, \frac{\partial p(\mathbf{v} \mid \mathbf{x})}{\partial s_n} \right) \tag{9.11a}$$

$$\alpha = \left\| - \frac{\partial^2 p(\mathbf{v} \mid \mathbf{x})}{\partial s_i \, \partial s_j} \right\| \tag{9.11b}$$

For convenience in computation we take the logarithmic form of the conditional probability density function and expand it into a Taylor series:

$$\log p(\mathbf{v} \mid \mathbf{s}) = \log p(\mathbf{v} \mid \mathbf{x}) + \mathbf{B}'(\mathbf{s} - \mathbf{x}) - \tfrac{1}{2}(\mathbf{s} - \mathbf{x})'\mathbf{A}^{-1}(\mathbf{s} - \mathbf{x}) + \cdots \tag{9.12}$$

where

$$\mathbf{B} = (b_1, b_2, \ldots, b_n)$$

$$= \left(\frac{\partial \log p(\mathbf{v} \mid \mathbf{x})}{\partial s_1}, \frac{\partial \log p(\mathbf{v} \mid \mathbf{x})}{\partial s_2}, \ldots, \frac{\partial \log p(\mathbf{v} \mid \mathbf{x})}{\partial s_n} \right) \tag{9.13a}$$

$$\mathbf{A}^{-1} = \|a_{ij}\| = \left\| - \frac{\partial^2 \log p(\mathbf{v} \mid \mathbf{x})}{\partial s_i \, \partial s_j} \right\| \tag{9.13b}$$

Then Eq. (9.12) can be approximately expressed as

$$p(\mathbf{v} \mid \mathbf{s}) = p(\mathbf{v} \mid \mathbf{x}) \exp[\mathbf{B}'(\mathbf{s} - \mathbf{x}) - \tfrac{1}{2}(\mathbf{s} - \mathbf{x})'\mathbf{A}^{-1}(\mathbf{s} - \mathbf{x})] \tag{9.14}$$

Specifically, our special interest is directed to the random signal with gaussian probability density function,

$$p_0(\mathbf{s}) = (2\pi)^{-n/2} |\mathbf{M}|^{-\frac{1}{2}} \exp(-\mathbf{s}'\mathbf{M}^{-1}\mathbf{s}) \tag{9.15}$$

From Eqs. (9.14) and (9.15), we have

$$p_0(\mathbf{s}) \, p(\mathbf{v} \mid \mathbf{s}) = (2\pi)^{-n/2} |\mathbf{M}|^{-\frac{1}{2}} J \, p(\mathbf{v} \mid \mathbf{x}) \exp(-\mathbf{B}'\mathbf{x} - \tfrac{1}{2}\mathbf{x}'\mathbf{A}^{-1}\mathbf{x}) \tag{9.16}$$

where

$$J = \exp(j\boldsymbol{\sigma}'\mathbf{s} - \tfrac{1}{2}\mathbf{s}'\mathbf{C}^{-1}\mathbf{s}) \qquad (9.17a)$$

$$j\boldsymbol{\sigma}' = \mathbf{B}' + \mathbf{x}'\mathbf{A}^{-1} \qquad (9.17b)$$

$$\mathbf{C}^{-1} = \mathbf{A}^{-1} + \mathbf{M}^{-1} \qquad (9.17c)$$

Although the optimal nonlinear transfer characteristic $\mathbf{x}(\mathbf{v})$ is obtained by applying Eq. (9.16) to Eq. (9.9), a more elegant approach is to invoke the definition of the conditional characteristic function given by[15]

$$\varphi(j\mathbf{w} \mid \mathbf{v}) = \int_{\mathscr{D}_s} \exp(j\mathbf{w}'\mathbf{s})\, p_0(\mathbf{s})\, p(\mathbf{v} \mid s)\, d\mathbf{s} \qquad (9.18)$$

Thus Eq. (9.8) becomes

$$\mathbf{x}(\mathbf{v}) = -j\,\frac{d}{d\mathbf{w}} \log \varphi(j\mathbf{w} \mid \mathbf{v})\big|_{\mathbf{w}=0} \qquad (9.19)$$

With the help of Eq. (6.86), the conditional characteristic function defined by Eq. (9.18) can be obtained by substituting Eq. (9.16) into Eq. (9.18)

$$\varphi(j\mathbf{w} \mid \mathbf{v}) = |\mathbf{M}|^{-\frac{1}{2}}\, |\mathbf{C}^{-1}|^{-\frac{1}{2}} \exp(-\mathbf{B}'\mathbf{x} - \tfrac{1}{2}\mathbf{x}'\mathbf{A}^{-1}\mathbf{x})\, p(\mathbf{v} \mid \mathbf{x})$$

$$\exp\left(-\tfrac{1}{2}\mathbf{w}'\mathbf{C}\mathbf{w} + j\mathbf{w}\mathbf{C}\mathbf{z} + \tfrac{1}{2}\mathbf{z}'\mathbf{C}\mathbf{z}\right) \qquad (9.20)$$

where

$$\mathbf{z} = \mathbf{B} + \mathbf{A}^{-1}\mathbf{x} \qquad (9.21)$$

From Eqs. (9.19) and (9.20), it is easy to show that

$$\mathbf{x}(\mathbf{v}) = \mathbf{C}\mathbf{z} = \mathbf{C}(\mathbf{B} + \mathbf{A}^{-1}\mathbf{x}) \qquad (9.22)$$

By using Eq. (9.13a) and

$$\mathbf{C} = (\mathbf{M}^{-1} + \mathbf{A}^{-1})^{-1} \qquad (9.23)$$

---

[15] M. Loève, "Probability Theory," p. 360. Van Nostrand, New York, 1955.

an alternative expression of Eq. (9.22) is found:

$$x_n = \sum_{k=1}^{n} c_{nk} z_k = \sum_{k=1}^{n} c_{nk} \left(b_k + \sum_{i=1}^{n} a_{ki} x_i \right) \qquad (9.24)$$

In the continuous case, since

$$c_{nk} = c(t_n, t_k)$$
$$b_k = b(t_k)\Delta t$$
$$a_{ki} = a(t_k, t_i)(\Delta t)^2$$

Eq. (9.24) may be written

$$x(t) = \int_0^t c(t, \tau) \left[b(\tau) + \int_0^t a(\tau, \tau') x(\tau') \, d\tau' \right] d\tau \qquad (9.25)$$

To show a more concrete form of Eq. (9.25) we make the assumption that the sampled values of the additive random noise are independent of each other and are followed by the gaussian probability density function. We may therefore write

$$p(n_i) = \frac{1}{(2\pi\psi_n)^{1/2}} \exp\left(-\frac{n_i^2}{2\psi_n} \right) \qquad (9.26)$$

Taking the statistical independence of **s** and **n** into account, we express the conditional probability density function as

$$p(\mathbf{v} \mid \mathbf{s}) = \prod_{i=1}^{n} \frac{1}{(2\pi\psi_n)^{1/2}} \exp\left(-\frac{(v_i - s_i)^2}{2\psi_n} \right) \qquad (9.27)$$

$$\log p(\mathbf{v} \mid \mathbf{s}) = \mu - \frac{1}{2\psi_n} \sum_{i=1}^{n} (v_i - s_i)^2 \qquad (9.28)$$

where

$$\mu = -\frac{n}{2} \log 2\pi\psi_n \qquad (9.29)$$

In this case from Eqs. (9.13) we have

$$b_i = \left.\frac{\partial \log p(\mathbf{v} \mid \mathbf{s})}{\partial s_i}\right|_{s_i = x_i} = \frac{1}{\psi_n}(v_i - s_i) \qquad (9.30\text{a})$$

$$a_{ki} = -\left.\frac{\partial^2 \log p(\mathbf{v} \mid \mathbf{s})}{\partial s_k\,\partial s_i}\right|_{s_i = x_i} = \frac{1}{\psi_n}\delta_{ki} \qquad (9.30\text{b})$$

With the use of these equations Eq. (9.24) becomes

$$\begin{aligned}
x_n &= \sum_{k=1}^{n} c_{nk}\left[\frac{1}{\psi_n}(v_k - x_k) + \sum_{i=1}^{n}\frac{1}{\psi_n}\delta_{ki}x_i\right] \\
&= \frac{1}{\psi_n}\sum_{k=1}^{n} c_{nk}[(v_k - x_k) + x_k] \\
&= \frac{1}{\psi_n}\sum_{k=1}^{n} c_{nk}v_k \qquad (9.31)
\end{aligned}$$

We must determine here c_{nk}. For this purpose we rewrite Eq. (9.23) in the form

$$\mathbf{C} = \left(\mathbf{M}^{-1} + \frac{1}{\psi_n}\mathbf{I}\right)^{-1} \qquad (9.32)$$

where the relation given by Eq. (9.30b) has been used; then we express it as

$$\mathbf{C}\left(\mathbf{M}^{-1} + \frac{1}{\psi_n}\mathbf{I}\right) = \mathbf{I} \qquad (9.33)$$

Furthermore, we may write this in the form

$$\mathbf{C} + \frac{1}{\psi_n}\mathbf{CM} = \mathbf{M} \qquad (9.34)$$

from which it is readily shown that the c_{nk} to be determined must satisfy the following equation:

$$c_{nj} + \frac{1}{\psi_n}\sum_{k=1}^{n} c_{nk}m_{kj} = m_{nj}, \qquad j = 1, 2, \ldots, n \qquad (9.35)$$

When the additive random noise $n(t)$ may be considered band-limited gaussian white noise, the use of Eq. (6.75) gives the continuous form of this equation

$$c(t, \tau) + \frac{1}{N_0} \int_0^t c(t, \sigma)\, m(\tau, \sigma)\, d\sigma = m(t, \tau) \qquad (9.36)$$

or

$$\frac{1}{N_0} \int_0^t c(t, \sigma)[m(\tau, \sigma) + N_0\, \delta(\sigma - \tau)]\, d\sigma = m(t, \tau) \qquad (9.37)$$

The quantity in the square parentheses expresses the autocorrelation function $\psi_v(\tau, \sigma)$ of the input $v(t) = s(t) + n(t)$, so we can finally obtain

$$\frac{1}{N_0} \int_0^t c(t, \sigma)\, \psi_v(\tau, \sigma)\, d\sigma = m(t, \tau) \qquad (9.38)$$

which is the so-called Wiener-Hopf integral equation. This has also been derived by Booton[16] for the linear filtering problem of nonstationary random processes. It is known that the optimal filter becomes nonlinear when the incoming signal has nongaussian statistics. Theoretical studies concerning this problem have been presented by Drenick[17] and the authors.[18]

9.3   Present Status and Future Problems

As we have indicated, decision theory provides a unified, quantitative approach to the optimal synthesis of adaptive control systems and includes such of the classical approaches as spectral-density analysis, the correlation method, and Wiener filtering theory. Modern control theory, for instance, is invoking statistical decision theory for the design of dual control systems. The concept of the dual control system has not been

[16] R. C. Booton, An optimization theory for time-varying linear filter with non-stationary statistical inputs. *Proc. IRE* **40**, 997 (1952).

[17] R. Drenick, *op. cit.*

[18] Y. Sawaragi, Y. Sunahara, and T. Nakamizo, *op. cit.*

analytically reviewed here, but the reader should not overlook the work of Fel'dbaum, who has introduced into his design methods a simplified concept of statistical decision theory and solved it by the method of dynamic programming,[19] originated by Bellman.[20]

Another application of decision theory to control problems that is worthy of note here is the combination of control theory, statistical decision theory, and game theory.[21] In spite of the fact that the application of game theory is still far from maturity, the theory has already been widely considered in communications engineering in relation to the reception of signals in the presence of random noise and the reception of radar signals under jamming conditions.[22] In recent years several applications have been made by Root,[23] Gadzhiev,[24] and Zetterberg.[25] Zetterberg has studied the problem of signal detection and obtained the response function of the reception filter. The theoretical background of his study is the theory of two-person games,[26,27] the signal-to-noise ratio being the payoff function. Nilson has studied the jamming of radar with respect to maximizing performance while enemy aircraft wishes to minimize it.[28]

Elementary discussion of automatic control have been presented by Grayson[29] and Welti.[30] Chinchinadze has studied game theory applied

[19] A. A. Fel'dbaum, Dual control theory. Pts. I–IV. *Avtomatica i Telemekhanika* **21**, Nos. 9 and 11 (1960); **22**, Nos. 1 and 2 (1961).

[20] R. Bellman, "Introduction to Dynamic Programming." Oxford Univ. Press, London and New York, 1957.

[21] J. von Neuman and O. Morgenstern, "Theory of Games and Economic Behavior." Princeton Univ. Press, Princeton, New Jersey, 1947.

[22] N. M. Blackman, Communication as a game. *IRE WESCON Conv. Rec.* (Pt. 2), 61 (1957).

[23] W. L. Root, Communications through unspecified additive noise. *Information and Control* **4**, 15 (1961).

[24] M. Y. Gadzhiev, Determination of the optimum variation mode of the usual signal and noise carrier frequency in detection problems based on the theory of games. *Automation and Remote Control* **22**, No. 1 (1961).

[25] L. Zetterberg, Signal detection under noise interference in a game situation. *IRE Trans. Information Theory* **IT-8** (No. 5), 47 (1962).

[26] D. Blackwell and M. A. Girshick, *op. cit.*

[27] J. von Neuman and O. Morgenstern, *op. cit.*

[28] N. J. Nilson, An application of the theory of games to radar reception problems. *IRE Nat. Conv. Rec.* Pt. 4, 130 (1959).

[29] L. P. Grayson, Analysis of competitive situation. *In* "Adaptive Control" (E. Mishkin and L. Braun, eds.), Chap. 14. McGraw-Hill, New York, 1961.

[30] G. R. Welti, Element of game theory. *In* "Control System Engineering" (W. W. Seifert and C. W. Steeg, eds.), Chap. 17. McGraw-Hill, New York, 1960.

to the analysis of self-optimizing control systems,[31] and Gadzhiev has tried to apply it to the optimal-control problem.[32] However, much lies ahead.

An area of particular importance is that of control systems containing nonlinear elements and time-varying parameters. With the growing application of the statistical decision theory we may expect a powerfully realistic method of dynamically optimizing control systems with time variant nonlinear characteristics in the near future.

[31] V. K. Chinchinadze, Logical design problems of self-optimizing and learning-optimizing control systems based on random searching; Automatic and remote Control. *Proc. First IFAC Congress.* Butterworths, London, 1961.

[32] M. Y. Gadzhiev, Application of the theory of games to some problems of automatic control. Pt. I. *Avtomatika i Telemekhanika* **23,** 1023 (1962).

Author Index

Numbers in parentheses are reference numbers and indicate that an author's work is referred to although his name is not cited in the text.

Subject Index

A

Adaptive control, 7, 73
  sequential decision making to, 139
Additive noise, 53
Averaging device, 117
Average risk, 62
  a posteriori, 27, 95
  in binary detection problems, 66
  in filtering problems, 202
  in ideal observer decision making, 89
  in nondata problems, 131
  in nonsequential decision approaches, 94
  in sequential decision approaches, 134
  in system identification, 106
Average sample number function, 149

B

Bang-bang control systems, 4
Bayes criterion, 63
Bayes decision rule, 63
  in binary detection problems, 69
  in nondata problems, 131
  in nonsequential decision approaches, 98
  in sequential decision approaches, 138
  in system identification, 107
Bayes theorem, 19
Bayesian system, 63, 95
Binary detection, 64
Binomial distribution, 164
Binomial sequential decision rule, 165
Borel field, 15

C

Characteristic function, 34, 45
  joint, 38
Conditional risk, 62
Correlation function, 45
Cost matrix, 53
Covariance, 45
Cross moment, 37
Cumulants, 35

D

Decision threshold, 81
Describing function, 3
Detection, 55

E

Elementary events, 14
Ergodic hypothesis, 44
Errors of the first kind, 67, 144
  of the second kind, 67, 144
Error probability, 78, 123
  total, 80, 87
Estimate
  interval, 57
  point, 57
Evaluation functions, 58
Expectation, 32
Extraction, 55

F

Filtering, 201
Fokker-Planck equation, 175
Frequency, 13

215